CARR

A NOVEL

By PHYLLIS BENTLEY

Author of "Inheritance"

Here is a ... Bentley, ne... America. It ... ing with the s... industry as ... Inheritance," though ... Carr" the emphasis is on the individuals rather than on the drama of the rise of the machine in England.

This is the story of Philip Carr, of his youth in the village of Carr Foot, in the West Riding of Yorkshire; of his love for Cordelia, the daughter of the man who had ruined his father; of his cousin Catherine, loyal and warm-hearted, but utterly unable to cope with life and constantly hurt by the people for whom she cares; of Lomas who married her for her money and defeated and subdued her by his mean tyranny; and it is the story of Phil Carr's manhood, his struggle to keep his mill going, his failure, and the new life which he and Cordelia and their two sons built up.

Carr called himself an ordinary man, and felt that he had accomplished no great thing, but his life was rich in love and kindness, laughter and joy. Phyllis Bentley has created in Carr a man whom one would wish to have known.

CARR

By the Same Author

INHERITANCE

CARR: *Being the Biography of Philip Joseph Carr, Manufacturer of the Village of Carr Foot, in the West Riding of Yorkshire, written by his grand-daughter, Mary Elizabeth Carr.*

by
Phyllis E. Bentley

NEW YORK
THE MACMILLAN COMPANY
1933

First English edition published in 1929.
First edition published in the United States June, 1933.

To avoid confusion I wish to state that the town of Hudley and the village of Carr Foot, with their houses, mills, streets, churches, newspapers and inhabitants, including the supposed author of this biography, Mary Elizabeth Carr, are all entirely imaginary. So are the circumstances of the life of Philip Joseph Carr. Only his character, his personality, is real; drawn from that of a real person, to whose beloved memory this book is dedicated.

PHYLLIS BENTLEY

But on the whole Carr was not a letter-writer; he preferred the spoken to the written word, and was apt to feel harassed and resentful when confronted with the necessity for a serious epistle.

II. *Letters from other of the persons concerned.*—These again are not many, as most of the persons concerned in Carr's career lived in the same town, and were not of the type to make intimate confidences to people outside the family. Lomas, however, was a letter-writer of the expansive and descriptive kind; but his remarks are so exceedingly flowery, and suffer so gravely in accuracy from their tendency to make Lomas Eastwood out a fine fellow, that they are almost valueless. Many letters of condolence written to my grandmother on Carr's death contain details of incidents, or estimates of character, which are important. Catherine's letters to her distant cousin and friend, Fräulein Minna Kirchner (afterwards Frau Schröter) of Leipzig, were all preserved for a considerable period in a tin box by the addressee, but during Frau Schröter's last illness, which took place in 1916, by her instructions they were all destroyed. Frau Schröter's letters to Catherine, with one exception, were also destroyed; the earlier ones were burned on the night before Catherine's wedding, as she records in her diary, and in her middle life it was Catherine's habit to destroy all correspondence addressed to her immediately she had read it. We may perhaps guess at the lamentable reason for this. The Catherine–Schröter correspondence was, of course, interrupted by the outbreak of war in 1914. The one letter of this series preserved, fortunately for us a very valuable one, was found between the leaves of Catherine's diary in a year much later than its own date, namely, in 1891 instead of 1881.

III. *Catherine's Diary.*—This, which covers the periods

from 1877 to 1891 and from 1917 to 1927, is simply invaluable, especially for the Catherine–Lomas affair, which played so large a part in Carr's career. The diary, which was left by will to Catherine's nephew, Eugene Carr, and failing him to the present writer, was found in its leather case in Catherine's safe deposit at her bank. It occupies eleven substantial leather-bound crown octavo volumes; the entries, at first dated daily, are not confined to a definite space, but spread over a few lines or several pages, according to Catherine's mood and adventures. Details of incidents, clothes, books and feelings are given at length, in a manner which, though rather school-girlish and high-flown, reveals the real delicacy, pride, shyness, feeling for beauty and scornful inability to understand anything base which formed the essential fineness of the unfortunate girl's character. It is pathetically significant that the entries become irregular the very week after Catherine's marriage, break off altogether a few months later, and when at length resumed in 1917 are in a totally different style—mere dry statements of fact put down as briefly as possible, with no reference to feelings (except on one notable occasion) and no semblance of literary arrangement. After March 22nd, 1927, the entries cease altogether.

IV. *Various Notes and Papers left by Eugene Carr.*—These include descriptions of houses and places, jottings on the Carr, Ainsley and Eastwood pedigrees, anecdotes of members of these families, outlines of some important incidents, and a short written sketch of Carr's career. The presentation of this material has been the subject of very careful consideration by myself and various other persons interested in this biography. At one time it was thought that the sketch should be given in full and *en bloc;* but as the account is in many ways incomplete, a great deal of repetition would have been involved; and it was eventually decided simply to use it as one of the authorities, quoting from it occasionally when its wording seemed particularly attractive, but usually incorporating its information into the present text in a summarised form and at the appropriate chronological point. The description of the office at Carr Foot Mills, on p. 137, and the felling of the chimney, on p. 296, are examples of this latter method; while Eugene's two interviews with Catherine during the War are given in full.

V. *Oral Tradition.*—This is the most important source of all. My grandfather himself was not much given to relating his own doings, but after his death nothing pleased my grandmother so much as to be led on to talk of him and their early life together. I have heard her describe a hundred times such incidents as the scene at the Carr Foot concert, the marriage preliminaries, the arrival of Carr at Scarborough with the fatal news about William Ainsley, the quarrel with Lomas on the Hough Hall doorstep, and so on. She had at that time a wonderfully accurate visual memory for details—the description of the dresses at the picnic, for instance, I took down verbatim as she uttered it—and she told her anecdotes with tremendous verve and zest, unconsciously acting each character as she went along. At such moments her faded blue eyes used to light up and sparkle with a kind of mischievous enjoyment, and the play of her still pure and delicate features was so delightful as to make one understand thoroughly the why and wherefore of the various events in which she was concerned. Besides her own first-hand knowledge she had naturally heard much both from her husband and from her father; also, with her shrewd insight into character, she had fathomed the secret of Ellen and Adelaide long before the letter referred to on p. 5 was found, and with her usual scornful impatience of anything insincere did not hesitate to let us know it. I recently read of a great modern writer describing his aunt as "one of the most powerful, attractive and formidable personalities I have known"; and how exactly this description fits my grandmother—even in her old age—the reader of P. J. Carr's biography is invited to judge for himself. Besides her testimony there is that of Eugene Carr, who during his holidays in the north loved to wander about Carr Foot, holding the present writer by the hand, and, pointing out to her places of interest in Carr's story, relate the anecdotes connected with them. Then, of course, there is the oral testimony of many friends and members of the family other than those referred to above, together with my own personal observations. The reminiscences of James Illingworth have also been very valuable.

VI. *The Hudley News.*—Acknowledgments are due to the proprietors of this newspaper (established as a weekly in 1861, and as an evening daily in 1892) for allowing me to print their notices of the wedding of Lomas and the funeral of William Ainsley, also extracts from various other of their obituary and wedding notices, and from their accounts of the fire and the felling of the chimney at Carr Foot Mills. I have to thank them also for very kindly permitting me to search their files for casual references to the Carr, Ainsley and Eastwood families. References in other newspapers I have disregarded as being necessarily derivative.

My thanks are also due to various gentlemen in Sheffield, who helped me to conduct the tedious—and not very successful—research into the ancestry of Hammond Carr the elder; and to the Hudley Registrar for similar information and help about the Carr and Ainsley families. The table on p. 11 is taken from the pages of "Carr Foot, its History and Antiquities," by kind permission of Mr. Sebastian Whitaker, the well-known antiquary.

Lastly, it will be well to state here that the persons in the biography are referred to throughout by name instead of by their relationship to the writer, as it was felt that constant references to "my grandfather," "my uncle" and so on would be tiresome and sometimes obscure.

MARY ELIZABETH CARR

Carr Foot,
1928–1929.

CONTENTS

I

Birth and Childhood (1858–1866)

II

Education and Apprenticeship (1867–1878)

III

First Love (1879)

IX

MIDDLE LIFE (1897–1913)

X

THE GREAT WAR (1914–1918)

XI

THE CLOSING YEARS (1918–1927)

PAGE

CARR

I

BIRTH AND CHILDHOOD (1858–1866)

It was on May 15th, 1858, at Number 4, Atack Place, Hudley, a county borough in the West Riding of Yorkshire, that Philip Joseph Carr was born, the hour being five minutes past one in the morning. The circumstances of his birth were somewhat inauspicious, for on the day but one preceding it his father, Hammond Carr, a handsome, clever and to all appearances successful young cloth manufacturer, had mysteriously vanished away from Hudley between the hours of midnight and dawn, leaving his young wife, then in daily expectation of the birth of her first child, asleep and ignorant of his departure. The mystery and alarm of this sudden disappearance no doubt accelerated the birth of the subject of this biography, but fortunately had no deleterious effects on his health or on that of his mother; for according to all the references Philip was a particularly fine child with large brown eyes and curly dark hair, while Ellen Carr's strength and energy were in later years the envy of her more delicate sister Adelaide.

At this distance of time Hammond Carr's disappearance is, of course, no mystery; it was due simply and solely to a misappropriation on his part of funds belonging to the widow of his partner, James Hallas, then lately deceased, who had made the young Carr—in whom he mistakenly placed great confidence—one of his two executors. The other executor, a young man of the name of Taylor Eastwood—he was a distant cousin of Mrs. Hallas, a printer by trade, and a man of remarkably independent and vigorous personality, as we shall see later—had in conversation with the widow that evening found reason to suspect the embezzlement. For some time previously he had been uneasy about Hammond Carr's repeated postponement of any definite statement on Mrs. Hallas's affairs; he now, though the hour was late, hurried impetuously round to Atack Place to demand an immediate explanation. He found a carriage standing at the gate of Number 4, and Hammond Carr on his threshold, just showing out his wife's sister Adelaide and her husband. Mrs. Carr herself was also vaguely visible, rather further back in the hall. Without a moment's hesitation Eastwood marched up to the young manufacturer, and demanded—rather fierily, we may assume—an interview. Hammond Carr, who probably knew only too well the aspect the interview would assume, replied with languid impertinence that his business hours were over for the day; but Eastwood was not to be denied; and fearing a scene in front of witnesses—which at that stage of the Hallas affairs would have been highly inconvenient—Hammond yielded the point with that graceful facility of manner for which his portrait prepares us, and concluding his farewells to Adelaide and her husband promptly, showed Eastwood into a back room. He stood at the door a moment—tall, careless, darkly elegant—to urge his wife not to sit up for him, and to bid her send the maids to bed, as he would himself see his visitor from the house; he then went into the room to face his accuser. His wife never saw him again. From her room upstairs she dimly heard sounds of voices, then other sounds which she took correctly to be those of Eastwood's departure; then while listening and waiting for her husband to come upstairs she fell asleep, and it was not till the morning that his absence was discovered. The anguish of the young wife, thus deserted on the eve of her confinement, may be imagined; and owing to some circumstances which had occurred before her marriage, her trouble was perhaps greater than anyone suspected at the time except her sister Adelaide.

These circumstances will appear in the course of a general view of our subject's ancestry, of which it is now time to give some orderly account. Little is known of Hammond Carr's parentage, beyond the fact that he was born in Sheffield in 1828, his parents being respectively Timothy and Bianca Carr of that city. He was probably their second son; at any rate we know of another son named Timothy, who early in life went to sea, and seems to vanish from notice there. There is extant an old letter from this Timothy to his brother, addressed to "Ammon Carr," which seems to show that Timothy was either a poor speller, or so entirely illiterate that he had to employ another person to write for him—either of which alternatives gives a definite clue to the Carrs' social status at that time. This letter is dated from Dublin, March 28th, 1848, and is rather a dashing account of Timothy's experiences there; it is endorsed in Hammond's writing with a note to the effect that it was the last letter he ever received from his brother. We must presume, therefore, that Timothy was drowned, or perished otherwise, between that date and the date of his nephew's birth ten years later, when Hammond left Hudley and his papers so abruptly behind him. Of the elder Timothy and his wife nothing more is known, save that Timothy is described in the births register as a cutler; nor do we know anything of Hammond's early life. The main, and indeed the only, point to remember about Hammond Carr's ancestry is, then, that he was not a native of Hudley, and not chants, in 1790, by Robert Carr, his brother Alfred Carr, and Benjamin Ainsley—described in the deed of partnership as a cloth merchant of Hudley—who in the same year married Catherine Carr, the sister of Robert and Alfred. In the next generation, during the trying times when Carr Foot Mills were being built and machinery established in them amid some rioting and disorder,[1] the internal goodwill of the firm had been still further cemented by another marriage, for Benjamin Ainsley's son John had married Robert Carr's daughter Elizabeth.[2] Of this marriage William Ainsley was the only issue, his mother having died in childbirth. Old Benjamin Ainsley seems to have been possessed of enormous energy and initiative. He was an entirely self-made man, the son of a hand-loom weaver; he is described as liberal-minded, intensely alive to the value of education, and very charitably disposed. In his later years he was twice Mayor of Hudley, one of the founders of the Hudley Literary and Philosophical Society, a governor of Hudley Grammar School, the donor of six almshouses for aged Hudley men, and so on. John, his son, seems to have carried on his father's public-spirited enterprises; we read of him being one of the original trustees for the erection of the Hudley Literary and Philosophical Society's hall, a governor in his turn of Hudley Grammar School, a great Liberal, a devoted Wesleyan, and a generous contributor to innumerable deserving Hudley charities. He died in 1856, a year before the marriage of his son William. The Ainsleys indeed make quite a considerable figure in such publications as "Hudley Worthies," compiled in 1865 by the Rev. R. D. Hamer, and "Biographia Hudliensis," by the

[1] *E.g.* Luddite risings in the West Riding in 1812, riot against power looms at Denbridge in 1826, Plug Riots at Carr Foot itself in 1842, and so on. [2] See table, p. 11.

same hand, from which the above particulars are taken. For further details of this family, their various portraits (one of Benjamin from no less a hand than that of Sir Thomas Lawrence), busts (some executed by Mr. Edmund Carr, of Rome, of whom more anon), residences, charitable bequests, magistracies, virtues and funeral orations, the reader is referred to these admirable and accurate works of reference.

But if the ancestry of William Ainsley on the Ainsley side was thus respectable, on the side of the Carrs it was ancient. References to the Carr family earlier than the sixteenth century are doubtful, but in 1596 a Robert Carre was already living at Carre Foot, for in that year he married a certain Susannah, daughter of Thomas Sharpe, gent, of Ribourne Hall. From thence the Carr pedigree is unbroken, but long and complicated; we will not trace it in detail, but pass down the centuries until we reach a certain Robert Carr of Carr Fold, who flourished from 1720 to 1775. His sister Dorothy was a noted local beauty of that day, and seems to have paid the penalty of this beauty and the Carr recklessness; for though we hear nothing of her marriage, there is a girl, significantly named Dorothy Carr, who is alluded to as Robert Carr's niece. This Robert had two sons, Robert and Alfred Carr respectively. Alfred married his cousin Dorothy, probably very much against his father's wishes—which seems to lend colour to the obscurity of Dorothy's birth—for we next hear of him writing home from Germany for money and forgiveness. It is interesting to note that at one period of his life he was associated with John Andrew Stein, whose pianofortes received the praise of Mozart in 1777. Eventually, however, after various vicissitudes, Alfred became a respectable merchant in Leipzig, and died there in 1837 at the age of ninety, leaving a widow and two daughters, from the younger of whom Minna Kirchner, Catherine's correspondent, was descended. His elder brother Robert had three children—Robert (born in 1765), Alfred (1766), and Catherine (1768). By the time these three had reached years of discretion, the Carr fortunes were in a very bad way, thanks to a series of gambling heads of the family. The family residence, Carr Fold, which had been destroyed by fire and rebuilt once since the 1596 Robert's days, was tumbling to pieces; and of the Carr acres there was scarcely a rood left. When, therefore, in 1790 their father died, worn out by drink and dissipation, at the early age of forty-eight, the two Carrs took a bold but wise step in becoming cloth merchants with the rising young Benjamin Ainsley, who, already a "warm" and coming man, was no doubt the more favourably inclined towards the brothers because he was already paying his addresses to their sister Catherine. In January 1791 the firm of Carr Carr and Ainsley bought by auction (for £30 2*s.*) room Number 120 in the second tier of the Hudley Piece Hall, where the cloth market was held on Saturdays. From an old account book we read that in 1793 they had in their room 267 pieces, valued at £642 8*s.* Later they rented a supplementary warehouse in Pritchard Street, for from the first the firm prospered exceedingly. Soon the Carrs built Carr Fold anew; while Benjamin erected a large, square, uninteresting mansion—which he named Hough Hall—on the main road from Hudley into Lancashire, a mile or so on the Hudley side of the village of Carr Foot. Later, as we have already stated, Carr Carr and Ainsley became cloth manufacturers, and prospered more than ever.

In matters other than business, however, they were not as fortunate. Robert and Alfred Carr both loved their German cousin Maria Carr; Robert was successful in winning her affection, and married her in 1791, while Alfred, thus disappointed, remained a bachelor all his life. The marriage of these two cousins was not a fortunate event for the Carr family; for of the four children of Robert and Maria, the eldest, Robert, died in infancy, and the youngest, Elizabeth, the wife of John Ainsley, died as we have seen in childbirth at the early age of twenty-two. Of the second and third children there is rather more to say. The third, by name Edmund Carr, born in 1793, had a quite considerable talent for modelling; he attracted the favourable notice of Sir Thomas Lawrence—who, as we have already noticed, had painted the portrait of Edmund's uncle Benjamin Ainsley—obtained a gold medal at the Royal Academy, and subsequently went to Rome to continue his studies. He remained there for the rest of his life, supported by a generous allowance from his father, and returning to Yorkshire only at intervals to execute busts or full-sized statues of local notabilities. One of these, of his uncle Benjamin Ainsley, who is represented as a full-size figure reclining on a mattress, is a curious piece; it was presented to the Hudley Museum in 1915, and now stands in the entrance hall there. Edmund's health was always somewhat uncertain: he probably owed his comparatively long life—he died in 1863—to his residence in Italy. He never married. Edmund's elder brother Alfred, the second son of Robert and Maria, though sharing the family delicacy, in due course attained manhood and became a partner in Carr Carr and Ainsley, succeeding his father as senior partner on his demise in 1835. When Alfred died, however, in 1857, he left but one son to succeed him; and this son, Alfred Walter, then twenty-five years of age, had always been ailing and sickly; it seems likely, from the various accounts of his illness which are extant, that he was tubercular.

From this somewhat protracted account of the Carr and Ainsley families it will be seen, then, first, that the Carrs were essentially territorial in their origin, while the Ainsleys were business men. Secondly, that by 1858 the firm of Carr Carr and Ainsley were sufficiently well-known and old-established to have great prestige and a considerable body of tradition. Thirdly, that thanks to the intermarriages of the Carrs in two successive generations, the only Carrs left at that date were the old bachelor artist Edmund, and the young Alfred Walter, whose health was extremely precarious; so that if William Ainsley should survive these two, which seemed only too probable, the whole of the Carr property would eventually devolve upon him, both his mother and his grandmother being Carrs by birth. It may as well be stated here that this did in fact occur, Walter's early death in 1861 preceding that of his uncle Edmund by two years. It is necessary that these facts should be grasped, or the later events narrated in these pages will not be understood. For the assistance of the reader a table of descent of the Carrs and Ainsleys will be found on the opposite page. The portion relating to the Carrs is taken, with some omissions, from Sebastian Whitaker's "Carr Foot, its History and Antiquities."

William Ainsley was fully capable of sustaining the burden of the Carr wealth; his portrait, painted in 1857 just before his marriage, shows him as a square, determined-looking young man, with crisp gingerish hair, fine full auburn whiskers, and a choleric blue eye. He was then thirty-six—it seems to have been a tradition in the Ainsley family to marry rather late. He had not had the privilege of a University education; but all the Ainsleys were well-informed men, keen students of politics, and by no means insensible to the finer pleasures of music and art. In business matters he was reckoned extremely shrewd and determined. His daughter Catherine was devotedly attached to him, and thought highly—except in one fatal instance—of his advice. Altogether he seems to have been a man of

TABLE OF DESCENT OF THE CARRS OF CARR FOOT

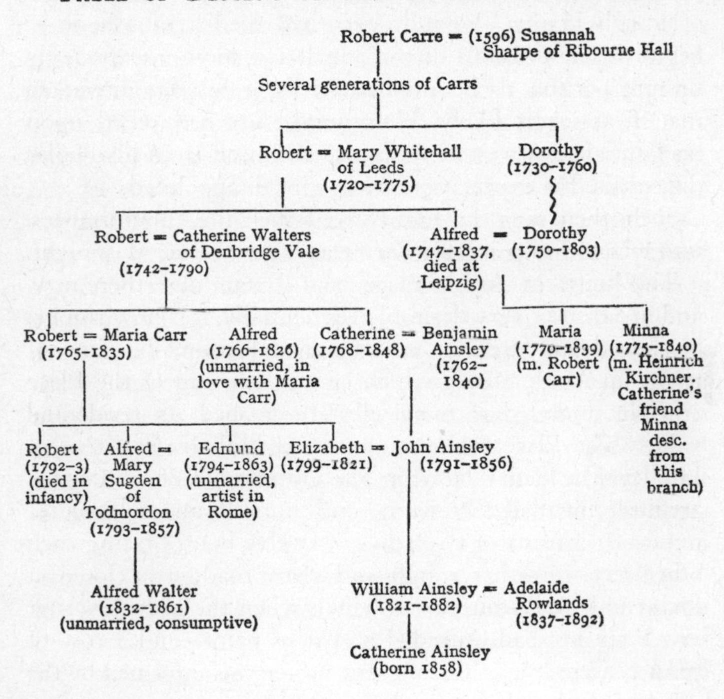

sound judgment and strong character; it may, in fact be safely assumed that William Ainsley, though passionately in love with his wife, was never quite as ignorant of Adelaide's preference for her brother-in-law as she imagined him to be. This appears from several passages in Catherine's diary, as well as from William's comment on P. J. Carr's marriage.

Before quitting once and for all what a biographer of Shelley has justly termed "the arid region of genealogy," it may be well to mention that Joseph Rowlands, the father of Ellen and Adelaide—their mother was Hannah, daughter of Joseph Hamer, linen-draper—had died a month or so before his grandson's birth. He left a most unexpectedly meagre portion to be divided between his daughters; so that if, as seems likely, Hammond Carr had relied upon his father-in-law's estate to extricate himself from his Hallas difficulties, his expectation was sadly disappointed.

Such, then, was the family, and such the circumstances, into which Philip Joseph Carr was born on that May night.

The house in Atack Place is still standing; then new, and in a district very desirable residentially, it is now smoke-blackened and dreary; and the introduction of a line of trams up Atack Street, which crosses one end of the Place at right angles, has materially diminished its residential value. The Place was designed and built by a native of Hudley, Mr. Henry Newton, the grandfather of the famous architect Sir Bales Newton, and himself an architect of repute. It consists of two rows of twelve houses facing each other across a rather rough and stony road; it is closed at each end by tall iron gates—which when the present writer saw them last badly needed a coat of paint—and a row of spear-head railings. The present writer was informed by the inhabitants that the gates always stand open, and are rather a symbol than an effective guardian of privacy. The houses themselves, though substantial and well-built, are not large, the frontage consisting of the width of the narrow hall and one room; they boast clumsy pillared porticoes and large old-fashioned sash windows; the rooms are high and square; until recently they had "cellar" kitchens; in front of each house is a small flagged area surrounded by despondent-looking rhododendrons, and the whole is railed in by more spear-heads on a smaller scale. Number 4 departs in no way from its companion residences, and to-day it looks a sufficiently dreary spot. But in the sixties of the last century, when the little Philip Joseph ran in and out of its heavy front door, and Atack Place was new and stylish, and much further from the commercial centre of the town than it is to-day, no doubt it looked bright and homelike enough to him. That Mrs. Carr was able to remain there at all was due to the generosity of William Ainsley, who took the affairs of the absconding Hammond on his shoulders and settled them all with characteristic ability. For when the widow Hallas had received her due there was nothing left for Mrs. Carr to live on, and Mr. Ainsley made her an allowance from that fatal May night till the day of her death.

It was, then, his money which fed and clothed the young Phil Carr during the early years of his life. Of Carr's childhood we really know very little, save that he had whooping-cough as an infant, though not so severely as to cause anxiety; and that he fell down the cellar steps of Number 2, Atack Place, the residence of old Mr. Newton, at the age of four. Fortunately the velvet suit he was wearing at the time saved him from any serious damage. Another accident from which he did not escape unscathed occurred a few months later, when, running to meet his cousin Catherine at the door on a wet day, he tripped over the mat and cut his upper lip on the tip of Mrs. Ainsley's umbrella. The scar of this mishap remained with him till his early teens; and till late in life Catherine had a very vivid remembrance of the incident, as the first time she had ever seen Phil cry. For from the first he was a very happy, merry little chap, and he and Catherine—who, born six months after himself (prematurely, to the great detriment of Adelaide Ainsley's health), was an ideal companion for him—spent innumerable happy hours together, either at Atack Place or in Catherine's home. At first after his marriage Mr. Ainsley naturally lived in old Benjamin Ainsley's house, Hough Hall. Of this house, which has recently been demolished to improve an awkward turn in the road, we shall hear more later; at this period Carr can have known very little of it. Before he was four the young Walter Carr died, and as Edmund Carr showed no disposition to leave Rome for the bleaker Yorkshire clime, William Ainsley took over Carr Fold on a lease and removed there, and it was not many years before it became his own property by the death of Edmund.

Carr Fold was—indeed, it still is—a very charming place for children to play in. To begin with, it is delightfully situated on a steep hillside, which commands an extensive view. In front of the big stone house its many lawns and paths and shrubberies slope down into a paddock, which is backed by a row of fine elms; to the right are more lawns, more trees, and through a gap in these a pleasing vista of stream, trees and hill. To the left the ground drops away, leaving the village of Carr Foot exposed to view, an irregular grey mass from which a crop of mill chimneys shoots up proudly into the smoky sky. The further prospect carries the eye over a succession of steep green hills and narrow winding valleys, rising and falling out of each other in the disconcertingly intricate manner peculiar to the West Riding; while in the distance another irregular grey mass and smoke cloud denote the presence of Hudley. One can imagine the two children—Phil dark and merry, Catherine fair and very serious—chasing each other round the clumps of rhododendrons, dabbling in the stream which tumbled down Carr Dene, plucking the red sorrel of the paddock, and jumping over the flower-beds. We know that Catherine's skipping-rope once decapitated a geranium, to her great grief, for she had an unmeasured passion for flowers and for animals. So great indeed was her grief that she fled, dropping her skipping-rope in the path—where Phil, puzzled, found it a few seconds later—to the house, and rushing up the stairs to her room climbed into her wardrobe, shut the door upon herself as well as she was able, and indulged in an orgy of tears over the broken flower, which she held in her hand. Here she was found half an hour later by Mr. Ainsley, come home for tea and anxious for the sight of his little daughter. There was always a very deep sympathy between Catherine and her father, whom she strongly resembled; and though Mr. Ainsley was anything but sentimental himself, he understood Catherine on this occasion. Phil, following his uncle upstairs, guided by the sound of sobs, entered Catherine's room and found her just emerging from the wardrobe in her father's arms. We can imagine how he stood aghast in the doorway, his brown eyes clouding with perplexity and trouble as he gazed, for he could never bear the sight of tears. That night when the two children were sitting on the huge steel fender in the Carr Fold kitchen, a piece of home-made currant tea-cake in their hands—it was their custom to devour this supper there after their nightly bath: "We ate it so slowly," said Catherine once in later years, "in order to postpone going to bed, that we almost limited ourselves to a currant at a time"—Phil threw his arm impulsively round the neck of his cousin who was still looking pale and sorrowful, and promised to buy her a new geranium with his Saturday penny. This was duly reported to Mr. Ainsley by Joshua the coachman, who as the husband of the Carr Fold cook was in the kitchen at the time; Mr. Ainsley was pleased to approve the scheme, and negotiations were set on foot by Phil and his mother for the purchase of a fine geranium from a Hudley florist. Catherine, however, did not wish the maimed geranium to be ousted; and the incident eventually terminated in the careful planting, by Phil's own hands, of a virginia creeper just beneath Catherine's window.

Joshua, by the way, often plays a part in these youthful chronicles. It was he who taught Phil and Catherine to ride and drive, allowing them to hold the reins of the trap but never, it appears, of the brougham; and there is one specially charming anecdote of him which puts Carr's character in an attractive light. One day, a year or two later than the geranium incident, the Ainsleys were driving over High Carr—a bleak, wild moor at the top of the hill whereon Carr Fold stood—to see the new waterworks, of the board of commissioners for which William Ainsley was an active member. Carr and Catherine were perched up on the box beside Joshua. It was a bright day of early spring; in the valley it had been warm and sunny, but up here there was a driving wind, and the children, who had valiantly protested that they would be perfectly warm, grew colder and colder. At length Joshua, who had been watching with concern their little faces grow blue, said to Catherine in a sympathetic tone: "Are you starved, lovey?" "Oh no!" replied the precise Catherine politely. "I'm not in the least hungry, thank you." She added truthfully: "But I'm a little cold." Joshua cocked his eye at her and seemed to ponder, for "starved" in the West Riding dialect means, of course, "cold through and through," "cold to the bone." Carr, who had taken Joshua's meaning correctly, was much distressed. He felt that for Joshua to realise that he had used an expression so Yorkshire that neither of them could understand it would hurt Joshua's feelings dreadfully; but, on the other hand, if he pointed out Catherine's mistake, Catherine's feelings would also be dreadfully hurt. (It may be noted in passing that this kind of supersensitive delicacy of feeling for others was very characteristic of Carr.) Something, however, *must* be done for Joshua, and Carr did it manfully. Leaning back so that Catherine should not see his face he gave Joshua an immense, portentous and worldly wink, signifying that Carr and Joshua were on a par as men of the world who knew the proper meaning of "starved," while Catherine was a mere ignorant female whose innocence had to be respected. Joshua, as may be imagined, returned the wink with interest; and it is easy to understand from this little incident how Carr became an immense favourite with the Carr Fold domestics, and could do nothing wrong in their eyes.

The slope of the Carr Fold garden encouraged many games which needed the action of gravity for their full enjoyment; and innumerable were the objects—suitable and the reverse—rolled down the steep paths from Catherine to Carr or from Carr to Catherine. The greater the bulk of the object the more delightfully headlong its career, and the greater the danger of the child who received it at the lower end. Disasters sometimes occurred; on one such occasion, we are told, Catherine gave a sharp scream of fright which brought the elders quickly out on to the terrace at the top of the garden. Adelaide spoke rebukingly to the dismayed Carr; whereupon Ellen suddenly flew down upon him, snatched him up and carried him away to Hudley in a fury. She would not even stay for a conveyance of any kind—which, however, William sent after her—and it was several days before she would allow Phil to resume the lessons which he shared at Carr Fold with Catherine, though Joshua called perseveringly for him every morning, and represented Catherine's grief at his absence as something tremendous.

Ellen Carr, indeed, was probably not a very happy woman at this time. Though there had been a rumour of her husband starting a wine business in Spain, she had heard literally nothing from him since the night before Phil's birth; she lived on her brother-in-law's bounty, and the difference between her younger sister's monetary situation and her own must have galled her pride, while Hammond's complete neglect of her and of his child was also, in its way, a kind of triumph for Adelaide. A daguerreotype of Ellen taken in the summer of 1865 shows her as a beautiful woman still—with that enormous plaited coil of hair which characterises the portraits of both herself and Adelaide, and dangling earrings—but her beauty is marred by a resentful petulance of expression; she has a haggard, defiant, almost angry look. That she loved her son deeply, nay passionately, there is no doubt; she looked after him with the most unceasing and vigilant care, sewed for him, watched over his health, taught him his moral and religious duties, taught him also, we must suppose, those excellent care-free manners which distinguished him from the mass of his rather stiff and homely West Riding contemporaries all his life. (They may, however, have been inherited from Hammond.) At times Phil's merry, lively ways won her to laughter, and they were happy together; but at times some turn of speech, some little characteristic gesture, reminded her too poignantly of his father, and Ellen remembered the falsity, the difficulty of her position, and fell aglooming. For months together she would not mention Hammond Carr to Phil at all; and then suddenly she would talk of nothing else, praising her lost husband, weeping over his portrait—which hung, in oils, beside the piano in the front room: a characteristic piece of extravagance on Hammond Carr's part—telling Phil how wicked men had persecuted him and driven him from home, and so on and so on. No doubt she thought she believed what she was saying, but somehow a profound instinct warned her to keep the matter vague to him, and she never went into details about these unknown (to Phil) wicked men. There were, in fact, two fundamental falsities in Ellen's attitude to her husband, and therefore in all her references to him; for she pretended that Hammond had loved her passionately, and that he was in all ways honest. Neither of these things was true, and she knew it; and Phil, with the intuitive but incomplete insight of childhood, believed all she said, but hated to hear her talk about his father. Whenever she began the subject he squirmed, and Ellen sometimes saw it and raged at him. The truth perhaps was that before Hammond's child Ellen felt all the guilt of her original treachery towards Hammond.

To all these complexities, of course, young Phil Carr held no key; he would only know that his mother was liable to sudden bouts of gloom and weariness, and sudden moments of angry passion; and would feel at these times that though, of course, he was devotedly attached to her, she really rather frightened and repelled him.

II

EDUCATION AND APPRENTICESHIP
(1867–1878)

In the autumn of 1867—the year, it may be remembered, when crinolines went out with a rush—three events took place which were of importance in Carr's career. To begin with, Hammond Carr was heard of for a brief moment again; this time he was dying in South America. Ellen wished to go to him, and angry scenes took place between herself and her brother-in-law, who put a complete veto on the proposition, and enforced it by declining to supply her with the necessary funds. Ellen spoke furiously of seeking help from some distant Rowlands relation, but before she could put this plan into effect, news came that her husband was dead. Ellen assumed widow's weeds, and wore them for what her brother-in-law considered a quite unnecessarily long period of time. Phil, of course, found his mother's mourning very suitable and natural.

The next important event of the year concerned Adelaide Ainsley. Immediately upon the reception of Hammond Carr's death certificate, Adelaide, who had already had two miscarriages since the birth of Catherine, gave birth prematurely to a still-born child, with consequences to her health so serious that it seemed unlikely at one time that she would recover. She did, however, struggle back to life; but was for many long years afterwards a delicate and broken creature. Her thick light brown hair began rapidly to turn grey, the pretty colour in her cheeks faded to an almost waxen white, she lost weight, and her features became painfully thin and sharp. Her springing gait, too, became limp and lifeless. From this time onwards, in fact, no one would have taken Adelaide for the younger sister of the two; and William Ainsley's hope of a son was quite extinguished.

The third important event—third in magnitude, though first in time—was Phil's first appearance at the Hudley Grammar School, which he attended from then until he was sixteen years of age. He did not distinguish himself at school, except in arithmetic, at which he was extraordinarily quick. He had in fact at that age, so I am assured by some of his schoolfellows, a very quick perception and a retentive memory, but no particular taste for learning. "Carr romped merrily through his lessons," writes his contemporary, the distinguished architect Sir Bales Newton, "learning the indispensable minimum without any great effort, and forgetting it with equal ease. At arithmetic, however, especially mental arithmetic, his facility was wonderful. I remember in the summer of 1868 there was an American 'Troupe and Brass Band,' supposed to be formed of negroes who had been slaves prior to 1865, performing at the St. George's Hall in Bradford. We were all rather interested in this; and one day our arithmetic master, who was a bit of a wag in his way, set us a tremendous sum about the number of banjo strings required annually for the whole troupe, if so many negroes broke so many strings in so many days. Hardly had he finished stating the problem when P. J. Carr jumped up in a flurry and cried out the right answer. I can see his look of laughing triumph now as he glanced round at us, while the master stood dumbfounded, and the class shouted joyously that Carr ought to have a ticket for the negroes' performance as a prize. I do not think this ever materialised, for Carr was not the sort of lad to press for it. At that time Carr was tall for his age, with easy, well-knit limbs, slender hands and feet, and very bright, glowing eyes. As I recall him he was always a lively, restless, spirited mortal, more ready to play than to work, but docile and amenable to authority when properly handled. I never heard him say an unkind word to anyone, and we all loved him." Another schoolfellow of his, Sir Charles Gill, head of that well-known firm of manufacturers Messrs. Gill and Barker—at that time his father, the Rev. Humphrey Gill, was vicar of the parish of St. Mark's, in the industrial depths of Hudley—writes as follows. "Phil Carr," he tells us, "like myself, always occupied a moderate position in class, rather nearer the bottom than the top, except when the subject was mental arithmetic, when he invariably shot up at once to the first place, and defied all efforts to oust him. What I chiefly remember about Carr's early days, however, is his prowess at football, though probably this belongs to the end of his schooldays rather than the beginning. His speed and nimbleness on the football field were quite renowned among us, and we all knew that he could be relied upon never to be a 'selfish' player. In fact Phil Carr could never be selfish at anything; he was too unselfish for his own good. Somehow or other he always got passed over when we were choosing a football captain, because we knew that he alone would be sure not to take offence."

We may also quote from the reminiscences of another, and much more intimate, friend of Carr's, namely, the solicitor, Mr. Nicholas Latham Whiteley. Mr. Whiteley was the only child of the well-known Hudley solicitor, Mr. Nicholas Whiteley (senior), his mother having died at his birth; he was handicapped all through his life by a slight lameness. In a letter sent to the present writer after Carr's death, Mr. Whiteley gives the following charming testimony: "Dear Phil! Looking back over fifty to sixty years I can see him now as I saw him on my first morning in school, laughing heartily at some joke against himself, his brown eyes sparkling, his whole lively person instinct with merriment and fun. The mere sight of him reassured me and helped me to face the alarming school life. I had been a rather sickly and backward child, and came to school when Phil had already been there two or three years; but to my great relief I was put in the same class with him. We were friends in half an hour, and have always remained so. As I had never been able to play games, I had devoted more time to studies than had been the case with many of my contemporaries, and even in the first week I was—rather to Phil's discomfiture—often near the head of the class. Never shall I forget Phil's triumphant glee when I lost a place or two in arithmetic and he, coming up the class at a tremendous rate, passed me outright and went up to the top. In my youthful egoism I was somewhat dismayed, but afterwards I got used to Phil's prowess in this line, and it was a joke between us. Most things have been a joke with Phil Carr; I never met a merrier, better-hearted fellow than he, nor one whom I would sooner have as a companion through life."

These extracts sufficiently show the kind of boy Philip Joseph Carr appeared to his contemporaries; and such as the boy was, such we shall find the man to have remained through all the vicissitudes of his long life.

This is perhaps the best opportunity for alluding to two photographs—one of Carr, the other of Catherine Ainsley—which were taken in the Easter holidays when they were both fourteen years old. Adelaide Ainsley had been, as she often was, ailing all through the winter; till finally William Ainsley sent her to Scarborough for a month of fresh air. Her sister accompanied her, Phil meanwhile residing at Carr Fold. It may be doubted by the reader whether Ellen's company was ever very beneficial to Adelaide, or *vice versa,* but this was not altogether the case; in the inexplicable way common to real people, who unlike characters in a novel are not single-motived mechanisms but living, complex beings, Ellen and Adelaide had underneath all their antagonism a genuine sisterly fondness for each other, at the same time as they hated each other heartily on Hammond Carr's account. The one motive led Ellen to decline to move from Hudley to Carr Foot to be near her sister, and to utter sharp sayings whenever Adelaide's situation gave scope for cynicism; the other led her to nurse Adelaide tenderly through all her trying and tedious complaints. But then Ellen had after all been Hammond's wife, whereas Adelaide belonged to William Ainsley; we may conjecture that Adelaide's hatred of Ellen was stronger than her love, though after the manner of weak and ailing folk she was glad to have her sister's strength at hand to rely on. Be that as it may, the two were at Scarborough together for a month; and William Ainsley had the two children's photographs taken as a surprise for them on their return. The faded likenesses lie on the table now beside the present writer. Phil's coat is edged with braid; he wears a broad dark tie with narrow stripes of a lighter hue; his collar, in some manner inexplicable to the modern mind, turns down in points at the front, but is open so as to reveal the tie at the sides and back of the neck. Here we see the long, sensitive, intelligent face, with the broad open brow: the crisply curling black hair, the full-modelled lips ready—

one feels—to break into a smile at any moment, and the beautifully bright and loving brown eyes, which were familiar to all who knew and loved Phil Carr at any stage of his life. His appearance changed extraordinarily little; his face, candid, youthful, and stamped with humour then, was on his deathbed just as candid, and perhaps bore an even deeper impress of humour, for time had etched lines of kindly merriment about his eyes and mouth. The contrast between his photograph and the one beside it, of Catherine, would be really amusing if it were not so pathetic in view of later events. Catherine is leaning her arm on the corner of a table whereon stands a nicely-clothed bust; in one hand she holds a fan; the sleeves and neck of her thick stuff dress are edged with white pleated frilling; she has velvet round her neck, and a kind of crinkly frill, very difficult to describe, about her substantial arms and down both sides of her chest. Poor Catherine was never beautiful in any generally accepted sense of the term, and though her features have here the smoothness and bloom of youth, her large light eyes—they were grey with a black iris—have already that rather fixed look, the lines of her face and mouth that rather heavy modelling, which they acquired so definitely later. Another of her characteristic features is also very much in evidence; for masses of straight heavy fair hair flow loosely across her shoulders and down her back as far as the bow at her waist, a thick coil of hair is plaited about her head, hair curls in about her neck and round her large well-shaped ears—where one feels it must have been very ticklish—hair even invades the plinth of the bust in the background. Catherine's hair was, of course, at once her pride and her dismay throughout her life. At this time she was a boarder at a select school for the daughters of gentlemen, kept by the Misses Thompson, in Ingleton; and her hair was a great trouble to her there—always hanging about her eyes when she worked or played her violin, and a source of agony at the regular school hair-washings, which took place *en masse* about once a month. It may be mentioned here that the elder Miss Thompson—who afterwards married Mr. Sebastian Whitaker the antiquary, of Thawholme Gate—seems to have been a very sweet and gentle woman with a rather curiously well-furnished mind, though her sentimentality seems rather excessive to modern taste. Her pupils were all devotedly attached to her; and it was no doubt from her that the young Catherine acquired that taste for the arts which was at once the ruin and the consolation of her life. Miss Thompson taught the girls literature, sketching, and (somewhat surprisingly) German; she encouraged the reading of poetry and the writing of long letters containing quotations therefrom, and Catherine's diary is probably a direct result of her influence. The younger Miss Thompson was of a very different type, shrewd and managing. Well, it is a rather plain but also a rather fine young face that looks out at us from the fourteen-year-old Catherine's photograph; from this distance of time we can pierce through the plainness and see its essential goodness and nobility. Her complexion may have lacked brilliance and her features delicacy, but her large eyes are very honest; there is character in the firm round chin and something lofty in the arch of the eyebrows; altogether she looks an exceedingly serious and rather sentimental but essentially generous young person; somehow she is on a large scale. Poor Catherine!

In 1874 Carr left the Grammar School, and began his apprenticeship in manufacturing at Carr Foot Mills. His contemporary, Charlie Gill, was apprenticed to Mr. Enoch

Barker at the same time. The young apprentices received no regular wage, but were paid one shilling per day for early morning work, *i.e.* from 6 to 8 a.m. We may think of the young Carr, then, rising early each morning and tramping out to Carr Foot Mills by six o'clock—there was a certain crossroad at which we used to encounter Charlie Gill, bound for Enoch Barker's mill at Denbridge Vale, *en route* —putting in a long day's work, and tramping back to Hudley again; for Ellen still refused to move to Carr Foot, and it was only occasionally that William Ainsley took his nephew up to Carr Fold to eat or sleep. Phil had his way to make, as William was fond of saying, and must keep his nose to the grindstone and expect no luxuries—though indeed he need not have trouble, for the lad was willing enough. During the four years of his apprenticeship (and indeed for many years after) Carr never once missed setting foot in Carr Foot Mills punctually at 6 a.m.; indeed sometimes, on leaving dances at three or four o'clock in the morning, he would make his way straight to Carr Foot, let himself into the mill with his key, and sleep for an hour or two on a pile of pieces, so as not to miss his daily shilling. It was, of course, during these three or four years that Carr acquired the thorough knowledge of his business which stood him in such good stead in later life. The Carr Foot establishment was a very large one, and carried on more processes than are usually found under one mill roof to-day. Carr spent some time in the spinning and winding departments, then passed on to the weaving, and later to the dyeing and finishing. In later years Carr's opinion on textile matters was highly valued in Hudley because of this early experience of his, and mill-owners would frequently ring him up and ask him to go round and give his advice on that everlasting subject of West Riding litigation, a damaged piece; for even as a lad he took to all things textile like a duck to water. His whole attention, which had never been fixed on school work, was easily caught by the practical and intensely interesting details of cloth manufacture, and he learned apace. Charlie Gill developed on different lines; a tough, stocky, plain, dark, bullet-headed lad with a good deal of ruthless determination in his make-up, he took more interest in the organising and financial aspects of Mr. Barker's firm than in the actual details of manufacture, though he applied himself to these with diligence. Neither Gill nor Carr were any good at designing—a circumstance which had a considerable, though indirect, influence on Carr's later career. Both Gill and Carr, however, knew a good design when they saw one, which was perhaps all that was necessary; at any rate, when their apprenticeship was over, their respective masters were sufficiently pleased with them to keep them on and pay them a small salary.

William Ainsley had probably always meant to do that for his nephew; but as regards the next step in Carr's career it is difficult to know whether William had always intended it, or whether it grew in his mind along with his gradually increasing fondness for the boy. Certainly it seems rather odd. It would not have been unnatural on William Ainsley's part if he had cherished a dislike against the son of his wife's first love, and indeed his kindness to Ellen and Phil was probably originally founded on a kind of grim determination to heap coals of fire on Hammond's head. Adelaide loved Hammond, and her husband tacitly knew it. Very well. Then Adelaide should be forced to admit that at least her husband knew how to behave with generosity to the man she preferred: nothing should be left undone to succour Hammond, his wife or his child. Of

Adelaide's feelings towards Phil, who was Ellen's child as well as Hammond's, it is difficult to speak with any certainty; but probably all this jumbled tangle of emotions was slowly straightening itself out under the influence of time and Phil's boyish candour during the period at present under consideration. That William Ainsley grew fond of Carr is very likely—for everybody was fond of Carr—but that he should take the extreme business step he did is only explicable on the supposition that Ainsley, like many another Yorkshireman, while priding himself justly on his sound common sense, possessed also a secret streak of romanticism; and the two strains of his nature mingled together to urge him on the same course. "Here," he perhaps said to himself, "here is an honest, decent, merry lad, good at the mill and fond of Catherine. I shall have to start him in life somehow, both for his sake and for the sake of my ancient grudge against his father. I have no son. Phil is my nearest male relation. Moreover, his name is Carr." Which of these motives was the most compelling will never be known for certain, but probably sufficient importance has not hitherto been attributed to the last one; for in Catherine's diary we find the following entry for February 6th, 1878. "A lovely day, very mild and bright. I continued my sketch down in the paddock, and read some more Schiller. Mamma seems rather better in the excitement of discussing plans for our German trip. I do *so* hope that Papa will allow me to remain in Leipzig for a year with the Kirchners, as he promises. Phil and Aunt Ellen to dinner. After they had gone, Papa told me that he means to make Phil a junior partner at the mill next year, on his twenty-first birthday. Poor Papa! It is a sad pity I am not a boy, but Phil will do just as well at the mill, or perhaps even better because of his name; while

Papa could not do without me to comfort him at home. Sometimes he seems very lonely. Perhaps after all it is selfish of me to wish to stay in Leipzig. I think this making Phil a partner will be a good plan." The other half of Mr. Ainsley's plan, though then obscure to Catherine, is perfectly clear to us to-day; Phil was to marry Catherine, live—a Carr married to an Ainsley—in Carr Fold, perhaps add Catherine's name to his, and in any case continue the glories of the firm of Carr Carr and Ainsley into the next generation. Again we may say, poor Catherine!

She gained her wish and spent her year in Leipzig, studying the violin and the German language; and returned in the March of the year following, looking rather German with her heavy fair features and a tremendous knot of fair hair rolling untidily in the nape of her neck. She was more addicted to the arts than ever, and though delighted to be at home again with her father, felt somehow just a little bit strange and awkward with her young English contemporaries, who all seemed to her to have the most atrocious taste in music and very frivolous views about life and destiny. Catherine, on the contrary, took a very serious view of her talents and duties, and would positively have liked to teach the young Hudleians to play the violin. But Mr. Ainsley at first laughed at the idea, and then rather sharply bade her not mention it again; and even Phil, though so sympathetic about all her other plans, rather opened his eyes about this one, and opined that Uncle William wouldn't like it—Aunt Adelaide too, so delicate; the sound of the scales would be sure to upset her. Didn't Catherine think so? He had had a tooth knocked out at football on the preceding Saturday, so Catherine did not like to contradict him too often. She offered sympathy about the tooth instead, which made Carr laugh heartily.

According to him they had splendid times at football; their team was absolutely unconquerable, and after each match they all went off together and ate a colossal meal somewhere, and then coming home in the train sang songs about the animals coming out of the ark, or John Brown's body, or other such cheerful ditties. Charlie Gill was a great footballer, a splendid half, but unfortunately had simply no idea of tunes—not that Phil had much, as he cheerfully admitted. Indeed he seemed to think this lack of musical ability a tremendous joke, but Catherine could hardly believe his amusement on so serious a subject to be genuine. Catherine, it appears, did not know Charlie Gill very well at this time. We may surmise that Charlie Gill was not encouraged by Mr. Ainsley to visit Carr Fold; Charlie Gill was a penniless young man with his way to make, and his name was not Carr.

The lad whose name *was* Carr spent a great deal of time with Catherine just then. They rode together on William Ainsley's horses—Catherine rode well, better than Carr. They danced together—this was rather a trial to Phil, who was a superb dancer, while Catherine made heavy going. They walked together—both were excellent walkers. They also talked together, probably with some mutual perplexity, for Catherine was soulful about the picturesque, while Carr was ignorant of its rudiments. Still, they had the ease together which comes of long intimacy in childhood; each was part of the other's familiar landscape; they were good friends. At this time Carr was, of course, as indeed he always had been, a perfectly outrageous flirt; but then such a handsome, merry lad as he could hardly have been anything else—the girls adored him! He made love admirably, like his father, but with a lighter touch and a more sparkling eye; and he was not the kind of sweetheart who left wounds behind. All that was very right and natural; his mother loved to see him doing it, and even Mr. Ainsley did not object to the light-hearted scattering of Phil's attentions. No girl, he thought, judging from his own rather bitter experience, liked a man less because he put her the highest of many. Phil was obviously good friends with Catherine, and after all that was the best foundation for a more permanent union; a little moonlight and propinquity, reflected Mr. Ainsley cynically, would do the rest.

But who shall know what Ellen and Adelaide respectively thought of this match, which seemed to be advancing so promisingly? If there had been great sympathy between Adelaide and her daughter, if Catherine had been like her mother, Adelaide, we feel, would perhaps have approved her marriage with Hammond Carr's son warmly. But Catherine was like her father: fair, earnest, noble, rather inhuman and very unfeminine. Neither was Ellen very fond of Catherine; and though for the sake of Carr Fold and the firm of Carr Carr and Ainsley and Phil's future generally Ellen tried to restrain herself, she could not help uttering sharp sayings sometimes on Catherine's dreamy ways and silly notions. Really Adelaide should not allow her to reveal her fancies so absurdly in her clothes! This led Phil, always a staunch and loyal friend, to defend Catherine, though he probably did not admire her "artistic" frocks any more than his mother; and Mrs. Carr felt more certain than ever that Catherine would at some not very distant date become her daughter-in-law. She reminded herself of William Ainsley's income, and of the fact that Catherine was his only child; and beamed benevolently on her handsome son.

III

FIRST LOVE (1879)

We now come to the evening of Carr's twenty-first birthday, that is, to the evening of May 15th, 1879, an evening which was, of course, to prove of such immense importance to all concerned.

Earlier in the day the deed of partnership between William Ainsley, cloth manufacturer, of Carr Fold, and Philip Joseph Carr, cloth worker, of 4, Atack Place, Hudley, had been signed with due Victorian solemnity at the office of Mr. Nicholas Whiteley (senior), who was Mr. Ainsley's solicitor. This deed, witnessed by the two Whiteleys, father and son, is still in existence, but follows the usual form for such documents, the only clauses of interest being numbers one and twelve. The first clause runs as follows: —"The said WILLIAM AINSLEY and PHILIP JOSEPH CARR will become and remain partners in the business of cloth manufacturers for and during the joint lives of the partners, under the style or firm of CARR CARR AND AINSLEY, but subject to the provision for determination hereinafter contained." While clause twelve specifies: "The partners shall be entitled to the net profits of the said business in the shares following: the said WILLIAM AINSLEY to seven-eighths, and the said PHILIP JOSEPH CARR to two-sixteenths." Carr's share was perhaps expressed in this rather unusual way in order to keep up the firm's tradition of two Carrs and one Ainsley.

The Carrs had dined at Carr Fold to celebrate the occasion, and toasts had been drunk to the success of the new partnership. In half an hour the carriage was to call to take the party to an entertainment which had been organised by the Carr Foot Wesleyan Chapel Young Men's Class, in aid of the new building fund. The previous chapel had been totally destroyed by fire in the January of this year. Mr. Ainsley had promised to give half the money necessary to rebuild it, on condition that the other half was raised by the congregation; and the building fund was the topic of the hour. Pending re-erection, the congregation met every Sunday in a large first-floor room in Carr Foot Mills, cleared by William Ainsley for the purpose. It may perhaps be mentioned here that another of Adelaide's grievances against Ellen was their division in the matter of religious practices. The Rowlands had been brought up in the Wesleyan fold, and William Ainsley was a staunch Wesleyan and a pillar—one might almost say, *the* pillar—of the Carr Foot Chapel; but Hammond Carr had belonged to the Established Church, and Ellen chose to follow in his footsteps and educate his son as an Anglican. Adelaide was the more irritated by this because the Carrs of Carr Fold had for centuries been Churchmen, and she saw no reason why her husband should not be a Churchman too. But William did not agree with her; the Ainsleys had always been Wesleyans, he said, and seemed to regard the matter as closed. A slight condescension was therefore usually audible in Ellen's deep, strong voice when she referred to any Wesleyan matters, but to-night, in honour of Phil's accession to the firm of Carr Carr and Ainsley, she was all affability and interest in the entertainment of which William Ainsley was naturally a patron, and a patron relied upon for liberal support. Indeed, had it not been so, the party would have gone to *Diplomacy,* which was then visiting the Hudley Theatre for two weeks; by previous arrangement the Carrs had come dressed for the theatre, and Ellen at least was privately much disappointed when she found that the secretary of the Young Men's Class had reminded Mr. Ainsley of his promise to go to Carr Foot that night. But she had put a good face on many more severe disappointments than this one, and she was very smooth and easy about it now.

While their elders within the drawing-room were thus chatting with rather more than their customary urbanity, Catherine and Phil were walking back and forth along the Carr Fold terrace, which was then bounded by a low balustrade, covered with ivy, and here and there decorated with stone balls. They both admired the view. Phil was a little disappointed about the theatre, but he thought that from this day onwards everything connected with Carr Foot ought to be especially dear to him, so he pretended he did not mind at all. Catherine, who was under the erroneous impression that at the Carr Foot entertainment she would hear some excellent music, was really pleased by the change of plan. The cousins exchanged ideas on this point, and Catherine was glad to find that they agreed so well; they then looked at the view again. The day, as we know from Catherine's diary, had been wild and showery, but had now settled into an evening calm. When they first came out upon the terrace the sky had been pale and clear, but it was now softening into the rich blue of a spring dusk, to which a slim young moon on the right obligingly lent a general air of silveriness and romance. We may imagine how they gazed out together over the familiar, well-loved lawns of Carr Fold, the shrubberies round which they had played as children, the tall elms not yet in full leaf up which Carr had so often daringly scrambled, the distant stream. Phil's eyes, we may be sure, turned fondly to the chimneys of Carr Foot Mills, which stood out tall and black and slender against the clear smooth pastel of the sky. To think that—through an act the quixotic generosity of which he did not yet fully appreciate—one-eighth of those chimneys belonged to him! To think that he was now entitled to draw cheques in the name of Carr Carr and Ainsley! How his young heart must have swelled with pride! Fortunately we need not go upon mere supposition here, for we have a detailed and, the present writer ventures to think, rather charming account of the young people's thoughts on that spring evening in Catherine's diary. How much is Phil and how much Catherine the reader must decide for himself.

"*May 15th.*—Dear Phil's twenty-first birthday. . . . In the evening I wore my new dress of periwinkle blue, which came from London this morning, made to my own design. The blue is quite an unusual shade, deep yet brilliant; the dress is made of very thick silk, and heavily embroidered round the neck of the bodice and the hem with flowers in thick rich colours. I like it very much, as I think it takes off the clumsiness of my figure and makes my arms and neck look white—such vanity!—but I can see that Mamma, and still more Aunt Ellen, think it strange. Papa, however, says it suits me, so I am content. While we were waiting for the carriage—it was really rather late; Papa says Joshua is getting too old for his work, but he drove for Great-grandfather Carr, so Papa likes to keep him—while we were waiting for Joshua to come round, Phil and I walked together on the terrace. . . . The dusk was now gradually falling, and lights sprang up one by one in the Carr Foot windows; their little yellow oblongs scattered about the twilit landscape looked somehow very romantic and appealing, and seemed to soften one's heart and arouse in one's blood all those 'sensations sweet' which Wordsworth has so beautifully described in the *Lines above Tintern Abbey*. I think we both felt the influence of the scene's tender charm; for Phil began to talk very confidentially to me about his ambitions. I could not quite make out what these were; but we both agreed that life ought to be a very much finer and brighter and more splendid thing than the last generation seems to have made of it, and we shall try to make *our* lives so. I said I was very ambitious, and Phil said so was he. I asked him again what his ambitions were, but he hesitated and said he did not know exactly, except that he wanted Carr Foot Mills to be the biggest and finest manufacturing mills in the West Riding, and the firm of Carr Carr and Ainsley to do very well and be very successful and be renowned all over Yorkshire for the quality of their cloth. I said it was a noble ambition to wish to be distinguished for the quality and beauty of the things one made; and Phil agreed, but not with any great animation. He kicked at the gravel of the terrace as we walked along, and seemed to be rather thoughtful or rather uninterested, I hardly knew which. Then Didymus" (Catherine's collie) "came towards us round the corner of the house. Dear Phil at once woke up from his pensive mood; he snapped his fingers and cried out: 'Well, Dido! Well, old man!' and fondled dear Didymus, who seems very much attached to him. We both stood still to caress Didymus, and afterwards did not recommence walking, but leaned against the balustrade, looking out over the peaceful scene, while Didymus wandered about the terrace behind us, sniffing at the plants. Presently he lay down with a thud and a kind of comfortable sigh, and went to sleep.

Then everything was very quiet. After a while Phil seemed to wish to say something to me, but hardly knew how to begin; he pretended to look over his shoulder towards Didymus, and told me in a mumbling kind of way that in the indenture he and Papa had signed that morning there was a clause which says that each partner shall be faithful and just to the other partner. I was deeply touched, and said: 'I am sure you will always be *that*.' Phil said no more; I think perhaps he was rather shy at having shown his feelings—though so noble and so creditable to him—to me thus. While we were standing silently there together the dusk had been deepening, and all of a sudden it was quite dark: the little yellow oblongs became twinkling points of light; the mill chimneys vanished; the elm trees by the paddock loomed but vaguely; the slim young moon shone out and ruled the sky. It was all so intensely beautiful that I felt I should like to stretch out my arms and fold the lovely dusky landscape to my breast. I could not help making one of my 'ausbrüche von schwärmerei,' as Miss Thompson used to call them, about it to Phil. How many lovely things, I said, there were in the world to look at! How exciting it was to think that at that very instant, while we were standing together on the terrace waiting for poor old Joshua to bring round the prosaic carriage, at that very instant far-off snowy mountain peaks were flushed with the last gleams of the setting sun, deep rivers were silently flowing through deserted canyons, waves were breaking in white curls on the darkening shores, immense trees were slowly rustling their massive branches in the wild and sombre forests, while in the great cities music was sounding and parliaments debated the fate of the world; everywhere great songs were being sung, great poems were being written, great dreams were being dreamed, great deeds were being wrought, while the stars looked on and the world turned slowly round. While I was saying all this (in my usual headlong manner) I quite trembled with excitement and enthusiasm, but when I had finished I felt nervous and uncomfortable, and said hastily to Phil that I did not expect he felt like that at all. With his usual kindness he replied cheerfully that, oh yes! he did; only he preferred to think that at that very moment trains were dashing all over the earth, proud ships clove the foam, machines stood quiet and calm in all the mills, waiting for the morrow's steam to move and thud powerfully in their iron beds; while in the great cities lights would be gleaming, dance-music sounding, cabs rapidly rolling, fair women smiling, and men striving manfully to please them; everywhere people were eating and drinking and loving and laughing, while the stars looked on and the world turned slowly round. I have perhaps not recorded his words *exactly* as he spoke them, but that was the gist of what he said. As he finished speaking he laughed heartily, and slightly pinched my left arm, in fun. I could not help feeling that though there was no *harm* in this view of the world, yet there was nothing very *good* either, and it showed that lack of seriousness (in viewing life) which I have often noticed in Phil. I was just beginning, in as kind a way as I could, to mention what I felt about this, when Papa's voice sounded from the window to say that the carriage was at the door, and we went in."

On the faces of their three elders there was no doubt an expression of benevolent inquiry as they entered; so much moonlight must surely have brought on a proposal which would once again unite an Ainsley with a Carr! But the young people had nothing to report. Catherine had left her cloak upstairs, and went off dreamily to fetch it; as usual when confronted by a mirror she discovered that her hair was coming down; she forgot the flight of time in readjusting it, and had to be shouted for from the hall by her father. At last, however, she came slowly down the great Carr Fold staircase—it was Carrara marble; its purchase and transport had been superintended fifty years ago by the sculptor Edmund, and it was flanked at its base by the full-length marble of Benjamin before referred to, and a bust of Edmund's sister Elizabeth. The party settled themselves in the waiting carriage. The two sisters sat side by side, in which position their family resemblance became marked; proud of their glossy and abundant hair they both still wore side curls, though the fashion for these was really over. Catherine, between them, looked very blonde and decidedly of another race. William Ainsley and his nephew sat with their backs to the horses; William feasted his eyes on his daughter, and Phil, having nothing better to do, rested his gaze on Catherine too.

"We shall be late," observed Mr. Ainsley in his rough full voice, drawing out his chronometer. "But I don't imagine that will matter."

Ellen and Adelaide seemed to agree, while Phil and Catherine exchange a glance of regret.

The carriage swept sedately round the broad curve in front of the house and turned into the drive; then passing out by the lower Carr Fold lodge began to negotiate carefully the steep and winding road which led down into the village.[1] Outside the Carr Foot Mechanics' Institute, of which Benjamin Ainsley had been one of the original founders, and from which there now streamed shafts of

[1] The preceding Saturday's issue of the *Hudley News* records the decision of the Carr Foot Local Board, of which William Ainsley was then Chairman, to purchase supplies of "Stone, sets and dross," for the repair of this road, which was known as Carr Bank.

light, heat and noise, the carriage stopped, and the party descended. A flight of steps led up to the door of the Institute, which, like so many other Carr Foot buildings, had serious inequalities of ground to contend with. The Ainsleys slowly ascended this, Adelaide, who found the steps painful, leaning heavily on her husband's arm; at the top they were met by the organising secretary of the Young Men's Class, who informed them in a whisper that the entertainment had begun—they had waited some time for Mr. Ainsley, but had concluded that he was prevented from attending, and had commenced the evening's proceedings without him. "Papa," says Catherine, "did not apologise for our unpunctuality, or attribute it to Joshua and myself, as he justly might have done; he simply smiled in a rather sarcastic way he sometimes has, and said that as the loss was ours, it did not signify. We then passed on, except Aunt Ellen, who felt ill and went home again." Catherine concludes her entry for that day as follows:—"The entertainment was rather odd, I thought. The voices were good, but so untrained, and the choice of music was very, *very* bad. Only one composer in the whole programme whose name would be known in Leipzig—Chopin. Still all the performers seemed so hearty and sincere about it that one did not mind. The exception was a very horrid man who sang, and I grieved Papa by not wanting to listen to him. Unfortunately the man's sister was sitting behind us, and heard what I said. It was all very awkward, but really the man *was vulgar*. I must learn to control my feelings more carefully, I know, and I ought not to close dear Phil's birthday on such a note of criticism; but he *was* a *horrid* man. Ugh!"

This is accurate (and convincing) as far as it goes; but we are possessed of information from other sources about the occurrences of this important evening, and must give a rather more detailed account of it. It must be understood, then, that the large room in which the entertainment was being held was entered by two doors from a corridor which ran beside it. One door gave access to the rear of the hall, the other, leading to the front seats, served also as entrance to the little platform, which was reached from the floor level by a couple of projecting wooden steps. The secretary guided the Ainsley party towards the second of these two doors, round which were clustered a few performers waiting their turn. As they approached these, one of them —a fair young man—turned to inspect them, whereupon Ellen suddenly said in her customary tone of irritable decision: "I shall not go in"; and turned away with an abrupt movement which set her long earrings swinging. Phil, looking at her in surprise, saw that she had turned pale, and that her breast heaved in agitation. Mrs. Ainsley also paused, and seemed to hesitate, but on her lips there was a curious smile—not altogether of displeasure—which Phil could not interpret. "Adelaide!" said William Ainsley at this point impatiently. Carr had heard that note in his uncle's voice before, and knew it to be ominous; William's face, too, bore an angry flush; so that Carr was not surprised when Mrs. Ainsley, with a mere slight compression of her lips, went on towards the performers, followed by Catherine, who as usual was in a dream, gazing upwards at the busts which decked the walls. "See your mother to the carriage, Phil," commanded Mr. Ainsley over his shoulder. The lad obeyed; fortunately Joshua had but just turned his horses, so there was no difficulty in recalling him. Phil put his mother in the carriage, and with his hand on the door asked, somewhat ruefully, if he should accompany her. Ellen's dark haggard face expressed angry surprise. "Certainly!" she threw out fiercely. Seeing her son's face fall, she added on a note of bitterness: "Well—never mind. Perhaps you'd better stay." Carr dutifully protested, and began to climb into the carriage, but his mother had by now collected her thoughts. "No," she commanded, with an imperious wave of her hand towards the Institute: "Stay—stay with Catherine. Shut the door and tell Joshua to drive on." Joshua, who had no mind to keep his horses standing a second longer than was necessary, immediately complied; and Phil was left hurt and bewildered—as his mother so often left him—standing at the foot of the Institute steps. He obeyed her instructions to the letter, however, as he usually did; for he entered the hall by the door in the rear, and made his way firmly up to Catherine, who was sitting beside the secretary in the row behind the one occupied by her parents. She gave her cousin an affectionate if rather absent smile, while from William Ainsley Carr received a backward glance which expressed decided approval. The lad sat down feeling more cheerful, and gave his attention, with the seriousness of youth, to the performance.

As this entertainment was reported in the *Hudley News* of Saturday, May 17th, 1879, we are able to give a detailed account of it. The items were of the kind customary to the period and place. A duet on the piano and concertina opened the programme. Then somebody invoked in song the dove with the white, white breast, and being encored tunefully besought the donor of a heart to take it back again: somebody else played a scherzo by Chopin: somebody (a bass) sang "Down in the Deep" with great gusto: somebody announced (with chords) that they had stood on the bridge at midnight: and somebody else (a Master J. Illingworth, who has an interest for us as being the coachman Joshua's grandson, and also for other reasons which will appear later) recited something very serious and moral, from Longfellow. There then came upon the platform that performer whom Catherine's diary stigmatises so severely as "a very horrid man"; he was the one at sight of whom Ellen had fled. He was, in fact, a mere youth, barely twenty-two, but he had a sophisticated air which made him look older. Of only middle height, but blond and slender, he was at this time considered by many critics —including himself—to be a very handsome fellow, with his fair face, as smooth and clear and pink as a girl's, his smooth fair head, his long straight nose, his large grey-blue eyes, his long fair lashes, and the aristocratic little mole on his right cheekbone. The only points in his appearance at which an unprejudiced observer could cavil were the expression of his eyes, which was to the last degree insolent, and the back of his head, which was lamentably straight. Of the second defect he was conscious, and tried to remedy it by keeping his chin well raised, and slightly pursing his full mouth; but he regarded the first as a merit, and liked to accentuate the boldness of his look by arching his fair brows and staring very directly at any person whom he wished to impress. At the moment this person was Catherine. As he was a native of Hudley, called in to add lustre to the entertainment by his comic songs, the fame of which had reached Carr Foot, he was not familiar with the Ainsleys, but he had been immensely pleased by the arrival of the Ainsley party, which he saw at once was composed of rich and important people, such as his soul loved. Obviously they had come in a carriage. A girl with them too! (A girl was always necessary to Lomas's full enjoyment.) Not a very pretty girl, certainly, but how striking she looked in that curious blue dress with those odd flowers! Her black cloak, too, so elegant with its squirrel hood and trimmings! Her brooch! One saw at once that she was truly distinguished! What a good thing he had put on his dress suit! His father did not know he had one, and Cordelia—bother her!—was sure to tell and make trouble, but at the moment that did not seem to matter. He could barely conceal his impatience for his own performance to begin, and made an attempt to move it to an earlier place in the programme, but this was thwarted by the other performers. At last it was his turn; with his head in the air and an important mien he entered the room and strutted on to the platform, preceded by the heavy Annie Hallas, who always played his accompaniments in those days—his sister Cordelia would not adapt her time to his; moreover, she disapproved of his songs, criticised his singing, and in general was likely to cause disaster. While Lomas waited for the rackety music to come to the end of the introduction he fingered his black bow, shot his cuffs and looked about him with a preoccupied air so as to display his fine grey eyes, which were undoubtedly handsome. (If he had been put to Catherine's "at this very instant" test just then he would probably have been thinking that all over the world handsome tenors in evening dress were facing brilliant and enthusiastic audiences: everywhere applause was sounding, fair women were admiring and yielding, men were triumphant and adored, while the chandeliers sparkled and the earth sped swiftly round.) Annie Hallas now gave him an alarmed and anxious look over her plump shoulder; he took his cue and began to sing, in his light genteel tones, an insinuating ditty which made "a starry night for a ramble" rhyme with "tripping o'er a bramble," and went on to state emphatically that if the singer *did* kiss a girl or two in a bushy dell there need be no harm done, for *he*'d never tell. His expression as he sang this suggested everything that could possibly be suggested in this connection, and he gave Catherine the full benefit of a look which he thought irresistibly rakish, but which really (owing to his youthful inexperience) rather resembled a bilious leer. Subsequent verses related his experiences in bushy dells with various girls who had obligingly tripped over brambles for his benefit.

The words of this song, which sound so mild to us today, then seemed decidedly more piquant, and they gained immensely in innuendo from the singer's look and tone. The whole performance was, in fact, extremely vulgar, having neither humour, grace, nor pleasant intention to redeem it from the crudest kind of pornographic appeal. Its reception was fruitful of the gravest consequences in Carr's career, and must be considered in detail.

What the audience in general thought of it we have, of course, no means of knowing. (The *Hudley News* merely records the name of the singer and the title of his song.) Mr. Ainsley, who had been made rather cynical about such matters by his disappointment in Adelaide, raised his eyebrows and gave a hard smile; his face then clouded abruptly and he shot a keen glance at his wife. Adelaide, however, cast down her eyes and made her face inscrutable; she probably did not dislike the sniggering coarseness of this young man—whose identity she thought she had guessed from her sister's abrupt withdrawal—as much as she felt it proper to simulate; but in any case she did not mean to let William Ainsley read her thoughts on the subject of the singer, in case it should prove that she had guessed aright. Carr, who very much disliked anything at all coarse or gross or in any way suggestive, put the singer down at once as an insufferable ass and a bounder eaten up with conceit: just the sort of fellow, in fact, that he simply could not stand. Having decided this, he ceased to listen to him and began to think about next Saturday's football.

Catherine's reactions were unfortunately deeper. If her feelings are to be understood at all, it must be borne in mind that both by nature and upbringing she was essentially grave, truthful and serious; that she rather lacked humour: that art of any kind, but more especially the musical art, was to her something lofty and sacred: that she was very young: and that insincerity, whether in art or in life, was not only odious to her but perhaps the deadliest of all the sins. At his very first appearance the singer's jaunty look and air had excited in her a shudder of repulsion; then the silly little jangling tune of the song sounded to her serious young ears meretricious, vile, nay, almost an offence against musical decency; and as for the words! How can one over-estimate their effect upon Catherine's chaste young mind? As the song went on the singer seemed to her so awful that she fixed her eyes upon him in a kind of fascination induced by horror; this was, of course, misunderstood by Lomas, whose look became more arch and insinuating than ever; and at the end of the verse he actually had the inconceivable audacity—and, we may add, for we must be fair even to Lomas, the youthful social ignorance—to look in Catherine's direction and wink. It was too much; every fibre, artistic and womanly, of Catherine's earnest nature quivered with a pure and righteous indignation; the colour mounted to her brow, and as she was not yet old enough or experienced enough to sit still under an outrage, she drew her cloak about her and rose to her feet. "I can't bear to hear this any more," she said. Her voice, though not raised, was sufficiently clear to be heard all over the room, and for a moment it caused—not unnaturally—consternation. The singer faltered in his amatory recital, and the smooth pink of his cheeks became scarlet; Carr, immensely startled, remained motionless, gazing up at his cousin from eyes round with astonishment; the alarmed secretary gulped his surprise; and a kind of horrified hush brooded over the room. Then the moment passed; Carr jumped up, Lomas pursued his brambly way, though with uneven voice and diminished confidence, and Mr. Ainsley, turning upon his daughter a hot face and a choleric eye, said in a tone of intense exasperation: "Sit down, Catherine! Sit down!"

Catherine, who had never heard that note in her father's voice before, was so bewildered by it that for a moment she remained standing, while Carr laid an irresolute hand on her arm. Suddenly a voice behind them shot out in furious jerky whispers: "Why can't you sit *down?* Other people want to see beside you! You're upsetting the singer."

"But he's so horrid," faltered the unnerved Catherine weakly.

"He's not!" cried the voice, tearful with rage. "You're very rude. He's my brother."

Intensely abashed, the cousins gave the speaker one startled glance of horrified apology, and sank down upon the form, Lomas stopped singing, a verse or two earlier than he had intended, and amid very faint applause made a confused exit; a buzz of conversation—naturally rather animated—rattled upon the heated air, then a young lady climbed the platform and stated her conviction (vocally) that "we'd better bide a wee," and the incident was over.

It was an incident, however, which Carr was never to forget as long as he lived, for during his swift backward glance he had seen the flaming auburn hair curling fiercely round a haughty, excited little face, the brilliantly clear complexion, the bright blue eyes, the pretty teeth, the charming ears, the small straight nose, which at that time lent such a tender youthful charm to Cordelia. Such was the cousin's embarrassment at their *faux pas* about the describer of starry rambles that during the ensuing items they held their heads down and went through an agony of blushing, but from time to time Carr stole a cautious glance behind him, and studied the pure delicate profile and soft agitated breast of the young lady whose stinging rebuke still smarted in his ears. Once he caught her glance; how her blue eyes sparkled as she indignantly glared at him! The soft-hearted Carr could never bear the thought that he had inflicted a wound on anyone, and not to be at peace with any of his neighbours made him wretched, so he ventured a timid and apologetic smile in her direction; she threw up her head and stared over his shoulder very haughtily, but her lips quivered, and Carr's remorse became painful. She was wearing a short sealskin jacket, very new and glossy; the effect of her bright hair against its soft furry blackness was really extraordinary—or so at least thought Carr, who could not keep his eyes from her sulky, silly, sweet little face.

The entertainment proceeded. The concertina, the Chopin player and the bass all performed again; the young ladies sang about the bells of Aberdovey and angels ever bright and fair; and Master Illingworth gave a temperance recitation. Between this and the next item, which was to be the last, a good deal of confused argument could be heard outside the stage door; and when this at length opened, to Catherine's intense relief Lomas did not appear. His place had evidently been taken by the bass at short notice, for the latter did not know the words of the duet—"Mrs. Wright, Mrs. Wright, you'll ruin me quite"—which he now performed with Miss Annie Hallas, very well. He sang it, however, so heartily and so guilelessly that he made a good impression in spite of his occasional blunders; and when the affair had closed with a speech from the secretary, announcing that they would have six pounds eight to hand over to the building fund, everyone except the Ainsley party and Lomas and Cordelia went home in a pleasant mood, though it was disappointing to find that rain had begun to fall while they were within.

Joshua and the carriage awaited the Ainsleys at the bottom of the steps; while Adelaide and Catherine were taking their places Carr hung politely back, and had the painful pleasure of seeing the young lady with the red hair —it was now concealed beneath a sealskin cap—and her obnoxious brother come quickly down the steps, followed pantingly by the accompanist, and hurry away through the village. What a pure, pretty little face it was! What a slender, delicate little figure! What energy was expressed in every line of her body as she walked! And *what* a temper she had! For the life of him he could not help smiling at this reflection, then grew sober again as the rain began to damp his crisp hair. What a shame for her new sealskin to get wet!

"Phil!" called Mr. Ainsley sharply from within the carriage.

Carr climbed in hastily, and they drove off.

At first they were all silent, but after a while the slow pace of the horses up the steep Carr Bank seemed almost to demand conversation, and Adelaide hazarded the remark that Joshua's grandson had done well. Mr. Ainsley gave an acquiescing grunt, and Catherine, who was feeling very unhappy about what she now regarded as her breach of manners, agreed with a show of enthusiasm. Carr longed to ask the name of the starry ramble singer, but dared not, for his uncle's brow was still uncommonly black; he reflected instead that Joshua's grandson lived in Carr Foot and might be sought out and interrogated on the point. He was spared the trouble of this, however, for the earnest Catherine, who had not even yet learned that there are times and places for the best of actions, began to express her contrition for the evening's occurrence. She did so regret having grieved her father! She was so sorry, too, that the singer's sister had been hurt!

"Let it be a lesson to you, my dear," observed Mr. Ainslay grimly, "always to be careful what you say in a public place."

Catherine said eagerly that it should be, oh, it should! (She did not know, poor child, just how true her words would prove.) There was a slight pause, then Adelaide, who had evidently now made up her mind what line to take on this subject, turned her face towards her husband, and looking him steadily in the eyes, inquired in her most languid tones what that young Eastwood did for his living nowadays.

Her husband gave her a black look. "Do you mean that fellow whose song Catherine objected to?" he then inquired dryly, while Carr pricked up his ears.

Adelaide mildly assented. "He's not with his father, I believe," she said. Seeing her mistake, she added hastily: "So Ellen tells me."

Mr. Ainsley gave her an even blacker look. She had, in fact, with her usual maladroitness, given herself away completely, had revealed that the family circumstances of Taylor Eastwood—for he, of course, as Adelaide had guessed and the discerning reader will long ago have perceived, was father to the Lomas and Cordelia whose acquaintance Carr had made that night—were known to her and of interest to her. And why should they be of interest to her, save because the man who drove Hammond Carr away from Hudley was of interest to her? No wonder William Ainsley's look was black. Carr, on the other hand, to whom the name of Eastwood meant absolutely nothing, except as that of the owner of the sealskin jacket, listened joyfully, his head bent forward, his brown eyes bright and eager. So her name was Eastwood! William Ainsley's glance rested for a moment on his nephew before he replied: "He's in the designing room at Enoch Barker's."

Carr leaned back, an enormous and pleasurable excitement suddenly filling his heart. The designing room at Enoch Barker's! In that case Eastwood—and his sister—would be well known to Charlie Gill. He could get to know them through Charlie. A vista of the most delightful possibilities opened out before him—that was, of course, if she ever forgave him. What was her Christian name, he wondered? Catherine was evidently wondering too, for she timidly put the question.

"Her name! No doubt your mother can tell you, my dear," replied Mr. Ainsley, in tones rather drier than before. He was perhaps realising that by announcing Lomas Eastwood's business so promptly he too had revealed that he was interested in the Eastwoods and had not forgotten those occurrences twenty-one years ago.

Catherine turned inquiringly to her mother. Mrs. Ainsley may perhaps have winced slightly beneath her daughter's earnest gaze; she may perhaps have reflected angrily that if William chose to be disagreeable about her interest in the Eastwoods, he should have something to be disagreeable about; at all events she coloured and said sharply: "I believe she's called Cordelia."

"What a curious name!" said Catherine, interested. She had that faculty of the noble-minded which enables them to admire fine deeds even when they are done in opposition to themselves, and now that her agitation had subsided and she was able to view the incident calmly, she admired Cordelia's fierce defence of her brother—Catherine would have done just the same for Phil, she thought, any day of the week. "I never met anyone of that name before—except, of course," she concluded seriously, "in Shakespeare."

"It suits her," murmured Carr.

His aunt glanced at him sharply, and gave her curious half-smile. She would perhaps have spoken, but at that moment the carriage began to negotiate the awkward turn from the road to the Carr Fold drive. Adelaide was always nervous at this turn; she paled now, clutched at the side of the vehicle, and held her breath till they had safely rounded the corner. "I wish you'd have that gateway altered, William!" she exclaimed petulantly then.

"Oh no, Mamma!" protested Catherine, shocked—the pillars of the gateway were, in fact, almost the only surviving relic of the Elizabethan Carr Fold. Catherine contended mildly for their preservation on the score of this antiquity; Adelaide argued the point; Mr. Ainsley smiled grimly at them, and Carr, looking out of the window, thought about Cordelia. The Carr Fold rhododendrons, wet with rain, gleamed in the light of the carriage lamps and vanished again; he thought again, sorrowingly, of the sealskin.

"But, Mamma," Catherine was crying, "you know, Papa always says——"

"I know you always agree with your father about everything," said Adelaide pettishly, drawing her shawl about her.

The carriage drew up at the Carr Fold door.

"Well, Phil," said Mr. Ainsley as they dismounted, with the usual undercurrent of sarcasm in his full tones: "I hope you've enjoyed your twenty-first birthday."

Carr assured him sincerely and emphatically that he had.

Ellen had already returned to Atack Place in Joshua's care while the others were at the entertainment; and as it was not to be thought of that the horses should do the journey twice, Mr. Ainsley invited Phil to stay the night at Carr Fold. But the lad refused; the walk home would do him good, he said, and the rain would do him no harm. Adelaide protested, Catherine frankly envied him the chance; his uncle, who did not believe in coddling young men even when they were partners in Carr Carr and Ainsley, gave him a kindly good-night and let him go; so that soon the young Carr found himself striding through the night with the wind in his hair and the rain on his face. (His new patent "Bismarck" flexible silk hat—as advertised in the *Hudley News* that week—he concealed beneath his coat for economy's sake.) He did not take the shortest way home, which lay across the hill, but slipped down into Carr Foot village again, approached the Carr Foot Mills, and striking a match read the name of the firm on the huge brass plate on the office door. As he stood there he suddenly threw back his head and gave one of his merry laughs; and as he could not possibly have been laughing at Carr Carr and Ainsley, we must conclude—indeed, we have it on the best authority: his own: for it is from his own lips that the story of this night has been compiled—that he was laughing about Cordelia. The darling! The haughty, angry little darling! She had thoroughly got the better of him in that encounter! The joke was against him, there was no doubt about that! Did she dance well?

He wondered, and hoped earnestly that she did, for of all the many girls he had seen and flirted with—and they *were* many—this one somehow took his fancy most. What a temper! What brilliant blue eyes! What hair! *He* did not care about its being red! He liked it! (It must be remembered that at this date red hair had not the vogue it subsequently gained.) What a swift, furious rush of words had come from her pretty lips! What a sweet, innocent, cross, determined little face she had! What a darling! He shook his head over her, and walked off through the wet darkness with a smile.

About this time Catherine was finishing her diary for the day with that emphatic "Ugh!"

It will be well to give a short account of the Eastwood family at this point, before proceeding to the events which followed upon their encounter with P. J. Carr and Catherine Ainsley.

Taylor Eastwood's father had been a cloth-dresser in the employ of Mr. Enoch Barker senior. Taylor himself early found employment in a printing works; and if told in detail his life would resemble one of the biographies retailed by Samuel Smiles. In brief, he was an industrious, vigorous, thoughtful, independent-minded man, a great leader, a man of the strictest integrity, a pronounced radical, and a most dauntless, dogged and persistent fighter for liberty wherever he thought he saw it oppressed. In 1858, when he was already married—to Mary Lomas, a Scotch serving-girl in the employ of Mr. Enoch Barker (junior), whose wife came from Paisley—and the father of a child, the great crisis of his life occurred. He heard Charles Bradlaugh speak at a meeting in Bradford, and forthwith became the determined atheist that he ever afterwards remained. To hear his idolised "Iconoclast" he went to

Sheffield, Doncaster, Bolton, Wakefield, Leeds; he was one of the audience at Sowerby Bridge when Bradlaugh spoke on "George Prince of Wales," while policemen, under a misapprehension as to the title of the lecture, were being poured into the town; and it was he who printed the handbills for Bradlaugh's debate in Hudley in 1875. He was a member of the National Secularist Society and of the Reform League; he took in the *National Reformer,* and read it with a fierce gusto which was rather increased than diminished by Messrs. Smith's refusal to sell it; and one of his most cherished possessions was a signed photograph of Mazzini, the back of which formed a receipt for his subscription towards the fund for the emancipation of Italy. Taylor's appearance agreed well with his character: for he was a short, thin, gingerish little man, full to the brim with a restless vigour which seemed to make his scanty hair positively bristle with determination. His heart beat fast, his breathing was rapid, his small blue eyes were very keen and bright; and he had a habit of clutching the lapels of his coat tightly in both hands, which revealed the man's argumentative and pugnacious character rather strikingly. In spite of the fierce antagonism which his religious and political opinions naturally excited in Hudley he prospered in his business career, for he was an excellent printer and a good sign-painter, and the fighting quality of the man aroused a certain amount of sympathy in his fellow-Yorkshiremen, who do not belong to a county noted for meekness.

Taylor was respected also for his conduct to the widow Hallas. His defiance of Hammond Carr was by no means unpopular in some sections of Hudley; and his stubborn pertinacity in extracting every farthing from William Ainsley which he could by any means be persuaded to pay on behalf of the defaulter earned him the admiration of those who had found the combination of William Ainsley and his solicitor Nicholas Whiteley too much for them in previous litigations. For a period of years Taylor Eastwood was the widow Hallas's guide, philosopher and friend—not a very enviable position, for Mrs. Hallas was a silly, helpless woman; Cordelia told the present writer that she always reminded her of Mrs. Nickleby, though in a lower walk of life. Then when the widow died, in 1869, Taylor took her youngest child—the others, of whom there were many, were all married—Annie, then a girl of fifteen, into his own household, and gave her every benefit which he gave to his own two children, putting aside her own meagre funds for her later use. At that time Lomas was a precocious twelve-year-old, and Cordelia a child of ten. Fortunately Annie was a mild, slow, simple creature; very fair and gentle, with a snub nose, a mouth which was usually open, and a soft, indeterminate, rounded face; she adored Lomas and was rather afraid of Cordelia. We say "fortunately," because had Annie been otherwise she would undoubtedly have clashed with Cordelia; even as it was, Mr. Eastwood's stern sense of justice and equal treatment of the two girls sometimes excited in his own daughter a turbulent jealousy. This jealousy was quite unfounded, for Cordelia was the apple of her father's eye and knew it; but Cordelia's passionate and excitable nature was not always amenable to reason, and any mark of favour showed by Taylor to Annie had often to be atoned for by a bigger favour to the younger girl. Mr. Eastwood had, for instance, given Annie a gold bracelet for her twenty-fifth birthday, and shortly afterwards had found it necessary to present Cordelia with a sealskin jacket by way of peace-offering—a most unwarrantable luxury, according to the married

Hallases and the Misses Barker, for a girl in her position. Beneath his rather alarming exterior, indeed, few men were warmer-hearted than Taylor Eastwood; he was almost excessively attached to his family and his home.

It now remains to indicate the characters and upbringing of Lomas and Cordelia. They present a very curious and interesting study in family likeness and differentiation.

Mrs. Eastwood, a large, loving, simple woman, a native of a small village near Paisley, was a Methodist, and in spite of his unflinching personal atheism, Taylor could not bring himself to hurt her by educating the children in his view. After one or two half-hearted attempts he gave it up, and they were both brought up in their mother's religion. Its moral tenets had had, however, very little influence on Lomas's character; and his father's austere precepts were first hateful, then tedious, and finally laughable, in his eyes—though he paid his parents' moral beliefs the compliment of lip-service. Cordelia, on the other hand, though she detested her father's politics and thought his lack of religion disreputable, was entirely saturated with his moral ideas. As regards morality in the narrow sense of the term, it must be stated frankly that Lomas was lax; and the presence of Annie in the house was not good for him. Cordelia, on the other hand, had a positively fierce purity, and hated caresses, even from her father. As a child Lomas caused his parents intense anguish by his habit of telling lies; and though the coming of years brought him discretion in this matter, it is to be feared that this childish habit was never entirely eradicated. He lied out of egoism, in order to further his own importance; Cordelia, on the other hand, was also egoistic, but her egoism made her furiously, fierily truthful—she was too convinced of the superiority of her own personality ever to deny it by a lie, or even by a polite evasion: politeness in fact was not Cordelia's strong suit. Lomas was habitually extravagant with money, excusing his fault by promises of future austerity; Cordelia longed with all the passionate intensity of her young heart to be extravagant, but some tremendous moral veto within her made her thrifty and careful. Both attached much importance to clothes and desired to dress well, but whereas Lomas went in for many and cheap, Cordelia always bought few and dear: the best within her reach was never quite good enough for her. Both brother and sister were indeed terrifically ambitious; they longed to get on, to be gentlefolk, to escape from the decent mediocrity of their house in Majorca Road to some large opulent sphere; but whereas Lomas wanted to be a rich gentleman so that he could indulge in pleasures now denied to him, Cordelia's ideas were far more earnest. When Cordelia thought of proud ships cleaving the foam, she thought of them as being in the charge of tremendously respected and responsible captains; when she thought of trains dashing powerfully over the earth, she thought of them as bearing distinguished people on highly important errands. Cabs, in her mind, were always hurrying celebrities to great state functions; she was always thinking of great careers taking their splendid course, of great empires exercising their terrific sway; life seemed to her to be composed of noble strugglings to conquer Fate and graceful acceptings of homage when one was successful. Cordelia, though in some ways sentimental, had inherited her father's grim sense of humour, and many things in art, poetry and music were a sealed book to her; Lomas, on the other hand, had no humour at all, but he had inherited his father's skill in sign-writing, was a very tolerable designer, and took a real pleasure—in so far as anything about Lomas was real—in the weaker forms of art. Lomas feared Cordelia without knowing why; Cordelia saw most of Lomas's faults very clearly, had a shrewd suspicion of the others, hated them, despised her brother, but would have worked her fingers to the bone, as the saying is, to make him worthy and successful.

To Mr. Eastwood and Cordelia, then, who were people of the strictest personal honour, and to Mrs. Eastwood, whose gentle soul was shocked by any deviation from her religious code, Lomas's lapses were a source of agony; and it was left to Annie to adore him fully, completely, altogether, just as he was. She it was who helped him in all his little deceptions, who learned his accompaniments and admired his songs, copied—feebly—all his attempts at fashionable manners, laughed at his smoking-room puns, and listened to his stories of his amorous conquests with large serious eyes. Everything Lomas did was right to her. It was, in fact, the gentle Annie who found the courage to suggest to Taylor, after a period of stormy misery at the close of Lomas's school-days, that it would perhaps be better if Lomas's work took him away from his father. Taylor Eastwood was immensely disconcerted and disappointed, but he always knew how to face facts; he considered the matter, decided that Annie was right, and took the necessary steps; and since Lomas had begun to work for Enoch Barker, Majorca Road had certainly been more peaceful.

The houses composing the lower end of Majorca Road, Hudley, have now been pulled down in the process of widening the main approach to Hudley from the south, which crosses Majorca Road at this point; and Number 39 (the Eastwoods' house) is no longer in existence. The roar and grime of the traffic have now made this district sordid and depressing; but even in 1879 Majorca Road was not at all a pretentious place, though it was doubtless pleasant enough, for one side of it then looked on to fields. The houses were of the superior workmen's cottage type, and Taylor Eastwood was probably the only man living there who owned the business he worked in. He liked the road because his printing works were just round the corner—they too are now demolished—and he had bought Number 39 and added to the premises in the rear. He also rented or bought—it cannot be ascertained which—an extra piece of land at the bottom of his small back garden, and here he grew celery, cabbages, potatoes and other such useful vegetables, for he was a tremendous gardener. In the garden itself he cultivated flowers: dahlias, southernwood, lavender, stocks, snapdragons, peonies and a few nasturtiums—though none of these, of course, in as great variety as we have them to-day—and along one side of his domain was a rockery which was his special pride. A long window in the back room of the house led down by one step into the level garden, and in the summer he was always in and out of this whenever he was at home.

Such, then, was the house, and such the circumstances, to which Lomas and Cordelia Eastwood and Annie Hallas were returning on the night of May 15th, 1879.

Now that Cordelia has entered Carr's life, our materials for his biography are very much fuller (see Preface, p. vii); and we are able to give a detailed account of many of its incidents as recollected by an actual witness. We know, for instance, that on this particular night the trio lost themselves rather badly as they walked home, owing to Lomas's obstinate persistence in a topographical mistake, in which he was, as usual, backed up by Annie; and that Cordelia, angered by this, broke a tactful silence about the events of the evening, and let fly at Lomas some severe sisterly criticisms. Hitherto Lomas had managed to exclude her from his public performances, and this was the first she had ever witnessed. His dress suit, his song, his voice, the management of his eyes and the way he shot his cuffs, all came in for Cordelia's angry scorn; and at one point in the discussion she summed up the performance in a pungent phrase. Lomas was accusing her of having no sense of humour. "I don't see any humour," said Cordelia hotly, "in making a fool of yourself."

Lomas, who was already in a very unenviable state of mind, positively trembled with rage and mortification at this.

"I don't know what those people in front would think of you, I'm sure," pursued Cordelia remorselessly.

"I don't know and I don't care," said Lomas in a high, strained voice, sustaining the facetious tone with difficulty. After a pause he added: "Who were they?"

Cordelia too was interested in this, and the ensuing discussion soothed their ruffled breasts.

Lomas opined that the fellow who stood up was called Carr—he had seen him once or twice with Charlie Gill. At that time Charlie Gill was rather a suitor of Cordelia's, but she did not like to be teased about him, so she said severely: "I'm surprised Charlie Gill should choose friends with such bad manners." After a pause she added: "Does he own Carr Foot then?"

"Who? Charlie Gill?" inquired Lomas tiresomely.

"You know perfectly well I mean the one who was there to-night," replied Cordelia with her customary severity. "You said his name was Carr."

Lomas thereupon explained with considerable picturesque detail—genealogies, especially when they were landed and aristocratic, were meat and drink to him—the well-known Hudley story of the extinction of the Carr Foot Carrs.

"Then what Carr is this one?" demanded Cordelia, a little disappointment in her tone.

"I think he's the son of the one who ran off with Annie's money," replied Lomas virtuously. His sister's silence told him that he had somehow scored. "Yes, his father was Hammond Carr, the man who ran off with Mrs. Hallas's money," he repeated with triumphant malice. "And he looks just the same kind of fellow, I think."

"At any rate he doesn't go about making a fool of himself on platforms," threw out Cordelia hotly, and in spite of Annie's soft murmur of protest the wrangle began afresh.

When they at last reached Majorca Road they found Taylor sitting up for them, as indeed he invariably did when his children were out at night. He was in an angry mood, exhorted them peremptorily to look at the clock, and administered a stern reproof for their lateness. Cordelia and Lomas were temperamentally inclined to receive all reproofs in a spirit of mutiny, which in Cordelia expressed itself by fierce retorts, and in Lomas by frigid insolence. To-night they reacted in their usual manner, but in a greater degree, and there was quite a sharp little family scene. (Mrs. Eastwood was in bed upstairs.) The gentle Annie, much distressed, cast about in her mind for some remark which would divert the conversation to pleasanter themes. Poor Annie was noted for her blunders of tact, and the remark she produced was the announcement that they had seen Hammond Carr's son at the entertainment.

"What!" shouted Taylor. He drew his scanty gingerish eyebrows together in a fierce frown, and announced succintly: "Hammond Carr was a rogue."

"We aren't *sure* he was that Carr," said Lomas in a mollifying tone; he probably feared that his father's objection to his performances—already strong—would be strengthened if Hammond Carr's son appeared to be connected with them.

"Who was he with?" demanded Taylor. Lomas described the party. "It would be him," said Taylor grimly. "Those would be the Ainsleys. They say William Ainsley's going to take him into the business because of the name, and marry him to his daughter. So much the worse for the daughter, say I."

"Well, she's no beauty," said Cordelia, tossing her head.

"Likely not, but she's an heiress," observed Taylor; and he went off into one of his customary political disquisitions on the unfair inequalities of rich and poor.

We may imagine how Lomas insolently yawned and Annie listened uncomprehendingly, while Cordelia sat with an angry, perplexed look on her vivid and expressive face. When, in later years, she was urged by the present writer to indicate her thoughts about Hammond Carr's son that night, she always replied: "I didn't know what to think. I just felt angry." When pressed to say with whom she felt angry, she replied with a flash: "Everybody!" This, and indeed the whole of her behaviour that night, was very characteristic of Cordelia; but there are so many incidents in Carr's biography which reveal Cordelia's character that if this were the only reason for narrating the dialogue set down in the foregoing pages it could well have been omitted. But there is another, and a very strong, reason for its insertion, namely this: it proves beyond any shadow of doubt that when Cordelia and Lomas next met P. J. Carr and Catherine Ainsley, the identity and circumstances of the cousins were perfectly well known to the Eastwoods. Cordelia's feelings in this intermediate period

I have just described; Lomas's unfortunately have left no record. This is indeed unfortunate, because from the mixture of anger, mortification, ambition and desire for revenge which we may suppose him then to have been feeling undoubtedly arose his whole subsequent course of action, which was so far-reaching and so important; and it would be interesting to know which feeling was predominant in his mind. But surmise on such a point is dangerous; and we can judge Lomas's thoughts only by his actions.

The meeting between Carr and the Eastwoods was not long delayed, for it took place in the following month, at a picnic given by Mrs. Gill to promote the engagement of one of her daughters, which seemed to be hanging fire after looking very promising. The Reverend Humphrey and Mrs. Gill had a family typically Victorian and clerical as regards size, for it consisted of four sons and five daughters. It will not be necessary to enter into particulars about all these Gills; suffice it to say that Charlie, who was the third son, differed considerably in character from the rest of his family. The Gills as a whole were careless, generous, jolly people; always poor—Mr. Gill was a scholarly dreamer, and had a very inadequate stipend—they yet kept open house, and somehow managed to be in at everything. No party was complete without a selection of Gills; but in order not to wear out their welcome they limited the number of Gills who should attend any function to four. Good-humoured wrangles were thus constantly in progress as to who should attend what; sometimes even the drawing of lots was resorted to; but it was noticeable that Charlie always had first choice. Charlie was steady, thrifty, saving; Charlie meant to get on in life; Charlie (unlike the rest of the family) was furious if his dress shirts were surreptitiously borrowed; Charlie never flirted with pretty girls, but sensibly kept up a constant attendance on one of Enoch Barker's plain tall daughters. It was thus a matter of intense glee to the Gills when Charlie fell in love with Cordelia Eastwood. Charlie knew Lomas Eastwood at the mill, of course; and though he disliked him as a person, he thought him a clever designer, worth "keeping on the right side of," as he expressed it. Lomas was flattered by Charlie's notice; he invited him to Majorca Road, out of policy Charlie accepted; he saw Cordelia there, and promptly, to his own intense disgust, fell in love with her. The Eastwoods encouraged Charlie's suit—it must be remembered that according to the ideas of those times the Eastwoods were "beneath" the Gills socially, and Charlie was quite a *parti* for Cordelia; also Taylor liked Charlie's thrift and his determination to succeed. Out of sheer perversity the young Gills encouraged Charlie's suit too; Mrs. Gill occasionally made a mild protest, but it was always drowned in a howl of joyous laughter from the rest of the family, who liked Cordelia for her spirit and enjoyed the spectacle of the calculating Charlie involved in an unprofitable love affair. Thus it was that when Mrs. Gill decided to give a picnic to encourage Emily's affair with young George Newton—the elder brother of Carr's schoolfellow Bales—the Gill family saw to it that Lomas and Cordelia were both invited.

Charlie and Lomas had both to request permission from Mr. Barker to be absent from the mill on Saturday morning in order to attend the picnic; Mr. Barker, having found that his own daughters were also invited and longing to go, peremptorily refused Lomas but granted leave to Charlie. Lomas, however, either in an access of fury at this second mortification or because the plans he afterwards carried out were already maturing in his mind, concealed his employer's refusal from everyone and attended the picnic. As the day for this approached it was found that the Gills' invitations had been given so indiscriminately that the affair had now grown altogether beyond their scope, and it was decided to conduct in on co-operative lines. The ladies met and decided what eatables should be taken. (Cordelia remembers providing a large home-boiled tongue.) The gentlemen looked up trains and planned conveyances. Carr had, of course, been invited, and Catherine was included by his request. The picnic was to take place at Bolton Abbey; and thither, first in a reserved saloon railway carriage, and then in two waggonettes, the party of young people, with Mrs. Gill mildly in attendance in grey alpaca as chaperon, went off one fine June morning. They looked so happy and jolly as they drove along that a carter whom they passed on the road was moved to ejaculate: "Eh, but it's lucky to be some fowk!" A burst of laughing agreement came from the picnickers, and Carr threw the man half a crown to brighten, as he said, his view of life. But probably the hearts in the waggonettes were not as free from care as the carter imagined. Emily Gill, in a printed sateen which had lost its first freshness, was just beginning to turn towards that refusal of George Newton which she afterwards so bitterly regretted. Miss Barker—in white piqué—was unhappy because Charlie Gill seemed to fluctuate between herself and Cordelia; while Charlie Gill himself was wretchedly undecided whether to pursue love or mammon. Catherine, in pale blue muslin and a hat with black streamers which did not suit her, felt nervous and out of things, as she so often did amongst her contemporaries; moreover, Lomas embarrassed her by fixing on her a pathetic and wistful gaze, which made her conscience very uncomfortable. Carr, feverishly excited, was even more than usual the life and soul of the party, for the blood was rushing madly through his young veins at the sight of Cordelia. He had not managed, or had not dared, to place himself beside her; but his lively brown eyes constantly returned to rest on her bright hair and vivid face. Indeed she must have been worth looking at that day, in all the bloom of her youthful beauty. She was dressed in holland piped in black, with a black sash and a Leghorn hat plainly trimmed with black ribbon. Everything Cordelia wore was always a miracle of freshness; the holland dress, which was not new, had been carefully boiled in hay a day or two earlier to preserve its colour; and from her severe hat to her neat black Pinet boots Cordelia's slender person did justice to her austere but excellent taste. Her face, however, was pensive and downcast this morning; for Cordelia too was unhappy. She had that feeling which so often precedes a great emotional decision, a feeling that her heart was full to the brim with perplexity and turmoil—perplexity about she knew not what, turmoil she knew not why. She was rather proud of her presence among these elegant Gills and Newtons and Whiteleys and Barkers, who were superior in education and "standing'" to her usual friends; at the same time she was angry because poor Annie Hallas had not been invited. She was irritated with Charlie Gill for hovering about Miss Barker, and at the same time felt (with a toss of her head) that Charlie Gill was nothing to her and Miss Barker was welcome to him. She hated Hammond Carr's son with all her heart—how dared he be frolicking about like that, with his handsome head and his elegant light suit, thought Cordelia indignantly (and inaccurately), on poor Annie's money! At the same time she hated Catherine with all her heart because she was the girl Hammond Carr's son was going to marry. Heiress-hunting! He knew which side his bread was buttered! How plain she looked in that frilly blue! She had *no* idea how to dress, thought Cordelia scornfully. At the same time Cordelia recognised something good and fine in Catherine's heavy face, and felt rather timid before her. Lomas as usual was making a fool of himself, reflected poor Cordelia; at the same time Phil Carr—as his name appeared to be—was making a fool of himself too, and everybody seemed to like it. With all these contrary sentiments beating in it simultaneously poor Cordelia's heart may well have been full and perplexed; and as she always resented her unhappiness as a crime on the part of the universe, her mood that day was undoubtedly very black.

The topographical details of the picnic are not important. We know that at some point—perhaps the famous "hole in the wall"—the waggonettes drew up and the party descended to view Bolton Abbey; Carr offered Cordelia his hand to help her down, and she disdained it. We know that the luncheon was eaten by the Strid. This is a spot on the banks of the River Wharfe, some two miles above Bolton Abbey; as Wordsworth explains in his poem *The Force of Prayer:*

> "lordly Wharfe is there pent in
> With rocks on either side.
> The striding-place is called the Strid,
> A name which it took of yore:
> A thousand years hath it borne that name,
> And shall a thousand more."

The poem narrates the tradition that a young Romilly from the neighbouring Barden Tower, jumping across from bank to bank as he had often done before, was checked in his leap by the greyhound whose leash he held, and falling into the deep and strong torrent was drowned. His mother founded Bolton Abbey as a memorial to him. Young Romilly may have been the first to lose his life at the Strid, but he is certainly not the last. As the opposing rocks are of unequal height, it can be easily and safely cleared from the right bank; but then the necessity for a two-mile walk apart from his companions has tempted many a rash young fellow to try to leap back again from the dangerous left side, with fatal results. On this day of the picnic the young men made the usual jokes and boasts about jumping it. At this a look of anxiety appeared on the faces of all the young ladies (especially, perhaps, on Cordelia's); but Mrs. Gill, emerging from the background where she had quietly remained all day, put her foot down and forbade any suicidal jumping with a firmness which showed that Charlie's characteristics were perhaps partly hereditary. The party then separated into couples and quartettes; Carr, after Cordelia's repulse of his hand on the waggonette steps, dared not approach her, and went off with Catherine and two Gills—their merry laughter could be heard at intervals from among the woods. Lomas followed them and could not be got rid of, though they tried all the cruel devices employed on these occasions by thoughtless youth. Charlie with a sigh attached himself to Miss Barker; Cordelia fell to the lot of Nicholas Whiteley, who was not able to walk very far. Cordelia liked Nicholas Whiteley, but also rather scorned him; at this period he was just down from Cambridge, and had rather a learned air; now Cordelia shunned anything learned—to her learning meant radicalism, Bradlaugh, and the disapproval of the neighbours. When, therefore, the party reassembled and drove off in their waggonettes to Ilkley, where they were to have tea, it is probable that the hearts of most of them—with the exception of Miss Barker, who had been successful, as she thought, in detaching Charlie from Cordelia—were still sore.

At Ilkley a surprise awaited them; the young men had engaged a room in the hotel where they might have dancing, and when they had eaten an abundant tea Mrs. Gill removed her bracelets and played a waltz. Carr had the first dance with Catherine, as it was right he should; Lomas secured an unimportant Miss Gill. Cordelia sat out with Nicholas Whiteley. By this time Cordelia was sick of Nicholas Whiteley, and hated him (temporarily) with all her heart. She sat stiffly by the wall, cold and cross, and answered all his remarks in curt, not to say snappy, monosyllables: the while she kept up a running mental criticism on Catherine's clumsy and undistinguished dancing. Her face was mutinous and sulky; she hated the picnic, she hated Nicholas Whiteley, she hated Charlie Gill and Miss Barker; most of all she hated Hammond Carr's son, who, now that the first dance was over, was standing by the door with a company of young men and maidens, making them all laugh with some nonsense or other. Cordelia was an excellent judge of dancing, and she had seen that he was easily the best dancer in the room. Mrs. Gill began another waltz—this time it was Cordelia's favourite tune *Venetia*.[1] A frown of positive anguish ap-

[1] The air of *Venetia*, by Caroline Lowthian, is as follows—

peared on Cordelia's fair young brow. If she had to sit this dance out too she simply would *not* be able to bear it. Her breast heaved with indignation and resentment, and tears began slowly to smart behind her eyes. Glancing down the room beneath her downcast lashes she perceived Charlie Gill looking in her direction. Would he ask her to dance? Did she want him to do so? She looked again, and saw that Charlie had moved, and was standing in front of Miss Barker. Rage filled Cordelia's heart, and she decided in a flash that Charlie Gill was definitely finished in her regard: she would have nothing more to do with him *ever*. But she would not sit out this next dance: she would *not:* if nobody else asked her, Lomas must come and fill the gap. It was his duty. He simply *must*. She raised her head to look for him. At that moment Phil Carr suddenly left the group by the door. He crossed the room, stopped definitely in front of Cordelia, and, with merriment sparkling in his eyes and on his lips, bowed his handsome head and asked Miss Eastwood for the pleasure of this dance. Cordelia gave him a look of fury, and stood up. He put his arm about her, and they whirled away together to the measures of the dance. He steered her marvellously, his step was light and bounding, his reversing was wonderful; he was not only the best dancer in the room, he was the best dancer Cordelia had ever met or seen or heard of; his dancing was *superb*. She hated him, and kept her brilliant blue eyes angrily lowered. Her beautiful red hair was parted accurately in the centre, and curled thickly about her neat little ears; her waist was trim and slender; she was not only the best dancer in the room, but the best dancer Phil Carr had ever met or seen or heard of; she was as light as a feather, and responded rhythmically to the slightest guiding touch. Carr's whole frame was steeped in a pleasure so intense as to be poignant; he suffered agonies and was in an ecstasy of bliss; and from that moment to the day of his death he could never touch holland without a loving, reminiscent smile—it was *par excellence,* the material of romance for him. The music stopped, but Carr broke into a burst of protesting clapping; the other dancers followed suit; Phil cried "Encore! Encore!" with fervent sincerity, and Mrs. Gill, smiling, complied and went through *Venetia* again.

Catherine was now sitting out with Nicholas Whiteley; she knew that he had just left Cambridge, and felt that here at least was a young man with whom she ought to be able to get on. He was reputed to be clever, and so, she knew, was she; she made several tentative advances to him, but her manner, as usual, was so heavily earnest that it seemed supercilious and overpowering; Whiteley became defensively sarcastic, and presently they fell into a hurt and uncomfortable silence, from which they were not sufficiently experienced to emerge. Catherine watched Phil and Cordelia dancing—indeed they made a striking pair, a couple to catch the eye—and somehow felt rather lonely. It was at this moment that Lomas Eastwood approached her. But we must have this part of the narrative in her own words.

"Alas!" begins the entry in her diary that night. "How true it is that the pleasures of anticipation far exceed those of realisation! The picnic to Bolton Abbey, which I begged Papa to let me go to, and which I looked forward to so keenly, has been a very uneasy and distressing day for me. We hardly stayed a moment to examine the Abbey, and my mind was not free enough to let me enjoy the scenery, for Mr. Eastwood and his sister were of the party. I worried myself a good deal at first, wondering whether I ought to make an apology to Mr. Eastwood for my thoughtless behaviour the other night, but at last I decided that such an apology would perhaps cause him more pain than silence, so I said nothing. He sat opposite to me both in the train and in the waggonette; and I could feel that he looked at me several times with an air of sorrow and almost apology that really upset me. I noticed that the others were not very nice to him—even Phil, who is so kind to everyone, snubbed him once when he began to tell a funny story. At the luncheon he did not eat much, and spoke scarcely at all; but his eyes seemed always turned in my direction, and I had a feeling that he wanted to speak to me. When we were walking in the woods I tried to make an opportunity for him to do so, but I am not clever at these things as some girls are, and the others seemed determined that he should not join himself on to our party, so it came to nothing. Then we went into Ilkley, and had dancing. I had the first dance with Phil, and then sat out with Mr. Nicholas Whiteley—he is supposed to be very clever, and Phil likes him, but *I don't.* He said some very cutting things to me, so that I really did not know what topic to try next with him, and then his glasses gleam so oddly. However, Phil and Miss Eastwood were dancing so beautifully together that it was quite a pleasure to watch them. I was very glad when Mrs. Gill stopped playing, but Phil and some of the others were very anxious for an encore, so she began the dance again. Just then Mr. Eastwood came into the room from a balcony where he had been standing. I saw his eyes quite gleam as he caught sight of me, so I looked away. But the next moment he was standing at my side, literally bending over me, with his hand on the back of my chair, asking me to have the remainder of the dance with him. His speaking voice is intensely irritating, light and genteel, and somehow mincing: he always seems as though he were just going to lisp, but never quite does so. However, Mr. Whiteley . . ." Nicholas Whiteley, in fact, whose opinion of Lomas was the same as Phil's, at this point leaned across Catherine and announced abruptly that Miss Ainsley was engaged to him for that dance. Catherine blushed and felt distressed; but Lomas seated himself beside her with apparent calm, and after a minute or two observed in a low tone: "I only wanted to say how sorry I am that my song displeased you the other evening, Miss Ainsley."

The unhappy Catherine blushed still more and stammered something to the effect that she was afraid she had been rude.

"No, no!" protested Lomas gravely. "You were right, quite right. I know but too well how my musical education has been neglected. No one regrets it more bitterly than I myself. I would embrace so gladly any opportunity of self-improvement in that respect." Between each of these sentences he paused, no doubt so that they should appear to come spontaneously, from the heart.

The instinctive part of Catherine warned her that he did not mean a word he was saying, and bade her distrust a young man whose periods were so very suave, not to say affected; but she disliked very much any form of snobbery or class prejudice, and she felt—perhaps rightly—that Lomas had been subjected to a large dose of it that day. She experienced also the quick sympathy of the artist for anyone whose performance falls short of his own ideal. Actuated by these sentiments she looked at him with serious kindness, but instantly looked away again, for his fair, smooth, specious face always gave her an unpleasant impression—whether of insolence, of insincerity, or of something worse, she could not tell.

"You, of course, Miss Ainsley," pursued Lomas, seeing that he had gained her ear, "have had such splendid opportunities." Catherine could not avoid looking interrogative, and Lomas added with proper gravity: "In Germany."

Catherine's face no doubt involuntarily brightened at the introduction of this word, and Lomas with his usual intuition followed up the opening skilfully. He told her that he had always longed to go abroad, particularly to Germany. What part of Germany had she been in? Catherine murmured "Leipzig," and Lomas repeated the word as though it were his Mecca.

"Ah, Leipzig!" he said with a brave, wistful smile. "You have indeed been fortunate." After a pause, during which he probably conjured up all he had ever heard about Leipzig, he added: "You studied there?" Feeling perhaps rather unsafe with Leipsiz, he then hurriedly returned to music, and told her that he loved music, and that as a child his great ambition had been to take it up professionally.

"Indeed!" exclaimed Catherine, aghast at such temerity.

Lomas saw that he had made a mistake, and instantly retrieved it. "But of course," he went on, shaking his head wisely and allowing a disillusioned smile to turn down the corners of his lips, "I soon learned that that was folly."

"At this point Mr. Whiteley," says Catherine, "folded his arms and seemed to give up listening. I hardly knew whether to be glad or sorry. I was ashamed that he should hear Mr. Eastwood's remarks, and imagine that our acquaintance was such as to justify them, but when he withdrew from the conversation it seemed to make it more intimate than ever." Lomas, having ousted his masculine critic, grew bolder, and asked Catherine point-blank what songs she would recommend for a tenor voice such as his own. Hesitatingly she named a few; Lomas listened avidly, his large eyes fixed on hers; then raising his eyebrows in what he fondly imagined to be a light, worldly manner, he said that a mere designer such as he would not be able to afford to buy them. He looked at her in such a marked way as he said this that poor Catherine had the alarmed conviction that he expected her to offer to lend them to him. She felt that there was no real reason why she should not, except that he somehow made her shudder. Perhaps she ought to offer the loan? She would like to do so just to show Nicholas Whiteley her liberal principles; but then Mr. Ainsley, she was sure, would not like it. See-sawing thus violently between duty and inclination in the matter, and not even quite sure which was which, Catherine was in a parlous state of mind, when "fortunately," as she continues in her diary, "just then the dance finished, and Mrs. Gill came and sat beside me. Mr. Eastwood said no more, and luckily had no further opportunities of speaking to me all evening. I must say this was a great relief, for he really nauseates me. His opportunities for culture have been so few that his errors of taste and outlook are not really his fault, but all the same he makes me feel really *ill*. He seems to think that any music which is popular is good, and that an imitation is quite as good as the real thing. I feel ashamed of disliking him so much, but the fact is, he spoiled my day completely."

If Catherine was relieved by the cessation of the dance, her cousin undoubtedly viewed it with quite opposite feelings. Tucking Cordelia's hand beneath his arm, he led her masterfully away to two chairs in an alcove rather apart from the rest of the room. Cordelia was still in a fury. Carr tried various remarks—on the Strid, the picnic, Mrs. Gill's playing, the lunch, the homeward drive, the absence of rain, and so on—but Cordelia would have none of them and received them in angry silence. She would not even look at Carr, but glowered fixedly at the opposite side of the room, making Charlie Gill exquisitely uncomfortable in his attentions to Miss Barker. Carr suggested that this idea of dancing had been a happy thought; but Cordelia merely raised her eyebrows and looked sulky.

"Don't you like dancing?" said Carr, surprised.

Cordelia opened her lips, said "Yes," and closed them again firmly.

"I thought you probably did," observed Carr in a complimentary tone.

Cordelia declined to say anything to this at all.

"Which dance do you like best?" pursued Carr, determined not to be beaten.

Cordelia looked away and appeared not to have heard.

"Do you like the *Venetia* waltz?" persisted Carr.

Cordelia turned and scowled at him. "I like the *tune*," she said with a perverse emphasis which implied that she had not enjoyed her dance with him.

Carr sighed and tried again. "Do you like——" he began.

"Why do you keep on asking what I like?" cried Cordelia angrily.

"I beg your pardon," said Carr stiffly, hurt.

There was a moment's pause, during which each sat erect, gazed away into the distance, and nursed their wounded pride; then suddenly—and very characteristically—Carr laughed. Turning suddenly on Cordelia and bending towards her so that his sparkling brown eyes seemed very near her sulky blue ones, he cried teasingly: "Do you ever smile?"

Cordelia, utterly taken aback, stuttered: "Oh—oh—oh—sometimes."

"I'll give you sixpence if you'll smile at me!" cried Carr, and he laughed again heartily.

For an awful instant, during which the fate of at least six people trembled in the balance, Cordelia gazed at him in an agony of indecision. She was caught between an immense fury and an overwhelming desire to laugh. He was so handsome! His crisp black hair was just exactly what Cordelia had always postulated in the man she meant to marry. And then his fine brown eyes, his merry look, his superb dancing! But the Hallas money! And his horrid behaviour to Lomas at the concert! But then again how he had deserted the rich Catherine to dance with the poor Cordelia! But his father was a rogue! Cordelia, her heart a tumult of perplexity and alarm—as well it might be, for upon this moment depended the whole of her future life—gazed wide-eyed upon Phil, and somehow felt the conviction grow upon her that *Phil* was not a rogue, whatever his father might have been. Oh, no! Oh, no, no! Phil was not a rogue! He was just the opposite! He was, in fact—it came over her with a rush—just the kind of man she liked best in all the world. All these epoch-making thoughts were over in a moment, while Carr's eyes were still fixed upon her in a look of mischievous inquiry; and suddenly, involuntarily, Cordelia's pretty lips parted in a tremulous, uncertain smile. It was enough; Carr seized her hand and exclaimed: "Cordelia!" He bent towards her.

"No, no!" cried Cordelia in a panic. "They'll see us from the other side."

"I don't care," said Carr recklessly. "It's only Charlie and that Miss Barker."

The careless contempt in his voice was balm to Cordelia's sore heart. But: "Please let go my hand, Mr. Carr," she said severely. For answer Carr, laughing, shook his head and twined his fingers in hers and looked into her eyes; and Cordelia suddenly surrendered. She smiled at him openly, lovingly, sweetly; and before either of them quite knew what was happening his lips had brushed her soft hot cheek. "Mr. Carr!" protested Cordelia weakly. "What *will* the others think?"

Carr's expression showed so definitely what he cared for other people's thoughts on this occasion that it was perhaps as well that Mrs. Gill, who having rescued Catherine from Lomas had resumed her seat at the piano, now crashed out the opening chords for a set of lancers. Of course the lovers danced together, and Carr had the exquisite pleasure of taking Cordelia off her feet on every possible occasion. (Now Catherine and Miss Barker were heavy and did not easily rise.) Indeed the pair danced all the subsequent dances together; and they walked to the station together, and somehow contrived to lose themselves together on the platform, and climbed into another compartment together away from the rest of the party, and were gloriously, glowingly happy throughout the tedious journey home. Carr did not kiss Cordelia again that night; he was always a chivalrous and respectful lover—indeed any other kind would have been repugnant to the austere Cordelia—and he took no liberties; but when at last the holland frock and the light check suiting parted on the Hudley platform, there was no doubt in the mind of either Phil or Dell (as he already called her) about their mutual love. Carr confided to Charlie Gill on the way home—how Charlie must have squirmed!—that he meant to marry Miss Eastwood; and Cordelia, when describing the incidents of this day to the present writer, invariably concluded her recital with: "And after that I always liked Phil Carr the best."

After that they were certainly always together; or perhaps it would be more accurate to say that they were always meeting each other. If there was a flower-show, Carr and Dell met there; if the Black Dike band played in the Hudley Park, Carr and Dell met there; if there were cricket matches, athletic sports, trotting races, school prize-givings, Carr and Dell somehow encountered each other at all of them. They both managed to attend the church bazaar where the new "telephone transmitter," with a connection to Bradford, was on view, kindly lent by Enoch Barker, Esquire; but a tempestuous scene took place in the Eastwood family because Taylor put his foot down and refused to let Cordelia accompany Lomas to the Hudley fair, whither Carr was going with a lively party. In August the Eastwoods went for a decorous fortnight to St. Anne's, while Carr accompanied the Ainsleys to Belgium; between these two distant spots letters passed with considerable frequency. September came; Carr and Dell both attended a "grand morning performance" of *H.M.S. Pinafore,* for among Taylor's peculiar tastes was fortunately a passion, acquired on a recent visit to London, for this piece. Archibald Forbes came to Hudley to lecture on the Zulu War and the finding of the body of the Prince Imperial; Carr and Dell went to that too, though Carr was not fond of lectures: anything Shakespearean, operatic or educational he instinctively shunned. October came; Carr and Dell went to the roller-skating rink, and saw "the king of all the skaters, M. Crowther." By this time, of course, they each possessed a tin-type of the other; Dell's shows her in the famous sealskin coat, with an enormous silver locket and a chain like a cable about her slender neck—a recent birthday present from her father. By this time too various pieces of music had been inscribed "Miss Cordelia Eastwood" in Carr's handsome flowing hand—the *Venetia* waltz of course; another favourite of Carr's called *Sonnenschein,* and the song *Twickenham Ferry.* Cordelia had developed an intense interest in football matches, and as Lomas too seemed rather interested in them, they watched the fortunes of the Hudley Wanderers quite closely. For, of course, when Dell met Carr she was at least nominally always in the charge of Lomas; while Carr was usually accompanied by Catherine. Somehow these meetings were never alluded to in Carr Fold or Atack Place; they meant too much to Carr, too little to Catherine; in Majorca Road they percolated into the consciousness of Mrs. Eastwood and Annie, but Taylor knew nothing of them. The Gills and the Barkers were much better informed; the subject of Phil Carr and that Cordelia Eastwood was handled with regular asperity at the Barker dinner-table—Barker as a manufacturer was a rival of Carr Carr and Ainsley—while the roomy, shabby vicarage inhabited by the Gills, down in St. Mark's Place, was always open to both Carr and Dell. The lovers were both great favourites with the Gills; and if Charlie chose to be sulky about it, that was his own fault —let him devote himself to his Miss Barker. This Charlie did with increasing assiduity as the mutual attraction of Carr and Cordelia became more and more apparent; and about the middle of November he apparently gave Cordelia up as hopelessly out of his reach, for he became engaged to Amelia Barker.

A large and jubilant party was given at the Vicarage on December 3rd to celebrate this occasion. Besides the young people, Mr. and Mrs. Barker and Mr. and Mrs. Ainsley and a few other middle-aged friends of Mrs. Gill's were present; Ellen Carr was invited, but it was the anniversary of her husband's death, and she would not come. A discussion arose in the Gill family about the presence of

Cordelia; some said that it would be more tactful to omit her, others that her absence would be rather too marked; others again—there were so many Gills that several shades of opinion were always represented—that even if invited she would not come. The matter was settled by Carr, who had of course been invited. He, simple open-hearted soul, having never perceived that the affair between Charlie and Cordelia had approached the serious, assumed that Cordelia was going to the party; and in the presence of some Gills he one day asked her to keep him a certain dance. "I haven't been invited," said Cordelia with a proud toss of her head. The invitation was immediately forthcoming; Cordelia at first haughtily declined, but then it struck her that Charlie might think she resented his engagement to Miss Barker if she persisted in her refusal, and so decided to accept, though Lomas was not included in the invitation. Taylor Eastwood, who was angry at what he regarded as Charlie's defection, backed her up in her acceptance, and said she should have a new dress to wear and a cab to go in—nobody should think she was daunted by the desertion of any mere Gill.

Tremendous preparations were therefore made on all sides for this party. The carpet was taken up in the Gills' front room, extra chairs were hired, the Gills practised dance music incessantly, and the wardrobes of all the feminine guests received great attention. Catherine wore a new dress; in her diary she calls this "my moonlight frock," but Cordelia describes it as being of the colour known that winter as "drake's neck," *i.e.* shot blue and green. Over this Catherine, between the dances, wore a white fringed shawl. "Mamma *would* make me have a white shawl," she writes, "though it quite spoiled the lovely shimmer of my moonlight frock. She said the green one

I should have liked made me look too old." Cordelia remembers her own attire very accurately; after much thought, and a careful study of the weekly fashion articles in the *Hudley News*—taken, so the column says, from *Le Follet*—she decided to make her last year's black silk frock suffice, and buy a new shawl. This was of pale blue crêpe-de-Chine, with a silky fringe; it was crossed in front so that the fringe covered all the bodice, and pinned at the breast with a silver filigree brooch. In her ears, which she had secretly had pierced, she wore a pair of long filigree earrings. From her roguish air whenever these were referred to, even after a period of fifty years, it is probable that they were a present from Carr, but she could never be persuaded to admit this fact. She undoubtedly, however, placed them in her ears while driving to the Gills' in the cab, for she describes graphically her anguish when one fell and became entangled in the floor rug; and as there was no reason for her to do this unless she wished to conceal the earrings from her father, the above surmise as to their origin is probably accurate.

Various incidents, slight in themselves, but fraught with considerable consequences for Carr, occurred on this December evening; they all resulted from the presence of Mrs. Ainsley.

Neither Adelaide nor her husband recognised Cordelia, for neither of them had had a good view of her at the Carr Foot concert; but there were quite a few young people at the party whom they did not know, so this circumstance did not at first call for comment. Carr, having dutifully danced the first dance with a Gill, hastened joyfully to Cordelia. At the close of this second dance he made his way to Catherine, who had been without a partner and was sitting beside her mother, but just as they reached her side she was borne off by Mr. Ainsley. Gallantly Carr invited Adelaide instead. His aunt with a smile declined; but just as he was withdrawing, she tapped his arm with her fan and inquired who the pretty girl was he had been dancing with. Blushing all over his candid young face Carr replied: "Miss Eastwood."

His aunt, startled, stared at him. "Eastwood?" she repeated. "Eastwood?" She paused, and inquired in a peculiar tone: "Is she Taylor Eastwood's daughter?"

Carr, continuing to blush, said that she was.

His aunt stared at him again, while her thin breast heaved. Suddenly: "You'd better not let your mother see you with her!" she threw out in a fierce undertone.

It was now Carr's turn to stare, and a question began to form itself in his startled eyes. But Mrs. Ainsley did not allow him to formulate it. "Go and take Catherine from her father," she bade him brusquely, her thin nostrils still quivering with agitation, and Carr obeyed.

But his aunt's remark weighed upon him; for the first time he began to ponder seriously the question of his marriage to Cordelia, and the obstacles thereto, if any. He had always understood from Cordelia that he had better not call at 39, Majorca Road, because her father would not like it; but he had thought that a serious proposal for Cordelia's hand would cause Mr. Eastwood's natural paternal objections to melt away. And now this hint that his mother would not like it either! He reminded himself that his Aunt Adelaide was a petulant invalid who always disapproved of everything, but he could not quite dismiss her advice from his mind; and consequently when next he danced with Cordelia he was rather absent and preoccupied. Cordelia pounced on this at once, and ruthlessly extracted from him its cause. When she had discovered it her head with its brilliant crown of hair drooped rather pitifully for a moment before she threw it back with her customary proud toss, her lovely eyes grew wet, and her pointed little chin quivered between grief and pride. She could very easily imagine a reason why Ellen would hate to see her son dancing with Taylor Eastwood's daughter—it was connected with the reason which would make Taylor Eastwood hate to see his daughter dancing with Hammond Carr's son. Cordelia was furious with Carr for having relations who dared to disapprove of her; and at the same time she was poignantly sorry for him for having a rogue for a father and not knowing it. Once or twice she opened her mouth to tell him furiously what the Eastwood family thought of absconders in general and Hammond Carr in particular, but she could not bring herself to hurt him by doing it, and was pantingly silent. Carr, seeing her confusion, thought she was distressed by his aunt's implied criticism of herself, and begged her with mistaken earnestness not to mind. His masculine obtuseness infuriated Cordelia. "Mind!" she flared. "As though I care what your family thinks of me! Your family is nothing to me!" She paused, and added with characteristic emphasis: "And never will be. Never!"

Against this Carr naturally protested. "Cordelia!" he said reproachfully, aghast.

The upshot of a conversation begun in this wise was, naturally, a lovers' quarrel, which reached rather serious dimensions. In the course of it Cordelia accused Carr of indiscriminate flirtation with any girl who was handy, and Carr made the counter-accusation that Cordelia had been much too nice to Charlie Gill. Cordelia said that if Carr really cared for her feelings in the slightest degree he would have—— She broke off, finishing the sentence with a mere proud toss of her head, but she meant that she resented —very perversely, for it was entirely due to herself—his never having contrived her entrance to Atack Place or Carr Fold. Carr, who felt guilty about this, knew she was referring to it, and retorted angrily that she never allowed him to call at Majorca Road, so what was he to do? Cordelia thereupon replied in a fury that he could do what he usually did, which was nothing. No, but really, protested Carr, others beside himself thought it was too bad of her not to let him call at her house; Charlie Gill and Nicholas Whiteley both thought so. Cordelia with the most cutting inflexion of sarcasm replied that she should be sorry to lose the good opinion of Charlie Gill and Nicholas Whiteley—she valued *their* good opinion very highly indeed.

"I don't know what you mean, Dell," said the harassed Carr.

Cordelia smiled loftily, but forebore to reply—indeed she did not know herself what she had meant except that her intent was to wound.

"Do you mean you don't value *my* good opinion?" persisted Carr, genuinely perplexed. Cordelia, maddened by being pushed into this corner and by the general exasperatingness of the situation, made one of those feminine twists which are so incomprehensible to lovers, and said coldly: "Why don't you go to your cousin? She's looking hard at you."

The implications of this quite inaccurate speech wounded Carr to the heart; he was miserably silent for a few moments, and when he at length spoke it was in a stiff, artificial tone—employed to conceal his hurt pride and quivering voice—and he referred merely to the seasonable weather. Cordelia was so hurt by his apparent coldness that she could not find a voice to say anything to this at all, and they separated for the next dance still unreconciled. For the rest of the evening the filigree brooch covered a sore heart, and Carr's gloom, as he danced with Catherine and the Misses Gill and the Misses Barker, was deep. Carr's face very easily expressed gloom, but as also he could never resist making jokes, even when he was in agony, it is probable that his depression was not particularly noticeable except to its cause. What is certain, at any rate, is that by reason of the curious chain of slight incidents narrated above, on the only occasion before April 1880 that William Ainsley saw Carr and Cordelia together, he was entirely misled as to their relations.

Mrs. Ainsley, however, had evidently seen enough in the course of one dance to give her a truer view; for we have another incident to relate before the chronicle of that night is closed. The concluding paragraph of Catherine's diary for December 3rd, 1879, is as follows:—

"In the evening we went to the Gills' party. . . ." (Here she describes her dress and her partners.) "Also Phil danced with me a great deal, so that altogether I enjoyed it very much. Just as I was writing those words in my bedroom after we got home, Mamma came in. I was surprised, as she does not often come to my room at night. She told me that she does not like my dear moonlight frock much, as it makes me look too old. I was sorry. She also spoke of other people's frocks, and the supper, and Miss Barker, and Charlie Gill—whom she does not like, and neither do I; we agree that he is hard and ruthless—and said that except for him all the Gill boys were nice. I agreed heartily. Mamma gave me a rather curious look then, and kissed me good-night and seemed about to leave me; but at the door she suddenly turned and said in an impulsive way very unlike her usual manner: 'Catherine, if you don't take care you are going to lose Phil.' 'Lose him? Why, is he ill?'

I cried, horrified. 'No, no! I don't mean like that,' said Mamma impatiently. 'But don't you see . . .' She stopped, and did not seem to know how to go on. Then she came slowly up to me—I was sitting on the bed—and began to run her fingers through my hair. 'I think your father intends that you should marry Phil, Catherine,' she then said, in that detached kind of voice she often uses when speaking of dear Papa. I was very much astonished, and I could feel the colour rising in my cheeks. Mamma went on: 'Though of course he doesn't confide his plans to *me*. But if you don't take care you are going to lose Phil.' She paused, and then added: 'To that red-haired Eastwood girl.' I had not really thought of it before, but as soon as she spoke I realised that I had really known for a long time that Phil is in love with Cordelia Eastwood. I saw it at once, quite plainly. I felt angry that Mamma should think that *I* should wish to keep Phil apart from the girl he loves, so I said rather haughtily: '*I* don't wish to keep Phil from Miss Eastwood, I'm sure.' Mamma seemed rather relieved than otherwise, I think; but she said: 'Have you no feeling of that kind for Phil?' I replied firmly: 'No, none at all. He is just like a brother to me. Mamma gave a sigh, I think of relief, but I am not sure; she then kissed me more tenderly than usual, and left me. When she had gone I found that I was quite trembling; I think I am excited and nervous from discussing such 'grown-up' and unusual subjects with Mamma. Fancy Phil being in love! I cannot quite get used to the idea somehow. I hope Miss Eastwood will make him a good wife. She certainly is very beautiful, but rather vehement and emphatic. But all the same I think she is *good*, very different from that *detestable* brother of hers. How I hate him! I must go to bed now, as it is late and I am very tired."

Poor Catherine! It would indeed be beyond her simple

powers to tell whether Adelaide's dark and tortuous soul was relieved or otherwise by the discovery that Phil preferred Taylor Eastwood's daughter to her own—or, rather, to William Ainsley's, for Adelaide undoubtedly usually regarded Catherine in that light alone. Did Adelaide love Phil better than Catherine, because he was his father's son, or hate him because he was his mother's? Did she want him to inherit the glories of Carr Fold and Carr Foot Mills, or would that seem to her as Ellen's ultimate triumph? Did she want him to marry her daughter, or would that too seem a triumph for Ellen? And what did she think of the Eastwoods? Well, at this distance of time it is impossible to say. Let it be put to Adelaide's credit that the impulse which led her to Catherine's room that night was a generous one: she wished her daughter not to lose the man she loved, whoever he might be, if she really loved him.

And what of Catherine after her mother had gone? We can imagine her undressing slowly, feeling "tired"—which may perhaps be interpreted as "rather dreary"—as she shed her moonlight silk, and trying to accustom herself to the idea of Phil's being in love. Perhaps she caressed Didymus, burying her face in his soft fur, rather more fervently than usual, with some idea that he alone loved her truly; perhaps she inspected her heavy features in the glass, as she brushed her thick hair, rather more despondently than was her custom. Perhaps she even shed a tear or two without quite knowing why; who knows? At any rate her diary is never quite as earnest, never quite as fervently desirous of reforming the world, never, in fact, quite as young, after December 3rd, 1879, as it was before. "Quite, quite plainly!" Poor Catherine!

IV

MARRIAGE (1880)

From December 4th, 1879, to April 6th, 1880, the answer to the question whether Carr would marry Catherine or Cordelia was still on the knees of the gods. We know from the testimony of Charlie Gill and Nicholas Whiteley that Carr suffered intensely during the weeks following the quarrel described in the previous chapter. It was his nature to be intensely uneasy, uncomfortable, harassed and altogether miserable when there was any misunderstanding between himself and one of his fellow-creatures. His was indeed a rather mercurial nature, easily exalted to high spirits, and as easily depressed into the depths of gloom; his loving heart hated to be at variance with anyone; and he was very apt to think himself to blame if one of the little social contretemps arose which inevitably occur from tility at all which could not be cleared away by a frank in- such cases he could never rest till he was reconciled with his enemy; and any long-continued hostility, indeed, any hostility at all which could not be cleared away by frank interview between the opponents, was at this time incomprehensible to him. It may be imagined, then, how a quarrel with Cordelia made him suffer; he went about his work with a perplexed and wretched look on his handsome young face, and obtained some measure of ease only when he was scheming to meet Cordelia or writing her beseeching letters. He had, it appears, written three of these—unfortunately she destroyed them—before Cordelia replied to him in the following epistle, which for its tempestuous fury and its brusqueness must surely be unique among love-letters. That it was a love-letter, however, all students of Cordelia's character will admit. Carr preserved it, together with a lock of her hair, in his pocket-book all his life. It is written in Cordelia's most emphatic and characteristic hand, with large black commas evidently inserted after the letter itself was written.

"Majorca Road,
Hudley,
December 17, 1879.

"Dear Phil,

"Please don't send me any more letters. Father is beginning to wonder, who they come from, and in any case, I don't want to have any more. You keep asking me what I meant at the Gill's party, by saying, that your family could never be anything to me. Since you ask, I will tell you. A long time ago, before you were born, your father, and mine, had a very serious quarrel about some money matters. So that, your family and mine, can *never* be friendly. I am sure your mother would say the same thing. So that it is no use our meeting each other any more, or writing any more letters. If you care to have the music back, I shall be glad to return it. I am sorry to say, that the *Venetia* waltz has become rather torn.

"With kindest regards and every good wish for your future happiness,

"Believe me,
"Yours sincerely,
"Cordelia M. Eastwood.

"You must *not* come here as you suggest. Father would be very angry. What you say about Charlie Gill is quite untrue."

It was probably the last sentence in this which kept up Carr's hope and caused him to write her yet another impassioned letter in his large flowing hand. Cordelia, however, remained obdurate and would not answer it; meeting him a day or two later in the street she cut him dead. It is difficult to tell exactly what was passing inside her haughty little head at this time; but probably the impulses which kept her apart from Carr were mainly good ones. If she had a proud and angry feeling that she would never intrude upon a family who did not want her, she had also a feeling of loving loyalty to her father and to poor Annie—the fact that Annie was rather a tiresome creature, below the average mentally, probably stimulated this feeling rather than the reverse, for Cordelia was a very staunch, warmhearted little person, with an instinctive maternal feeling towards the weak. Yes, there was her father, and Annie, and Phil's superior social position—never should it be said that Cordelia Eastwood entangled a man richer than herself without his family's consent!—in the one scale; and in the other just her love for Phil. Now Cordelia was also an austere and puritanic little person, with an inclination to think that what was pleasant was wrong, so poor Carr's chance of triumphing in her heart was not very great.

That he did triumph was due entirely to the opportune arrival of Christmas. The bright-berried holly and pale suggestive mistletoe, the crowded brightly lighted shops, the exciting rows of geese and turkeys, naked save for their feathery necks, the making of Christmas cakes and mince pies and rich plum puddings—Cordelia was a splendid cook—the preparation of presents for those one loved, the carol-singing choirs, the seasonable sprinkling of snow, the frosty red afternoon skies, the consciousness that one's complexion was really excellent, one's cheeks delightfully rosy even in this nipping weather, all worked Cordelia's heart in Carr's direction, the more so perhaps because Taylor Eastwood, who of course disapproved of Christmas, was always very grumpy and cross-grained at this season of the year. Cordelia loved Christmas, and found her father's veto on it silly; she permitted herself to wonder vaguely whether Hammond Carr were not perhaps an ill-used man after all. In any case, was all that old affair Phil's fault? Of course not! This was a season when everyone should be happy and love one another; Cordelia's heart was full of love, but she was not happy—oh, not at all happy! Suddenly she could not bear it any longer; on Christmas Eve she abruptly rushed out and, between laughter and tears, fury and love, bought one of the tiny Christmas cards which were then the vogue—a little scrap of cardboard about two inches long by an inch wide, with a tiny spray of leaves and flowers along the left side, and a stilted Christmas wish in gold lettering in the centre—and addressed it in the Post Office to Mr. P. J. Carr, 4, Atack Place, Hudley. As she stood at the counter wrestling with the abominable pen she communed rapidly with herself whether to put "Esquire" or "Mr." Annie, who was with her, advised "Esquire," but Cordelia decided—very characteristically—that it was always better to be on the austere side than on the flamboyant, and accordingly Carr received the lesser title. One cannot avoid the conclusion that this was rather a favourable symptom, that Cordelia really regarded Carr as belonging to herself and therefore needing no excessive ceremony. Charlie Gill, one feels, would have had the "Esq."

The card in its envelope was duly delivered to Carr on Christmas morning, and after an agonised hour or so in church at Ellen's side, while he wondered what Cordelia meant and what he ought to do, he rushed to Majorca Road and pulled the bell of Number 39 with great vigour.

Annie let him in; and was so flustered by the sight of him that she led him straight to the back room, where the family usually sat. Fortunately Lomas was out, and Mr. Eastwood was at the far end of the garden. Although Christmas dinners as such were forbidden in the Eastwood household, some extra furnishings were usually added to the midday meal on that day, and Taylor was at present engaged in getting in some of his celery, in which he took particular pride. Annie thrust Carr into the room and vanished, speechless with agitation. Cordelia, who was sitting by the fire reading about Dr. Lorock's Pulmonary Wafers, and the visit of Miss Annie de Montford, Mesmerist, in the last week's *Hudley News* with an irritated sense that everything was very stale and unprofitable, looked up at her lover between ecstasy and horror; and in Mrs. Eastwood, who faced her across the hearth, the horror undoubtedly predominated. The table was set for the approaching meal; Mrs. Eastwood apologised for this and incoherently bade Carr be seated. With his eyes fixed on Cordelia he took a chair, and an awful moment of tense silence followed. The situation was saved by the Eastwoods' cat Cherry, a handsome young tortoise-shell animal who suddenly appeared at the French window leading to the garden, and mewed to be let in. Mrs. Eastwood, intensely fluttered, admitted him; behind her back Carr murmured: "Cordelia! Dell!" Cordelia gave a gasp, but Mrs. Eastwood had turned to them again, and was explaining quite unnecessarily the cat's habits. It was not in Carr's nature to be ill at ease with anyone for long, especially with such a simple and kindly person as Mrs. Eastwood, and he entered into a discussion of feline manners heartily. As if to repay him for this interest the cat served him well, for it climbed to the table and had to be lifted down, leaped upon chairs, stuck a tentative claw into various cushions, and showed a disposition to scratch the table legs, all in a highly reprehensible and unusual manner which quite disconcerted Mrs. Eastwood, who kept exclaiming fondly: "Naughty!" and rising to rescue it from various unsatisfactory situations. This gave Carr snatched moments with Cordelia, which he used to indicate somehow that he loved her, always had loved her—here Mrs. Eastwood broke in again with further apologies about the cat—and would she marry him very shortly? Cordelia simply did not know what to say; her eyes were full of tears, her mouth quivered into a terrified smile, she felt really distracted; while Carr admits that to him too the scene was a mere confused whirl of bounding tortoise-shell cats, Mrs. Eastwood's large bulk and soft black eyes, and the parting in Cordelia's hair.

These moments of blissful anguish were terminated by the sudden appearance of Taylor Eastwood at the window. At this Cordelia's hand flew to her mouth in the gesture of horrified dismay since popularised by the Gish sisters; Mrs. Eastwood paused, cat in hand, and looked at the young couple with an air of troubled sympathy; Carr alone, unconscious of any real reason why Cordelia's father should dislike him, stood his ground manfully, his head in the air, his usual merry smile lighting up his handsome face. Taylor perceived him through the window, and he already wore a very black scowl when he entered the room. He was, as has been indicated, a small man; he was wearing his old garden coat, and his hands were full of celery sticks and earth, but Carr—always an excellent judge of character—knew at once that he was formidable.

"And who's this?" demanded Taylor in a tone of intense disgust, pausing in front of Carr and fixing his sharp blue eyes on him in a piercing stare.

"It's Mr. Carr, father," said Cordelia weakly from her armchair by the fire.

"Are ye Hammond Carr's son?" demanded Taylor in a heavy menacing tone, thrusting his face up into his visitor's.

Carr, a little staggered by this unexpected fierceness, of course said that he was.

"Then you can clear out!" said Taylor Eastwood emphatically. "I want none of his sort here."

"I don't know what you mean!" protested Carr with an indignant flush. He added simply: "I want to marry Cordelia."

At this Cordelia gave a little scream, and Taylor's face became empurpled. "What!" he shouted. "What do you mean, you young jackanapes? What does he mean, Cordelia? You've been flirting with him, that's what you've been doing. That's why that young Gill has got engaged to Miss Barker."

"Father!" exclaimed Cordelia, infuriated. "How dare you! Don't mention Mr. Gill's name to me, please!"

"I want to marry Cordelia," repeated Carr, clinging firmly to this point as the only stable part of the universe just then.

"Well, you never will with *my* consent," replied Taylor, grimly emphatic. "Nor with your mother's either, I'm thinking."

At this Cordelia, quite overwrought with the emotions of the past few months and this culminating scene, burst into hysterical sobs and cried in a high, strained, trembling voice: "I *shall* marry him if I want to!"

"You've taken leave of your senses, child!" cried her

father aghast. "You ought to be ashamed. But you'll never marry Hammond Carr's son with my consent," he added with a relentless determination. "Never. I grant you he's a handsome lad enough, but I want none of his sort here."

He turned aside contemptuously, the sticks of celery dangling limply from one hand, and threw open the door into the hall. Carr, hot, miserable, and more mortified than he had ever in his young life been before, was utterly at a loss what to do. Mrs. Eastwood still stood by in a petrified attitude, clasping the cat to her waist: Cordelia wept bitterly: Taylor, with contempt in every line of his withered countenance, was indicating the open door. Carr took a step towards Cordelia, but was instantly warded off by Taylor, and stood still in the centre of the room, fingering the brim of his hat, his young face angry and perplexed. He felt that he ought now to do something very firm and heroic, but could not for the life of him think what. "We shall see," he stammered at length with a youthful attempt at bravado. "We shall see, Mr. Eastwood."

"I daresay we shall, Mr. Carr," returned Taylor with biting sarcasm. "But we shan't see *you* here again in a hurry, I'll be bound."

Carr, utterly disconcerted, somehow found himself in Majorca Road.

When he had gone the storm broke forth. Cordelia raged; her blue eyes shot forth lightning, and her brilliant hair, becoming disordered, seemed to wave the banner of rebellion. She stamped her foot and sobbed and wrung her hands. Taylor remained fairly calm; he reiterated the admission that Carr was a handsome lad enough, but concluded each time, with relentless decision, that he wanted none of Hammond Carr's sort there. Mrs. Eastwood ventured timidly to suggest that this young Mr. Carr was in a very good position; he was a partner with Mr. Ainsley, she understood.

"Aye! He will be if he marries Ainsley's daughter, I don't doubt," said the implacable Taylor.

At this Cordelia's sobs rattled on the air like musketry. Her father approached her and laid a soothing hand on her hair; but this touched some spring in Cordelia, and she flew from the room like an arrow and hid herself upstairs. A few minutes later, however, to Annie's alarm she suddenly entered the kitchen with a hasty step; though she was not now crying, her lips were fiercely compressed, and her breast heaved in sudden quick pants as a result of the late storm; tying herself vehemently into a large apron she dished up the dinner with so much speed and fury that poor Annie was quite disconcerted and did not venture to gainsay her, though Lomas had not yet returned to the house.

An extract from Catherine's diary may be useful here:

December 25, 1879.—Phil and Aunt Ellen were very late for dinner, which was supposed to be at half-past one to-day. This made Mamma rather cross, and she spoke rather sharply to Phil at table when he forgot to pass her the salt. Phil was indeed very gloomy and preoccupied; his eyes were quite large and fixed, gazing away into space all the time. While we were at dessert the choir came and sang Christmas hymns to us; I thought they sang remarkably well, and even Aunt Ellen was not as scornful as usual about them, but Phil seemed weary of them long before they had finished. After dinner Phil and I took Didymus for a walk over High Carr; Phil was still very depressed, and I began to feel rather miserable too. I should like to have asked him whether he had seen Miss Eastwood lately, but feared he might be vexed if I did, for Phil is very sensitive beneath his high spirits, so I said nothing. As we returned the sky was beautifully red and wintry, and I said I thought there would be skating again soon. Phil brightened again at this, and said they had told him at the skating rink that the ice from the last frost had never really melted, so that a very short frost would make it safe again. I hope it freezes *hard* to-night; it has been growing colder all evening, so I think it will."

Catherine was granted this wish, for that night snow fell and frost set in, by Saturday, December 27th, the ice was firm, and most of the young people of Hudley disported themselves gaily on the rink to the sound of the rink band, which played daily, with short intervals, from 10 a.m. to 10 p.m. Catherine and Phil were excellent skaters; Cordelia was not so good—her ankles wobbled and had to be bound—while Lomas never ventured upon the ice at all, regarding it instead with a look of haughty condescension from the land, in company with the timid Annie.

The site of the ice rink, though now occupied by a garage and a picture house, is well marked by tradition, so that we can form a very definite idea of the scene which met Carr's eyes as he flew rapidly round the ice with Catherine that afternoon, awaiting the hoped-for arrival of Cordelia. (He had written to her to suggest this rendezvous if the weather should favour it, but had not ventured to brave Taylor and call to see her, on the preceding day.) The situation of the rink was in itself prosaic, being only a few hundred yards or so off the main road from Hudley to Lancashire. But from almost every inch of ground in Hudley there is a fine view of hills, and this site is no exception to the general rule. There was a light powdering of snow on the ground; the air was clear and keen; all round the horizon white hills and round slender black chimneys rose up against the red wintry sky with an almost terrifying beauty. The heavy whirring sound of steel on ice was music in Carr's ears, the joyous, swift, rhythmic movement invigorated his young blood and drove away the depression he had felt since his meeting with Cordelia's father. Of course it would all come right in the end! Taylor Eastwood would relent, and Cordelia should surely marry him. He laughed joyously, and was about to do a beautiful outside edge with Catherine, when he caught sight of Cordelia's neat little figure—rather extravagantly clad in the sealskin—standing forlornly at the entrance between Lomas and Annie Hallas. At once he darted off to her.

Cordelia had been definitely forbidden by her father to speak to Carr again, but she had replied to this veto merely by a haughty toss of her head and silence, so she felt morally free to act as she wished. Up to the moment of her arrival at the rink, however, she was in doubt as to her own wishes on the point; but when she saw Carr, bareheaded and handsome, dashing towards her the minute she came in with his merry welcoming smile, when she saw how well he skated, how admirably he walked across the hard ground at the side without a single quiver, when above all he knelt before her in the snow and fitted her wooden skates on her trim little boots with his strong slender hands, and pulled the straps tighter and more secure than the united efforts of Lomas and her father had ever made them before—then she decided, finally and irrevocably, that she loved him. Clinging to his arm with one hand, and waving her little round muff distractedly about in the effort to keep her balance with the other, she wobbled to the ice's edge, and timorously lowered herself upon it. Carr took her hands in the traditional style, and at once Cordelia felt perfectly safe. With slow and irregular strokes the two sailed round the square of ice together for the rest of the afternoon. The red sky faded into misty twilight, and then into clear cold dark, the moon came out above the white hills, torches planted on high poles round the rink flared luridly, and still Carr and Cordelia moved round or paused or sat upon the frozen benches in each other's dear company. They were discussing the future, and had a great sense of having settled all that and made the most satisfactory arrangements for disposing of all obstacles, though in reality they had settled nothing except to go on loving each other and keep it from Cordelia's father and Phil's mother for the present. For the present only, of course; something was sure to occur to make things all right shortly.

At length they awoke with a start to the realisation that it was rather late and that none of their friends seemed to be about; they sought for them hither and thither about the ice, but found only George Newton practising figure eights in a corner by himself—very gloomily, for Emily Gill had just refused him. Newton informed them that the rest of the party had gone off long ago, Miss Eastwood's brother with the rest. At this the lovers left the ice and took their skates off hurriedly, and hastened out of the rink in the direction of Majorca Road. As this was some way distant there was quite a chance that they would overtake Lomas and Annie before they reached home, but Cordelia's ankles had the stiff, leaden feeling consequent on several hours' inexpert skating, and she was daunted by the thought of having to face another family scene if she returned late and alone. Being thus tired and uneasy, she became a little cross, and Carr was protective and remorseful. The situation was saved by the appearance, in Prince's Road, of an empty cab lumbering slowly townwards, its elderly driver wrapped in rugs. Carr sprang forward and hailed him, almost before he drew up opened the door and whisked Cordelia in, then rather belatedly asked the fare to Majorca Road. The cabman, his half-closed eyes roving about Carr's well-cut clothes and dashing mien, murmured grumpily: "Seven and six."

"I don't want to *buy* the cab, you know," protested Carr with a merry look, one foot on the step. "I only want to ride half a mile in it."

At this the cabman involuntarily gave an appreciative snort, but he immediately repented it, and replied sourly: "Eh, lad! Ye're so sharp ye'll cut yeself one of these days."

"It's too much, Phil," cried Cordelia from within at this point, severely. "We'd better walk."

"As it isn't Boxing Day," continued the cabman, "I'll tak ye for five bob."

"Done!" cried Phil with a laugh. Jumping into the cab he bade the man hurry, get some speed up, make his horse run for once if it could. With a defiant growl the driver took him at his word, and the cab rattled over the snowy roads at a pace considered in those days quite alarming. Cordelia, always nervous in vehicles, was quite seriously frightened, screamed a little occasionally, and once in a panic at a corner seized Carr's hand. Is it to be wondered at that Carr's arm found its way round the sealskin's waist, or that he stole a kiss or two from his love's soft warm cheek? Cordelia herself, though she rebuked him severely, did not altogether blame him. Suddenly at the corner of Atack Place, Gills, Newtons, Barkers, Lomas, Annie and Catherine —good heavens! Phil had forgotten all about Catherine— were seen chatting around a lamp-post. "Oh look!" cried Cordelia. Carr threw down the window and shouted "Stop!" The saturnine cabman at once hauled in his horse, so abruptly that Dell was precipitated on to the front seat, while Phil banged his head against the side of the door. Carr had a few hot youthful words to say about this, the cabman glancing over his shoulder at him the while with an air of grim satisfaction. Carr then turned to Cordelia, and handed her out tenderly. Cordelia was a little fussed, a little disarranged; her cheeks were hot, her blue eyes wide; red curls showed beneath the sealskin cap more lavishly than usual. In the lamplight all this was distinctly visible. The cabman, cocking his eye meditatively at her as she descended, observed suddenly, in tones of heartfelt though humorous conviction: "Eh! I wish I wasn't wed!"

Cordelia exclaimed indignantly that the man was drunk, but Phil gave him seven-and-sixpence.

For the next six weeks matters remained in pretty much the same position; that is: Carr and Cordelia deeply in love, meeting each other daily but not in any real sense clandestinely; Mrs. Eastwood, Lomas, Annie, Catherine and most of Carr's friends cognisant of this, but for various reasons saying nothing to the parents concerned; Taylor Eastwood imagining that he had nipped the affair in the bud; Mrs. Carr and William Ainsley entirely ignorant of it. Then on Saturday, February 14th, disaster fell upon the lovers, through the medium, typically enough, of a piece of music entitled *The Sweethearts' Waltz* and the old custom of St. Valentine. Carr had sent the one to Cordelia in order to observe the other; and Cordelia (who though *not* a good pianist according to Catherine, being devoid of real musical taste, had a considerable facility in sight-reading) was thumping the waltz out on the little piano in the front room when her father came in to his Saturday's dinner. The lilt of the refrain caught Taylor's ear; he hummed it to the best of his tuneless ability, then put his head round the door and asked his daughter jocularly what trash it was that she was playing. The ingenuous Cordelia gave a guilty start and coloured. Taylor's face immediately changed; he advanced sternly into the room—Cordelia's blush deepening with every stride he took—and snatched the music from the piano ledge. Its title, and the masculine handwriting on the front page, completed Cordelia's betrayal. "What's this?" demanded Taylor fiercely, tapping its coloured frontispiece. Cordelia, trying to pluck up her spirit, faltered that it was a Valentine. "From that young Carr, eh?" pursued her father. Cordelia's head drooped and she murmured a faint "Yes."

Taylor was extremely angry. It was not only that Cordelia's continued friendship with Carr cut across his expressed determination that his daughter should have no dealings with the son of a man whom he had good cause to regard as a rogue; what hurt him, as Cordelia in later life came to see, was that his daughter, hitherto so candid, so fiercely open in all her dealings, should have deceived him in a matter so important. Lomas was untrustworthy, Lomas told lies, Lomas was not straight—that his father knew; but he had hitherto trusted Cordelia implicitly, and to find that she too was unreliable and truthless (as he thought) was a bitter blow to the upright Taylor. He dragged the girl off to the kitchen, and there was a terrible domestic scene; the waltz was consigned to the flames, and Cordelia, Annie and Mrs. Eastwood wept unrestrainedly, while Lomas stood by silently sneering at his father's fierce denunciations of them all. When his wrath had sufficiently expressed itself Taylor locked Cordelia into her own bedroom, and went out, taking the key with him. When he returned late that evening he announced abruptly that Cordelia was going to Scarborough first thing on Monday morning; old Mr. and Mrs. Newton had taken a house there, and now Mr. Newton was ill, and Mrs. Newton needed a bright young girl to be with her and run errands for her and that sort of thing, and Mrs. George Newton (the mother of George and Bales) was going over on Monday and would take Cordelia with her. Mrs. Eastwood exclaimed miserably that she could not bear to be parted from her little girl; but Taylor, his withered face haggard with disappointment, turned a deaf ear to her pleading. "How long will she be there, then?" wailed poor Mrs. Eastwood, and Taylor replied sternly: "Till she comes to her senses." He remained adamant on the point, saying that Cordelia was lucky to have such a chance—many girls would be delighted with the opportunity: it was most fortunate that Enoch Barker, to whom he had gone for advice, had heard of old Mrs. Newton's requirements, and that Mrs. George Newton thought Cordelia suitable.

"Mr. Carr may go to Scarborough after her, father," suggested the unhappy Mrs. Eastwood timidly.

Taylor snorted. "I'll take good care he doesn't," he said grimly, sticking out his chin.

Accordingly, on Monday morning a weeping, sullen, rebellious Cordelia was conveyed to the Hudley station by her father and handed over to the care of Mrs. George Newton (a rather tart and unsympathetic woman); while on Tuesday morning there was delivered at 4, Atack Place a letter which threw Ellen Carr into a fury. Phil, of course, had already gone off to his work in Carr Foot Mills, and Ellen was obliged to keep her rage bottled up within her till the evening. No sooner, however, had Carr entered the house in the evening—rather quiet and miserable, for Cordelia had naturally failed to keep her rendezvous with him for the last two days—than he heard his mother's voice sharply calling him. He went to her, and found her standing by the fire in the drawing-room. She was very pale; out of her haggard, twitching face her eyes gazed black and burning.

"What does this mean?" she demanded in a harsh tone, extending Taylor Eastwood's letter towards him. Phil, bewildered, took it from her hand and read it. This letter is unfortunately lost, but its terms were no doubt sufficiently brutal, and Carr flushed as he replied that Mr. Eastwood had no right to speak like that—he had already told him that he wanted to marry Cordelia.

At this Mrs. Carr, drawing herself to her full height, exclaimed passionately: "Never!" The veins on her temple throbbed alarmingly. "Do you mean to tell me, Phil," she burst out again in a vibrating tone of scorn and anger, laying her hands violently on her son's shoulders, "that you've been paying serious attentions to Taylor Eastwood's daughter?"

Poor Phil said staunchly that yes, certainly he had—he wanted to marry Cordelia.

His mother almost threw him aside and stormed about the room. "Never! Never!" she cried passionately. "Never!" She came close to Phil, clutched his arm and gazed into his eyes. "Taylor Eastwood drove your father away from me to his death!" she told him pantingly. "And now you dare to stand there and tell me you want to marry his daughter. I don't know how you dare." She flung away from him to the door. "You can put her quite out of your mind," she told him fiercely. "Never mention her name to me again."

"But, mother," protested Phil, beginning to regain his senses, which had been somewhat scattered by the sudden and unexpected character of the attack, "I'm engaged to her." (This was not strictly true, but the impulse to utter it was undoubtedly an honourable one.)

"Then you can get unengaged to her," threw out Ellen scornfully. "You see her father objects to you—he's sent her away so that you shan't see her. The insult of the thing!" she broke off in a fury—"that Taylor Eastwood should send his daughter away out of reach of my son! It's not to be endured! However," she continued in a milder though more contemptuous tone: "you acted in ignorance, I'm willing to believe. Let me hear no more of it. The girl has gone away somewhere, and you won't see her for long enough. And whatever you do, don't let your uncle hear a word of this nonsense—he'd be very much vexed."

"Mother," cried Carr in a loud quick tone, "don't treat me as a child!"

It was very rare for Philip Joseph Carr to lose his temper and say harsh things, but on this occasion he undoubtedly did so. Like that of many gentle and good-natured people, Carr's temper, when it did occasionally burst the bounds of his habitual kindness, was for a few moments simply devastating—a foaming fiery flood. It became so now. The course taken by this interview is known to us because Carr later confided it to his wife, but as to what happened next his memory is vague. He only remembers announcing that he meant to marry Cordelia whatever happened, that he cared nothing for his mother and less for Taylor Eastwood, that what her father had done was not Cordelia's fault, and in any case he meant to marry her, that if William Ainsley didn't like it he would leave Carr Foot Mills and be damned to them, and in any case he meant to marry Cordelia. His temper was then exhausted, and he became again the gentle, kindly, rather perplexed lad that he had been on entering the house. But his mother had had a fright, and began to feel that she might drive him into serious opposition by taking a high hand with him—after all, he was twenty-one, and he might consider that that deed of partnership made him financially independent. Trembling with genuine anguish, she adopted a pathetic tone. Could not Phil understand her feeling against Taylor Eastwood? "The night before you were born, Phil!" she wailed. The soft-hearted Phil understood it only too well, and wished sincerely that—he could not say he wished that he had never seen Cordelia—that, that, that it had not happened so. Ellen, seeing she had made an impression, no doubt, followed it up with vigour; throwing her arms round Phil's neck she forced him down into a chair, and kneeling beside him told him between gasping sobs that all the unhappiness of her life came from Taylor Eastwood, and now he was proposing to marry Taylor Eastwood's daughter! He would break her heart! Her forlorn widow's heart! Rising to fierceness again, she declared that he should never marry an Eastwood, never, unless he wanted to do it over her dead body. She grasped his hand feverishly in hers and turned her wild haggard face, wet with tears, beseechingly to his. Phil, troubled to the depths of his soul, turned aside and suffered: at last his young manhood broke down and he too gave a deep sob. Ellen, we may surmise, wondered rapidly whether to venture upon a hint of Catherine and Carr Fold, and with her usual astuteness decided against it. She took Phil's head upon her breast, stroked his crisp curling hair and kissed his white young face; the simple Phil put his lips obediently, if with rather an abstracted air, to her cheek, and felt almost mad with wretchedness. Happy days of love with Cordelia seemed to recede like a golden dream impossible of fulfilment, and life closed about him its black and cruel fangs.

He gave an involuntary groan, and covered his eyes with his hand. At this a slight smile of relief and triumph stole round his mother's lips. "Understand me, Phil," she said in a mild but inexorable tone, "I absolutely forbid you to have any further dealings with this girl."

"I shan't promise anything," said the wretched Phil.

His mother, however, did not choose to hear this; instead she rose and floated away across the room, and pausing in front of the portrait of Hammond Carr by the piano, fetched a deep (and very audible) sigh.

We, who know all Ellen's story, and may hazard a surmise that these were the methods with which she worked upon Hammond Carr to marry her, may perhaps wonder that Phil was so deeply affected by this scene, for though Ellen's feeling on this occasion was undoubtedly genuine, there was artifice in its expression. But we must take the opportunity of recording here, on this the first important occasion of their exhibition, the two qualities which were at once the virtue and the defect of Carr's character. First, then, he had that quality, so often called simplicity by more worldly-minded people, which makes its owner extremely reluctant to believe evil of anyone, indeed almost incapable of doing so until faced by the most incontrovertible proof. This was curiously combined, in Carr, with a kind of instinctive knowledge of character. At that time, for example, Carr, if asked his opinion of Lomas Eastwood, would have replied at once in condemnatory terms; but he would have been immensely astonished and taken aback and almost wounded to find Lomas actually behaving in a scoundrelly manner. Carr had then, we may conjecture, an instinctive comprehension of Ellen's character which was fairly accurate; but to imagine that she was actually being rather selfish, rather vulgar and rather histrionic to *him* was beyond his capacity altogether. His second quality we slightly touched upon at the beginning of this chapter. Carr was a peace-lover. He hated to be at variance with even the meanest of his fellow-creatures. To oppose anyone for a long time single-handed was impossible to him; and though he had quite high and fine and generous ideas on what a man's conduct ought to be, he did not find it easy to defend them when they were attacked by those he loved. To feel that he was at variance with his mother and making her suffer was torture of the most agonising kind to him. The only thing which could torture him more was to feel that he was making Cordelia suffer, and fortunately for his own happiness he felt that if he deserted her he would be doing that. We need not, therefore, follow him in detail through the hesitations, the perplexities, the miseries and the precipitancies of the next two months, but give a mere brief sketch of them and then proceed at once to the morning of April 3rd, 1880.

It was an easy matter for Carr to find out Cordelia's address from George Newton—who as a disappointed lover himself was very sympathetic—and to correspond with her through the friendly medium of Emily Gill. Her letters maddened him to the pitch of desperation. Poor little Cordelia's independent spirit suffered greatly in her new position. The work she did for old Mrs. Newton—a kindly, gentle, but probably rather fussy old lady—was not as hard as that she did at home; but at home she was the daughter of the house, one greatly beloved, who ordered her goings and comings pretty much as she chose. To be at another's beck and call fretted her high spirit terribly; she was not used to taming her frank speech and subduing her haughty manners to please anyone but herself. To feel that she was a dependent, a person earning her board by soothing compliance with another's wishes, aroused in her a fury of rebellion. She wept at nights, tossing from side to side of her narrow bed and biting the sheets between her firm white teeth; and next morning naturally felt sulkier and less agreeable than ever. She knew no young people in Scarborough, and Mrs. Newton's ideas seemed dowdy and old-fashioned; it was dreadful to feel doomed to live with them for ever! Then her loss of Carr gnawed at her heart. A little distance often throws a character into clearer perspective for us, and Cordelia saw how true and loving, how kind and merry, how faithful and considerate, her lover really was. At first in her letters to him she proudly pretended to him that she was well and happy, but soon this little deception quite broke down, and her letters became tear-stained, homesick, pathetic little affairs which wrung Carr's heart. Cordelia, his bright Cordelia, forced into a menial position! It was not to be endured! At last there came a letter which said that Cordelia had weighed herself at a chemist's and discovered she had lost two pounds. Considering that she was less than eight stone already, Carr felt that this was a terribly serious matter, and he made up his mind to act at once. Cordelia was unhappy without him, yet her father and his mother would never give their consent to their marriage, it seemed. Very well, thought Carr as he shaved one morning, in a blinding flash of revelation; then they would marry without it! Easter was approaching; George Newton and a Gill or two—not Charlie; Charlie was going to Brussels with the Barkers—were going to the Isle of Man for an Easter holiday; Carr asked his uncle's permission to join their party and be absent from Carr Foot Mills for a fortnight, obtained it, and made all the necessary arrangements. Newton was in his secret; knew that he was really going to Scarborough, and promised to explain his absence to the Gills so that they should not mention it in their letters home. Cordelia, too, knew that he was coming, though not perhaps the alarming nature of his errand, and had arranged the time and place of their meeting. Almost at the last minute all these plans were upset because of the General Election. The Hudley election was fixed for Wednesday, March 31st, and the Gills declined to be in the Isle of Man while there was so much "fun," as they expressed it, going on at home. Their outing was therefore postponed from the Thursday before Easter until the following Saturday, April 3rd. Carr was almost frantic at this delay, but feared to rouse suspicion of his purpose in his mother if he did not accede to it; so letters passed again between him and his love, and their meeting was arranged for ten o'clock on the morning of April 3rd, at a particular spot on the Esplanade in Scarborough. It is interesting to trace how the workings of the great political struggle of the last century influenced even such remote emotional events as the marriage of two young West Riding lovers; for, as it chanced, Cordelia's twenty-first birthday fell on Easter Sunday (March 28th) in that year; and had Carr attempted to marry her before that date—as he undoubtedly would have done but for the General Election—he would have found all the majesty of the law arrayed against him. Cordelia's parents might have been informed, and the whole course of innumerable lives, present and to come, been changed. Carr, of course, being entirely ignorant both of the marriage laws and of Cordelia's age, went blithely on, quite unaware how the course of his love was being favoured by electoral circumstance. By Easter Sunday he felt that everything was in readiness for his marriage—except for his perplexing lack of money. Carr very often lacked money, for it slipped through his generous, easy fingers like water. Had he really been going to the Isle of Man he would have borrowed the necessary funds from his mother—to whom, of course, he made a regular weekly contribution towards the upkeep of the house—but he was not going to the Isle of Man, and somehow he could not bring himself to ask his mother for money with which to go and marry Cordelia. Yet money must be had from somewhere. The fatal day drew near, but the money was not forthcoming, and Carr's face began to wear a harassed look, when suddenly—and to him inexplicably—he obtained it from a most unexpected source, to wit his Aunt Adelaide. One night as they were sitting together in the Carr Foot drawing-room—the attention of the others being momentarily given to Didymus, who was balancing a lump of sugar on his nose—Adelaide observed softly that he looked worried. Carr, very conscious, squirmed and gave a deprecating murmur, but Adelaide persisted. Would a little money help? Carr started, blushed, stuttered that it would—that it didn't matter—that his aunt was not to bother—that, in short, he needed nothing. Long before he had come to this conclusion his aunt had given his arm a little meaning pat, and bidden him come upstairs now with her. He followed her in a dream, waited outside her bedroom door in acute embarrassment, and presently found her stuffing a little roll of gold wrapped up in banknotes into his hot hands. Carr, of course, had not the vaguest idea of her possible motive, and even at this late date we may wonder whether Adelaide suspected his designs on Cordelia or not. That she did and that she favoured the match as a species of revenge on her sister may perhaps be inferred from a remark of Ellen's. She had observed Phil's absence from the room, and on their way home together that night asked what his aunt had wanted with him. Phil truthfully replied that she had made him a present of money. "Have you ever told her about that affair with Cordelia Eastwood?" demanded Ellen sharply at this. "No," muttered Phil, feeling very guilty and in half a mind to tell his mother everything. "See that you never do," commanded Ellen. Something harsh and domineering in her tone hardened Carr's heart, and on Saturday, April 3rd, he left her to catch his early morning train without telling her anything of his intentions.

The lovers met at 10 a.m. on the Esplanade according to arrangement, and ran off at once—Dell in the joy of seeing Phil again needing little persuasion—to the Registrar's. Here they were met by a disappointment, for, having satisfied that gentleman with difficulty that they were both of age [1] and that Cordelia had resided in Scarborough for more than fifteen days, they found that they could not be married until the following Tuesday. One clear day had to elapse between the giving of notice and the marriage, and Sunday—perversely, irritatingly, stupidly, as they felt—did not count as a day. This dashed them a good deal; and Cordelia, who was really in a run-down and nervous condition owing to the tedium of her late experiences, wept and showed a disposition not to get married at all—she could not possibly wait till Tuesday, and therefore, with a logic characteristically Cordelian, thought they had better wait years for the consent of their parents. At this, Carr in the desperation of his young love began to talk wildly about getting a special licence from the Archbishop of Canterbury or running off to Gretna Green; Cordelia immediately became very sensible and practical, and pointed out how much simpler, less expensive, more correct and in

[1] Fortunately Cordelia had a letter in her pocket from her father, congratulating her on attaining her majority.

every way better it was to wait till Tuesday. She could continue to live in the Filey Road with the Newtons; Phil could stay at a nice quiet boarding house. (Carr, conscious that his bag was already reposing at that excellent hotel the *Crown,* slightly winced at this.) They could meet from time to time, but must take great precautions, for unfortunately Mrs. George Newton was coming over for the week-end—in fact she was almost due now, and Cordelia must hurry back to meet her. They arranged a rendezvous for later in the day and parted, exquisitely happy and intensely miserable.

The programme sketched by Cordelia was faithfully adhered to, except that the precautions they took were hardly great enough for the occasion. Once they had to fly down a side street to avoid Mrs. George, once she almost fell over them by the gate in the dark. Yet a third time Cordelia took three-quarters of an hour to post a letter in a pillar box perhaps three minutes distant, and Carr accompanied her to within ten yards of the house. He was also not quite as invisible at church on Sunday morning as he fondly imagined, and Cordelia found it impossible to get to the evening service—Mrs. George attended it alone, and no doubt saw Carr again behind his pillar. At any rate, by some means or other suspicion was undoubtedly awakened in Mrs. George's tough breast. The old Newton couple had their breakfast in bed every morning, and Mrs. George had done so likewise on her previous visits to Scarborough; so the lovers had arranged that Cordelia should slip out between eight and nine on the fatal Tuesday morning, join Carr on the Esplanade, and walk about with him till ten o'clock, the hour fixed for the marriage. At ten minutes to nine Cordelia perceived, from the dining-room window, that Carr had got tired of waiting on the Esplanade and was standing by the Newton's gate, looking as obviously an eloping lover as if he had had a placard to that effect tied round his neck. With beating heart and trembling limbs Cordelia ran upstairs, put on the sealskin, took up the little bag of necessaries she had prepared overnight, and tiptoed down and across the hall again. She opened the door; Carr saw her and ran up the steps; he took the bag, she stepped across the threshold; they were almost out of the house when Mrs. George Newton's harsh voice sounded from the stairs, and Mrs. George Newton herself, in a frilled nightcap and a wrapper, stormed across the hall to them. The lovers stood aghast. "Just tell me one thing, you two," said Mrs. Newton in a tone of sound, determined common sense. "Are you married, or is it only that you ought to be?"

"We are!" cried Carr, furious at this slur cast on his Cordelia. He repeated the lie with all the emphasis at his command. "We *are* married."

"Then I wash my hands of you," returned Mrs. Newton, with a certain natural irritation. She shut the door with a slam, and Cordelia found herself alone on the steps with her lover.

He took her arm and urged her away. All down the steps and along the roads Cordelia wept bitterly; she was terrified by Carr's lie, and felt convinced, tragically desperately convinced, that they never would be married now. Carr would be run over at a cross-roads, or there would be some hitch in the licence—never, never would they be married, and her character was gone! Carr pooh-poohed all this, and tried to assure her that in less than an hour they would be man and wife; but he too felt that he had tempted Fate by his audacious lie, he too felt nervous at the cross-roads; his heart beat fast, his hands trembled with emotion, his young face was drawn and haggard as he supported the weeping Cordelia towards the office of the Registrar. They were before their time, and had to wait; and they went through a period of intense agony—an agony which crystallised, as it were, their love for ever, for it made them realise that no torment could be worse than separation. At last, however, they were before the Registrar; strangely enough there was *no* hitch in the licence, nor had Phil forgotten the ring; and a few minutes later Dell was safely transformed into Mrs. Philip Carr.

Immediately they both forgot the agony which had gone before; Cordelia was surprised to find the front of the sealskin damp, and dried it solicitously; Carr was in the wildest spirits. Why should they stay in Scarborough beneath the critical Newton eye? Why not go to London and enjoy themselves? Cordelia, who had never been to London, agreed joyously; and off they went—in a first-class compartment, secured to themselves alone by a lavish tip to the guard. They lunched on the train; when they reached London they put up at the new Holborn Viaduct Hotel; shops were inspected, the sealskin supplemented—in particular by one of the fashionable "fishwife" costumes, with thirty-two buttons in a row down the back, over which they had the first quarrel of their married life because Carr buttoned it awry—sights were seen, restaurants sampled, theatres visited. Cordelia, who had lived always a narrow, careful life, strictly bounded both by the limits of a small income and by her father's peculiar views, was in the seventh heaven. She loved the lavish way Carr drew out half-crowns on the slightest provocation; she loved his easy, dominating manner in hotels; she loved each instance of the undoubted fact that he was nearly always the handsomest man in the room; she loved to see Londoners admiring him. And all this rich, splendid London life, this flash of lights—and the feeling that it was genuine, authentic, not a mere poor provincial imitation—all this appealed to Cordelia immensely. Oh, she was happy, immensely happy; and Carr was immensely happy too. They must have made a striking pair as they entered restaurants and theatres together; Carr tall and dark and dashing, with crisp wavy hair and merry brown eyes: Cordelia small and very slender, with an exquisite complexion, eyes of brilliant blue, a crown of flaming hair very severely dressed, and a touching expression of innocent purity which marriage had not destroyed.

On Saturday, April 10th, an incident occurred. By a piece of tremendous good fortune they had been trying to book at the Opéra Comique for *The Pirates of Penzance* at the very moment when three seats were returned, and by bribery and corruption—perhaps also by his youthful charm and that of Cordelia—Phil secured two of them. Hence they witnessed that delicious foolery from the stalls, and clapped ecstatically, with the rest of the packed house, at the irresistible strains of *Poor Wandering One*. ("Take any heart, take *mine*," was a sentiment very much in tune with Cordelia's feelings at that moment.) At last the curtain came down, the lights went up; Carr turned sideways to allow his neighbour to pass out, and found himself looking into the eyes of Charlie Gill.

"Hullo!" he exclaimed in intense surprise.

"Hullo!" returned Charlie dully, looking rather pale and gazing fixedly at Cordelia.

"What are you doing here?" pursued Carr cheerfully. "Fancy meeting you here!"

Charlie, his eyes still on Cordelia, who was wearing the blue shawl and the filigree earrings, explained that he had been abroad with the Barkers and was on his way home.

"I thought you were in the Isle of Man," he concluded.

"I've been doing a thing worth two of that, my boy!" cried Carr, laughing heartily. "Allow me to introduce you to my wife."

"Oh!" said Charlie, brightening a little. "I see." He offered congratulations, shook their hands, asked a few particulars, smiled stiffly, and vanished. The curtain rose again, but he had not returned; nor did they see him again that evening. Carr reminded himself that he was, of course, Charlie's successful rival with Cordelia, and strove to take pride in that thought. But he could not; and somehow the incident cast a shadow over the evening—it seemed as though everyday Hudley life had stretched out its grimy hand over their romance. When they reached the song *He loves me, he is here: fa la la la, fa la la la,* they turned to each other with a smile, and reflected that after all they were married and nobody could part them; but when Mabel went on *He loves me, he is gone,* Cordelia's heart was nearly broken by the pathos of it; her eyes became quite wet, and she unconsciously shrank towards Carr's shoulder for protection.

Although they went next morning to St. Paul's—Cordelia was already a *convinced* Anglican—and in the afternoon to Richmond Park, somehow their spirits did not rise to their former heights. They had become conscious that alarming interviews lay ahead of them; moreover, they wondered whether Charlie Gill had yet gone home, and if so, whether he would tell of his meeting with them or not. Carr, judging Charlie by himself, thought not; but Cordelia more shrewdly thought that he would. She woke up on the Monday morning with the determination fixed in her small head to go home that day and get these awkward interviews over. Left to himself Carr would probably have stayed in London until his money was done, but he was no match for Cordelia when her mind was made up, so they took an early train, and reached Hudley between one and two o'clock that afternoon.

Their state of mind at this moment seems almost incredible, but must nevertheless be accepted, for the accounts of both on this point are clear and emphatic. It must already have occurred to the discerning reader to wonder why neither of them thought of announcing their marriage to their respective families by letter. The answer to this query is, that till the moment of their arrival in Hudley on the afternoon of April 12th they both fondly imagined that their parents were still quite ignorant of their elopement from Scarborough, and still believed them to be in the Filey Road and the Isle of Man respectively. Such a belief is, as the reader must feel, almost incredible in view of the various circumstances of the case—Mrs. Newton's witness of their departure, for instance—and can only be explained by the suggestion that they were so intensely preoccupied with each other, so completely and utterly engrossed in the fulfilment of their love, that their ordinary common sense was in abeyance, and they really lived in a romantic dream from which everyone else was excluded. That this dream was very different from the reality must, of course, be obvious. Immediately after their departure from her mother-in-law's house, Mrs. George Newton sat down and wrote an indignant letter to Taylor Eastwood, stating that his daughter's husband had removed her (Cordelia) from her (Mrs. Newton's) care; and that she (Mrs. Newton) was no longer responsible for her. Then, on reflection, she became very much troubled by the idea that Carr's announcement of their marriage might have been the lie that in fact it was. Horrified by the thought of Cordelia's position if such were indeed the case, she went out and sought wildly about Scarborough for the lovers; then, not finding them, sent off a telegram to Taylor which exploded like a perfect bombshell all over Hudley. Taylor, pale, quivering, almost mad with rage and grief, found time to call in at Atack Place on his way to the station, forced himself into Ellen's presence, and had a perfectly atrocious scene with her. He thought Hammond Carr's son capable of any infamy, and did not believe that Carr and Cordelia were married; but in Ellen's presence he swore that they should be, if he had to horsewhip Phil into acquiescence. Ellen, beside herself at this suggestion, with a bitter smile gave vent to the wicked and cruel wish, as it seemed to Taylor, that Phil should never marry the girl—thus he would revenge his father. She insinuated that Cordelia was no better than she should be, and had thrown herself at Phil's head and tempted the lad into dishonourable courses; whereat Taylor shouted at her and advanced on her with uplifted fist. Just in time he recollected himself and staggered back without striking her; then putting one hand to his head he somehow got himself from the house.

Meanwhile the rumour of the elopement was spreading all over Hudley. Adelaide, who was shopping in town with Catherine, heard it, and hastened to Atack Place. She found Ellen in a fearful state of rage and anguish, not fit to be left alone; and after some argument carried her off back with her to Carr Fold. There they found William Ainsley in a rather bad humour, eating his midday meal alone; he had waited till long past his usual hour for his wife and daughter, and at last could wait no longer—Phil being away, he must get back to the mill. Adelaide immediately, with a rather sardonic, curious little smile, broke the news to him as he sat at table. The blood rushed to William

Ainsley's head. "The fool!" he broke out passionately. "The damned fool! He doesn't know which side his bread's buttered on. The damned romantic fool!"

"They may not be married, William," said Adelaide in a mincing tone.

"I'm sure they're not!" cried Ellen, her eyes glittering feverishly.

"Of course they're married!" said William Ainsley, glowering. "Don't you know your own son better than that? Did you know aught of this, Catherine?" he added sharply, turning to his daughter.

"Yes, papa," said the truthful Catherine. "That is, I knew they were in love with each other."

Her father stared at her from bloodshot eyes. "Well, go and take your things off," he said roughly to Adelaide. As she went from the room, supporting Ellen, we may surmise, with a great show of sisterliness, William Ainsley rose from his chair and laid a heavy hand on his daughter's shoulder. "Why didn't you marry Phil yourself, Catherine?" he demanded. "Don't you like him?"

"Yes, Papa," replied Catherine steadfastly. "But not in that way."

"Rubbish!" said William Ainsley—with what degree of truth the reader must determine. "You're like all women—don't know your own mind till it's too late." He took a few steps up and down the room. "It's a great disappointment to me," he said heavily. "Very great indeed." He sat down again at the table. "The damned fool!" he repeated in a tone of intense irritation.

"She's very pretty, Papa," put in Catherine, "and good."

Her father gave an angry exclamation, and struck the table with the palm of his hand. Seeing Catherine shrink, he said hastily: "Well, there, say no more about it. But it's no use your aunt thinking they aren't married," he added bitterly. "I know Phil better than that. An idea of that sort would never come into his head."

The entry in Catherine's diary from which the account of this scene is taken closes with the words: "With this I absolutely agree. Dear Phil is incapable of dishonourable or calculating thoughts of any kind."

This, however, was just what Ellen could not be convinced of: and all that night she cherished, she positively hugged to her breast, the thought that Phil, by seducing and betraying Taylor Eastwood's daughter, had nobly revenged all his father's wrongs. Life, however, with its customary irony, had a poetic justice of another kind in store for her. After an exasperating journey Taylor Eastwood had reached Scarborough in the early evening of April 6th; being a man of sense and experience, after a brief consultation with Mrs. Newton he went at once to the Registrar's office. The office was closed; he invoked the aid of the police and sought out the Registrar at his private house. The Registrar, having daughters of his own, was extremely sympathetic; moreover, he remembered Carr and Cordelia —as who would not? The office was unlocked, the record produced, and Taylor's most pressing anxiety set at rest. As soon as the post offices opened next morning, he sent a consoling telegram to his wife, and also one to Ellen Carr, announcing the marriage in the crudest terms consistent with proof which would carry conviction. The telegram was delivered at Atack Place early that morning, and at once sent on to Carr Fold by Mrs. Carr's cook, who with considerable good sense took it down to Mr. Ainsley's Hudley office and urged its immediate delivery. Ellen, Adelaide and Catherine were sitting together in the drawing-room overlooking the terrace when this telegram was brought in on a salver by a young housemaid. The girl, who in common with all the other Carr Fold domestics knew the circumstances, was really afraid to hand the orange envelope to Mrs. Carr; she timidly proffered it instead to Catherine. Catherine with characteristic vagueness did not notice the address; jumping to the conclusion that it was a telegram from Phil to herself she opened it, read it, realised her mistake, looked at the envelope again, turned pale and faltered: "It's for you, Aunt Ellen."

"Read it!" almost screamed Ellen, jumping to her feet, one hand pressed to her wildly beating heart.

So Catherine read it. ("I blame myself for not having considered more before doing so," she reproached herself in her diary that night. "I ought to have prepared Aunt Ellen for the blow, I ought to have softened it down for her. I shall never cease to blame myself terribly for what happened.") "'Philip Joseph Carr,'" she read in clear if rather shaky tones, "'and Cordelia Mary Eastwood were married by Scarborough Registrar April 6. Taylor Eastwood.'"

There was an awful pause; then from Ellen there came a kind of horrible animal groan; she stared stupidly, from wide dull eyes, at her niece and then at Adelaide, who wore her curious little smile; she seemed to make an immense effort to speak, but could make no sound save a repetition of that dreadful open-mouthed groan, and then fell headlong on the carpet. Catherine's diary, though it blames her so severely for her thoughtless behaviour on this occasion, shows too that she found her aunt's agitation surprisingly excessive; but then Catherine did not know all the circumstances. That Adelaide's child should be the one to inform Ellen that her son had married Taylor Eastwood's daughter lent a fearful bitterness to the news. Life had avenged

Adelaide, oh, avenged her terribly for Ellen's theft of her lover! Perhaps too in that last conscious moment—for Ellen was struck down by a cerebral hæmorrhage from which she never recovered: she was never again conscious, did not recognise Phil when she saw him, and died within twelve days—in that last conscious moment Ellen had perhaps remembered Adelaide's gift of money to Phil, and suspected her of helping on the marriage. At any rate she fell thus, stricken.

The doctor was summoned, and pronounced that it was a matter of time only; and the question then became, how and where to find Phil. Nobody knew where he was, not even young George Newton, who was recalled from his holiday and severely questioned by his angry parents. Carr had never mentioned any plans for after his marriage—probably never made any. The facilities for tracing disappearing persons were not then as great as they are now; there was no wireless, no cinema. Taylor had a certain amount of vague evidence that the pair had left Scarborough by a London train, but could trace them no further. William Ainsley and he communicated with each other daily in the hope of news from the eloping pair, but as we know none came; Carr and Cordelia were lost in the void until Sunday, April 11th, when Charlie Gill arrived in Hudley. He, of course, had no more idea than Carr and Cordelia themselves of all the excitement in Hudley consequent on their elopement. He had not returned to *The Pirates* the night before because he simply could not bear the spectacle of Cordelia as the wife of another man; and he returned to Hudley on a Sunday because Mr. Barker wished him to be at business on Monday morning, and he had dallied in London on the Saturday in order to see the new Gilbert-and-Sullivan—which, as he was a single individual, he thought he might manage to do from one part of the house or the other. When, however, at the Gill supper-table that night he brought out—not without effort—the announcement that he had seen Carr and Cordelia at the Opéra Comique the previous night, and he supposed they were married, naturally the excitement was intense. The circumstances were explained to him by several people talking at once. Mrs. Carr was dying, and Phil was lost. He and Cordelia had eloped, and were goodness knew where. Did he know where they were staying? Charlie thought Phil had said the Holborn. This was immediately communicated to both the Eastwoods and the Ainsleys by the friendly Gills; and early on Monday morning telegrams were despatched from both households. Carr and Cordelia, however, left too early to receive them.

One can imagine, then, the astonishment of the newly-married pair when they emerged from the Hudley station and found Joshua waiting for them, and yet understand that this was a perfectly natural phenomenon. Joshua had been ordered to meet all London trains that day—putting his horses up between whiles at the Pack Horse Inn in Hudley—for Mrs. Carr's condition was now dangerous. Joshua was extremely fond of Phil—perhaps fonder of him than of Catherine—and though like Mr. Ainsley he thought it was a pity Phil did not know which side his bread was buttered, he admired the young man's spirit in eloping with a girl of whom his mother disapproved. (None of the Carr Fold servants liked Mrs. Carr.) Joshua was quite prepared to forgive Cordelia if he liked the look of her, and he found that he liked the look of her very much indeed. Consequently he was most fatherly and respectful to her; handed her into the carriage most tenderly, arranged rugs about her with an aged deferential hand, and several times called her "Mrs. Phil," which the ingenuous Cordelia adored. Meanwhile Joshua explained to Carr all that had been happening. His instructions were to drive the young people straight to Carr Fold, but in Joshua's opinion Mrs. Phil had ample time to call round and see her father first if she felt inclined. Cordelia felt very strongly inclined; so the carriage rolled away to Majorca Road. So rarely do human emotions fulfil conventional expectation that the young people were secretly relieved by Joshua's shocking news—though of course they pretended to be horrified. Carr was very glad indeed that their marriage was known to everybody, so that he would not have to break the news—an operation peculiarly trying to sensitive natures—and his mother's recent opposition to his marriage had alienated his affection from her, or perhaps we might say that his increasing alienation from her had culminated in their recent disagreement. Cordelia was equally glad that their marriage was known; she could not help feeling relieved that the haughty wife of Hammond Carr was not going to make their lives miserable by her disapproval; she rather liked being the heroine of an elopement, and she decidedly enjoyed driving in a carriage. They reached Number 39 and went in.

Taylor had not returned to business for the afternoon. He was sitting in the back room previously described, reading the *National Reformer,* when Cordelia and her husband burst in upon him.

"Well, Mr. Eastwood," cried Carr, laughing heartily. "I hope you're going to forgive me for taking Dell away from you."

Taylor, lowering the paper, looked at him over his spectacles and snorted.

Various slight circumstances, however, inclined him to a

reconciliation. To begin with, Taylor was in a good mood with the world just then. The election had resulted in a sweeping victory for the Liberals all over the country. Bradlaugh was positively in for Northampton, and though there were rumblings which threatened a storm about his taking of the oath, Parliament had not yet assembled, and that was all in the future; at present Taylor's beloved Bradlaugh was in, positively in, and Taylor felt that the world was going the right way at last. Then there was the appearance of his daughter. Cordelia was clad that day in the fishwife costume, the sealskin, the little round muff, some new boots and a Regent Street hat. On her left hand she wore an indubitable wedding ring and a very nice diamond ring presented to her by her husband, and she had ingenuously removed her glove so that these should be seen. She looked blooming; her cheeks were bright and rosy, her blue eyes sparkling, her smile deliciously joyous, her gait bounding; obviously she was as happy as the days were long and very proud of being Mrs. P. J. Carr. Then there was Carr himself; he was undoubtedly a handsome lad, with his erect figure, his bright brown eyes, his crisp black hair and his jolly candid smile; and he had undoubtedly preferred the penniless Cordelia to the heiress Catherine. Then he had called Cordelia "Dell." Taylor very much disliked nicknames, as a general rule; but there was something homely and friendly, something non-standoffish, something true and loving, something just the opposite of Taylor's idea of Hammond Carr, in Phil's quite unthinking and natural use of his wife's pet name. Then again—and perhaps not least—the Eastwoods' fine cat, Cherry, had advanced to Carr as he entered the room and reached up a paw to his elegant trousers. Carr was not particularly fond of cats, but he was simply incapable of consciously hurting the feelings of any animal, as of any human being; he stooped down to the cat, said "Well, then!" in a soothing tone, playfully shook its paw and ran a caressing finger beneath its soft chin, all in a purely natural and unthinking manner. He behaved thus because it was his nature to behave thus, and because no false notions of dignity or calculations of effect ever came into his head to prevent him from behaving naturally; and Taylor Eastwood, who was no fool, could not help seeing this. Instinctively he felt that while Carr had not perhaps a great deal of wisdom, his heart was in the right place. Carr was obviously tremendously proud of Cordelia, and head over ears in love with her. He appreciated her at what Taylor had always felt to be her true worth. Finally, Taylor felt just a trifle guilty about Mrs. Hammond Carr. His telegram had killed her—or would do so in a day or two. His old score with Hammond might, therefore, surely now be counted quit.

"Well," he said grumpily, "the milk's spilt now, I suppose."

At this Cordelia threw herself into his arms (crumpling the *National Reformer* shockingly); and Carr wrung his hand, really moved. In the background Mrs. Eastwood and Annie wept happily, while Lomas unobtrusively withdrew. This charming domestic scene was broken upon by Joshua's violent ringing of the front-door bell; really Mr. and Mrs. Phil must come on to Carr Fold now. Carr, agreeing, tenderly helped Cordelia to her feet, dried her eyes and adjusted the sealskin, kissed Mrs. Eastwood and shook hands with Annie heartily. Taylor Eastwood scorned carriages and the people who owned them, and would not have driven in one for the world; as he stood at the door of Number 39, clasping the lapels of his coat with his customary air of pugnacity, and watched Joshua drive the young couple away, he shook his head over them, but in his heart he reluctantly admitted that P. J. Carr was a fine young fellow. At Majorca Road the reconciliation was complete.

The reconciliation at Carr Fold was on a different footing. William Ainsley, to whom the dignity of his daughter was precious, had no mind to advertise his disappointment at her loss of a husband to the world at large, nor did he relish dwelling upon that aspect of the matter to Phil. After his first impulse to cast the Carrs utterly away and see them no more, his sound common sense and love of justice reasserted itself. Nobody knew better than William Ainsley that a man cannot love (or cease to love) to order, when his reason commands; moreover, Phil had never been informed of his uncle's marital plans for him. Mr. Ainsley told himself that he had been a fool to count on anything so uncertain as a young man's fancy, and that his disappointment was entirely his own fault; but that reflection, while it prevented him from dissolving the partnership and throwing Phil on the world, did not make his disappointment any less. He made up his mind to pretend to Hudley that Mrs. Carr's dislike of Cordelia as Taylor Eastwood's daughter was the only objection entertained on Carr's side of the match, and he insisted on keeping the young couple at Carr Fold until Mrs. Carr's fatal illness should terminate; but he felt vexed, cross, exasperated, and he received Cordelia gruffly, with an irritation only just concealed. This, of course, sent Cordelia's head up at its haughtiest angle. Like this she looked prettier than ever, and we may imagine Mr. Ainsley to have been still further irritated by the contrast between the pretty, silly, uneducated little thing—as he quite erroneously thought her—and his own earnest, accomplished but so plain Catherine.

Not a detail of the fishwife costume, the sealskin, the Pinet boots and the diamond ring escaped him; he cursed Carr in his heart for an extravagant, besotted young fool, and would have liked to give himself more consolation of the same kind by sneering at Cordelia's taste, but could not, for Cordelia's taste was excellent, and the ring did not appear in the mornings. There were, however, other points on which Mr. Ainsley was able to be sarcastic. Cordelia was, for example, afraid of dogs—she had never lived with any—and shrank from the peaceful but massive Didymus, straining away from him when he approached her with a quite piteous expression of panic. Mr. Ainsley teased her once too often on this subject, whereupon she suddenly flew out at him in a manner utterly unprecedented at Carr Fold, and told him that he was unkind and cruel and that she hated him. "*My* father never speaks to me like that!" she cried, and forthwith burst into vehement tears and fled from the room in an angry swish of silk. Carr, horrified, followed her, casting a look of reproach at his uncle as he went. Mr. Ainsley raised his eyebrows and said something cutting about Phil's having caught a Tartar, but he was really rather tickled by the girl's spirit, and treated her with more consideration after her little outburst of temper. He had not yet brought himself to express any opinion on his nephew's marriage directly to Carr, and an uncomfortable feeling of suspense—among other uncomfortable feelings—brooded over Carr Fold. Catherine had made up her mind to love Cordelia, and she was extremely, persistently kind to her; but Cordelia was not comfortable with Catherine. Much shrewder than her husband, she understood perfectly William Ainsley's scheme and its failure; moreover, she was by no means sure that Catherine's fondness for Phil was merely that of a sister. As Catherine was feeling a little dreary just then, and Adelaide was inscrutable as usual, Carr had probably rather a wretched time of it during the next week, while his mother lay dying in a room above.

All these various conflicting feelings were, however, soon concealed under the decorum rendered necessary by the presence of death. Ellen Carr, as has been said, never regained consciousness, and she died at three o'clock on the morning of April 19th. None of the three young people had ever seen death before, and they were naturally much distressed. Carr in particular was bowed down by a natural sorrow, and by that feeling which so frequently afflicts those who stand beside an open grave: namely, that his shortcomings towards the dead had been terribly many. All the careless words, all the unsympathetic glances, of which he had ever been guilty towards his mother returned to his mind with a dreadful force; and as regards his marriage with Cordelia he felt so unutterably criminal that he was almost ashamed to kiss her. In the early morning after his mother's death, while the family were wandering vaguely about, feeling useless and miserable, he blurted out something of this feeling to Mr. Ainsley. His uncle, who like Taylor Eastwood was a man of sense and experience, saw that the boy's life might very well be ruined if he allowed this remorse to prey upon him. He therefore took Carr apart with him into the library, and talked to him in a sensible, sober and downright fashion. He told Carr that while it would have been better if he had confided his love to his uncle and altogether taken a more open course about it, yet a man had a right to marry to please himself. That he had fallen in love with Cordelia was perhaps unfortunate from several points of view. To begin with, the girl was beneath him socially—at this Carr looked black. But in Mr. Ainsley's experience real genuine hearty affection such as Carr and Cordelia seemed to have for each other—Carr's brow cleared—was a very good foundation for married life. Nothing, in fact, said Mr. Ainsley—rather pathetically, if Carr had but known it—was better. Then Cordelia was Taylor Eastwood's daughter. But Mr. Ainsley hinted that Ellen's animosity against the Eastwoods was not well grounded. Seeing that Carr did not grasp the implications of this, and loth to destroy the boy's faith in his father too abruptly, he suggested that Ellen had never got over her husband's flight; it had been such a terrible shock, that perhaps her judgment on the Eastwoods had never been quite sound, quite reliable, since then. Ellen's death was, in fact, due as much to events which had happened before Phil was born as to Phil's marriage; in any case, the thing was done now; it was no use brooding over it; Carr's first duty was to Cordelia. Cordelia had made herself very useful that morning, in those gloomy hours while the servants still slept, improvising a fire and an unexpected cup of coffee and producing Adelaide's shawl just when she required it; and Mr. Ainsley's heart was softened towards her.

"You've married to please yourself and not to please me, Phil," concluded Mr. Ainsley, "and considering what I've done for you I think I was entitled at least to be consulted. However, Cordelia seems a good girl, though a bit of a Tartar,"—at this Carr looked black again—"and we won't say any more about it. I won't let it make any difference to you at Carr Foot while I'm alive; but I may as well tell you frankly that I shall alter my will."

As the thought of Mr. Ainsley's will had never previously entered Carr's head, this did not depress him as much as it might have done if he had been of a more calculating nature. Mr. Ainsley no doubt saw this, and it probably did not diminish the affection he had for his nephew. "Though I daresay," he added in a kinder tone, "I could trust you always to look after Catherine's interests."

Carr said "Of course," and meant it. Mr. Ainsley gave a sigh which we may surmise was rather exasperated, and the interview ended. Carr was pleased that all was now clear between himself and his uncle, and felt that he had been let off lightly; characteristically he forgot all about Mr. Ainsley's will, which indeed he would have been ashamed to remember.

Ellen's funeral took place at St. Mark's, Hudley, on April 22nd; her will, which was very short and left everything she possessed—this being practically only the house in Atack Place and its furniture—to Phil, was duly read; next morning the young Carrs returned to Atack Place and took up their abode there; their marriage was an accomplished and acknowledged fact, and they began their life together, which was to last through so many and such diverse years.

V

CARR CARR AND AINSLEY (1880–1882)

TIME passed on; and it is interesting to note how soon life under the new conditions became accepted and regarded as ordinary by those concerned. It was very tragic about his poor mother, thought Carr, certainly; but after all she was at rest now, and probably understood everything better; and however tragic it was, somehow Carr could not but take pleasure in the sight of Cordelia installed opposite him at his own dinner-table in his own house. (She looked charming in mourning.) William Ainsley too accepted the new conditions with a rapidity at first sight astonishing. But as a matter of fact Ellen's death seemed to lift a load off Carr Fold. That old story of Adelaide's love for Hammond seemed to have slipped years back into the past now that the two principal actors in it were gone. Adelaide seemed to breathe more freely, to be able to lift her head and look around; for the first time in twenty-two years it seemed to occur to her (this comes from Cordelia) that she had not done badly for herself in marrying William Ainsley. Her health undoubtedly improved from the day of her sister's death, and she became both more affectionate and more cheerful. Her husband and her daughter both felt the effects of this; Catherine observed it with a mournful surprise, but William undoubtedly (though a trifle cynically) enjoyed it; and a kind of Indian summer of happiness set in for these two. A photograph of Mr. Ainsley taken about this time shows him as rather plumper in the face than we have been used to thinking him; his crisp, gingerish hair has receded somewhat from his forehead, his abundant moustache, whiskers and beard show traces of grey, and he wears an eyeglass on a cord; but his expression is still that of a powerful and determined man: he looks as able, as choleric and as prosperous as ever, and rather more self-satisfied than before. Now that Hammond Carr's son was married to Taylor Eastwood's daughter, and Hammond Carr's wife was dead, the tongues of William and Adelaide were somehow loosened: they were able to discuss their daughter's future freely, and even at times to make an excursion into the past, from which the sting had now strangely been drawn. Under the influence of his wife's new cheerfulness Mr. Ainsley was able to remind himself that there were plenty of other young men in the world besides Carr, that Catherine was an heiress who should have no difficulty in finding a husband, that this husband could take the name of Ainsley outright, and the firm could then still be Carr Carr and Ainsley: finally, that the project which had gone awry for this generation might be fulfilled in the next. By endowing Carr with a son and Catherine with a daughter he arranged everything very satisfactorily, and as the months went on one of these hopes, at least, drew near fulfilment. Carr's eldest child, a son, was born on February 12th, 1881, and was christened Hammond Taylor Carr.

To an observer unacquainted with the previous history of the Carr and Eastwood families, this name would no doubt seem the perfectly natural outcome of the Victorian custom of bestowing the name of each grandfather on the eldest grandson; but those who have followed Carr's biography so far must be astonished to see the name of Taylor Eastwood in such close and familiar juxtaposition with that of his ancient enemy. It can, indeed, only be explained by a study of the relations of Carr with the Eastwood family during the winter of 1881. These relations were, simply, of the most cordial and satisfactory kind. To begin with, Carr was an extremely tender and considerate husband. Nothing was quite good enough for his Cordelia, and he never thought of concealing that he felt so. There are households in which the husband always has the best cut of the joint and the best piece of cake, but Carr's was not one of them; in his house the best of everything belonged automatically to his wife. The young couple were deeply in love with each other, and scarcely left each other's side except for the daily routine of business. (It may be mentioned here that William Ainsley's hostility to Cordelia vanished under his increasing conviction of Cordelia's sense of duty and idea of the importance of business. Carr still maintained his early morning visits to Carr Foot Mills; it now fell to Cordelia to waken him and get him off, and in this she never failed. She had a very strong sense of the importance of the firm of Carr Carr and Ainsley; and was quite ready to move into a house nearer Carr Foot if business seemed to demand it.) Throughout the winter of 1880–1881 poor little Cordelia suffered a good deal from sickness and other disabilities of her condition—she was, for instance, unable to eat her Christmas dinner at Carr Fold, and had to lie down in another room during its progress. She had always previously enjoyed superb health, and disliked being ill very much indeed; sometimes it made her really rather cross. Carr's devotion during this trying period was all that a loving, generous and truly delicate heart could make it. He gave up football, he gave up dancing, he gave up going to the swimming baths with young George Newton; and he gave them up, not because he thought he ought to, but because he really wanted to abandon anything which kept him away from his dear (though cross) little wife. This naturally was not unperceived by the Eastwood family, and Taylor—who had seen so many marriages—could not but feel that a young man who behaved like that had not very much wrong with him at bottom. Then too, although Carr was a Tory and a high-ish Churchman, while Taylor was a Radical and an atheist, after one tremendous political quarrel they experienced the phenomenon not unknown among opponents of high personal character, and found that they had more in common with each other than with some of the people who agreed with their views. Carr, again, who in his childhood had spent hours standing beside the gardener's wheelbarrow at Carr Fold, watching with those bright eyes of his the mysterious slow processes of cultivating the earth, was interested in Taylor's garden and sometimes able to offer good advice. Moreover, he occasionally begged a root or two from Carr Fold—Catherine was always very eager to oblige in this respect. We may imagine, then, the tall handsome Carr and the small withered Taylor ambling round Taylor's little garden together on winter Saturday afternoons, pausing by the chrysanthemums, expatiating on the celery, discussing the next year's peas, getting a little heated about Sir Stafford Northcote, about whose attitude to Bradlaugh Carr was fortunately rather dubious, while Cordelia, blooming in her new blue poplin, pouted charmingly at them through the long window. On her lap would be some article of the exquisite trousseau she was preparing for her child. No material was too good, no labour too excessive, to be bestowed on this prodigious infant, and Taylor as well as Carr felt that it was right that it should be so. (William Ainsley, on the other hand, sometimes wondered how a one-eighth share in Carr Carr and Ainsley stood it.)

Terrible agitation was experienced in Majorca Road from February 1st, the conjectural date of the young Carr's arrival, to his actual appearance on February 12th. Taylor was always turning up on Carr's doorstep with his face full of suspense and inquiry; and Carr drew him in eargerly anxious to confide to him all his latest hopes and fears. When at last the child was born it was felt by all concerned that he was well worth waiting for. Catherine may perhaps be allowed to speak on this point. At the actual moment of the child's birth she was away in Ingleton attending the wedding of her former schoolmistress, Miss Thompson, to Sebastian Whitaker the antiquary; so she did not see the baby until four days later. "This morning," she writes on February 16th, "I went with Mamma, to see Phil's beautiful baby. He is indeed most beautiful; a fine big boy, with an exquisitely pure fair skin, like Cordelia's, and beautiful blue eyes, like hers too. He has quite a lot of hair, of a colour I can only describe as bronze—dark brown with ruddy gleams in it. His face did not strike me as at all like his father's, but his limbs and dear little hands and feet, and the way he was lying in the nurse's arms, were quite comically like Phil. Dear Phil is naturally intensely proud of him. He wants to call him Hammond Taylor Carr, after his two grandfathers, which seems to me very nice."

To Cordelia, on the other hand, Phil's joyous announcement of this suggestion was in the nature of a bombshell. From her pillows she stared up at her husband in amazement. Could he have forgotten so soon the antagonisms which had made their marriage a secret one? As a matter of fact he had; utterly incapable of bearing malice himself, he imagined that everybody else forgot a grudge as soon as he did, which unfortunately was not often the case. Cordelia had not yet brought herself to tell Phil that she shared her father's views of Hammond Carr, and she could not do it now; instead she murmured, with rather less than her usual vehemence, that she had thought of "William," after Mr. Ainsley. Carr's face fell at this, for the suggestion was obvious and reasonable; and he was overjoyed to find, when he consulted Mr. Ainsley next day on the subject, that his uncle emphatically did not wish the child to be named after him. "I rather thought of 'Hammond Taylor' if you didn't want 'William,'" explained Carr eagerly. Mr. Ainsley raised his eyebrows, and said: "An excellent suggestion," in a rather dry tone. Meanwhile Cordelia at home was breaking the proposal to her father. Taylor Eastwood snorted, coloured to the roots of his gingery hair, and almost bounded away from the bed at the outrageous suggestion.

"Don't say anything to Phil, father," pleaded Cordelia. "He doesn't know anything against his father, you know."

"Then it's time he did," snorted Taylor.

Cordelia sighed, and her eyes filled with tears; her father remembered that she was still weak, and subsided into inarticulate grumblings. In the course of a day or two he came so far round to the suggestion that it rather tickled him. Besides, he liked Phil so well nowadays that he was able to see Hammond Carr not as a melodramatic villain but just as a piece of ordinary weak human nature. And then again, as he reflected bitterly, who was he to cast a stone, with a son like Lomas? After suggesting that "Taylor" should abdicate in favour of "Charles," the name of his beloved Bradlaugh—a suggestion which was prudently buried in Cordelia's bosom and not allowed to emerge—he tacitly yielded. Cordelia herself, who at first had terrible qualms at the thought of saddling her beautiful boy with an ill-omened name, was gradually seduced by the lofty, Mayfair-ish, aristocratic sound of it. "Sir Hammond Carr"—it sounded well.

On March 15th, therefore, Hammond Taylor was duly christened as such by the Reverend Humphrey Gill at St. Mark's, having as godmother Catherine, and as godfathers Charlie Gill and Nicholas Whiteley (junior). Joshua had the privilege of driving him to the church from Atack Place—it was, in fact, the last time but one that he drove for the Ainsleys, for he had now been superseded by his son-in-law, the father of the Master James Illingworth who performed at the Carr Foot concert. The young Hammond behaved admirably throughout the ceremony, at first sleeping, then, as the water touched him, opening surprised but placid blue eyes. His bronze hair was much admired by the many friendly spectators, who after the ceremony all returned to Atack Place and drank the baby's health.[1] William Ainsley, glass in hand, presented him with a fifty-pound bank-note, at which Taylor, who was a teetotaler and had given the child only five pounds, became rather gloomy. Indeed this meeting between the Ainsleys and the Eastwoods was, like previous meetings of the same kind, not very comfortable; and it is not difficult to understand the sequence of ideas which led William Ainsley to speak to Catherine and Adelaide, on their way home behind Joshua, of the terms of his new will.

[1] The cork of the bottle of champagne drunk on this occasion is in the writer's possession; it bears on the flat lower end, printed in Carr's characteristic bold hand, the child's name and the date of the christening.

After describing the provision made for Adelaide—which consisted of a fund held in trust for her, the capital of which was to pass to Catherine at her death—and expressing the hope that he would live to see Catherine happily married, with her husband a partner in the business and children of her own growing up to succeed him, so that these arrangements would be invalidated, Mr. Ainsley explained that apart from certain charitable bequests, and a one-eighth share in Carr Carr and Ainsley to Phil, the whole of his property descended to Catherine absolutely. (At this Adelaide made a *moue.*) It may be surmised that Mr. Ainsley made this rather rash arrangement, as it is usually regarded nowadays, because in the event of Catherine's dying without issue there were no Ainsleys to whom his wealth could return, and he wished her to have the disposition of her own property, and be able to enrich those who were kind to her. It was expressly stated, however, as Mr. Ainsley's wish, that so much of Catherine's capital as was at the time of his death invested in the firm of Carr Carr and Ainsley was to remain with that firm—of which she would then own a three-fourths, and Phil a one-fourth share. She was only to withdraw it if she thought Phil's conduct of the business unsatisfactory and likely to prove unfavourable to her interests; but if she seriously thought this, then the power to withdraw at six months' notice was hers. Mr. Ainsley explained that the threat of this would enable Catherine to prevent Phil from doing anything of which she disapproved. "But, Papa!" protested Catherine, aghast at the thought of disapproving anything in a business she did not in the least understand. "For instance," pursued Mr. Ainsley grimly, "you can prevent Phil taking that fellow in."

"Which fellow?" queried the alarmed Catherine.

"Cordelia's brother," replied Mr. Ainsley, very grimly. "Always remember, Catherine, that Carr Carr and Ainsley is yours and not Phil's, and you can do as you like with it without feeling that you are injuring him. Don't you ever be persuaded into letting him take another partner in, or anything of that kind. Cordelia's brother has no claim on you, even if he *is* a good designer."

The passage in Catherine's diary which describes this incident concludes: "I can see that Papa is irritated by Cordelia's brother. I am troubled about this on Phil's account, for I am sure Cordelia would defend her brother if Papa criticised him, and then Papa and Phil might quarrel. I shall not make things worse by telling Papa about Mr. Eastwood, though he irritates *me* beyond description!"

This last sentence requires a comment, for the last time Catherine's diary was quoted at any length on the subject of Lomas was on the occasion of the picnic at Bolton Abbey. But there have been many entries concerning him since then, and it will be well here to bring the history of Lomas's relations with the rich Miss Ainsley up to date.

These relations consisted, simply, in a pursuit which was none the less relentless because it was not so much dogged as insinuating. Carr's courtship of Cordelia meant that Catherine was always being thrown into Lomas's society. For the last six months of 1879 she met him almost every other day; and whenever he saw her he hastened instantly to her side, advanced his smooth fair head near hers, smiled his specious smile, gazed at her intently from his insolent eyes, and began in his genteel, lisping voice to gush some personal musical anecdote into her reluctant ear. Catherine shivered and shuddered away from him, replied to him in scarcely audible monosyllables, hung her head and tried not to see him or looked into the distance and pretended he was not there; but she was generally forced into uttering two or three reluctant sentences to him by his gentle, suave persistence in asking her musical questions. Apparently encouraged by this scant response, Lomas hung round her on every possible occasion—except when there was a chance that Mr. or Mrs. Ainsley might see him he was always behind Catherine's chair or at her side, and did not scruple to push himself into any group of which she was a member. This had rather the effect of creating a void round Catherine, for Lomas was emphatically not popular in decent society, and we find from time to time exasperated little entries in her diary on the subject. On September 30th, 1879, for instance, when the young people had gone to hear Archibald Forbes lecture, we find: "Mr. Bales Newton, who used to be a friend of Phil's and is now an architect in London, was there. Phil introduced him to me—a clever, ugly, interesting fellow—we were just talking about Fountains Abbey when Mr. Eastwood came up and spoiled everything, as *usual.*" On November 22nd we read: "We drove down to Denbridge Vale to see Phil play in the football match. As soon as I got there I saw Mr. Eastwood and his sister and cousin[1] in the distance. I looked the other way and kept close beside the Newtons and Emily Gill, but of course Miss Eastwood is a friend of Emily's, and very soon that horrid Mr. Eastwood was beside me again, *as* usual. He monopolised me all the afternoon; the Newtons would not talk to me at all, and I did not get a word with Emily. What a bugbear that man is to me! He talked of nothing but Charlie Gill's engagement to Miss Barker, and kept on admiring Miss Barker's 'condescension,' as he calls it. Ugh!" On December 27th we have the following rather pathetic little note:

[1] A very natural mistake about Annie.

"To skate at the ice rink with Phil. We were just having a lovely round together when the Eastwoods arrived. Phil ran off at once to Miss Eastwood. Her brother monopolised me all the afternoon, as usual, calling out to me from the side in a most disagreeable way, but as nobody else seemed to want to talk to me I suppose it did not matter."

From time to time Catherine made spasmodic efforts to rid herself of her incubus, and snubbed him ferociously, but Lomas always found means to render her snubs ineffective—he either appeared not to notice them at all, continuing his plausible strains, which always had an effect of condescension, smoothly; or he allowed himself to seem so utterly, so despairingly dejected by them that Catherine's conscience was alarmed, and forbade her to continue administering such cruel rebuffs. From time to time also she considered the expediency of complaining about Lomas to her father or to Phil, but—as indicated on the day of Hammond's christening—it seemed to her so cruel to poor Phil, who would inevitably be driven into a quarrel either with Cordelia or with his uncle if she did so, that she held her peace. Phil's marriage to Cordelia of course delivered her more than ever into Lomas's hands. People who had never thought of inviting Taylor Eastwood's son to their houses could hardly avoid inviting Mrs. Philip Carr's brother, and Lomas was more in evidence than ever. He now, of course, was known to Mr. and Mrs. Ainsley, and as Cordelia's brother could hardly be expected to refrain from talking to Catherine and dancing with her. Nor could the soft-hearted Catherine embroil the two families and make Phil unhappy by refusing to dance with him or by complaining of him to her father; while unfortunately she was not sufficiently intimate with Cordelia to mention the matter to her, and Phil and Dell were too busy with their own affairs to notice it. Accordingly, we find this very bitter note after a hospital charity ball on January 12th, 1881,—just a month before the birth of the young Hammond. "As usual Lomas Eastwood advanced on me as soon as I entered the room. I could have screamed when I saw him—he exasperates me to such an absurd degree. He danced with me three times, two ordinary dances and one extra. He is a good dancer, and though not as tall as I am manages very well with me, but I hate dancing with him, hate it, hate it! But I suppose I ought rather to be grateful to him for asking me, as my other partners were decidedly few and far between. He talked insufferably and unendingly, as usual. When we were sitting out after the extra dance he positively let flow, amid a torrent of long words, a remark which, if I believed a word he says, I should have construed into a declaration of love. But of course I don't believe a word he says!"

The reader will doubtless be struck by the much more mature and experienced tone of this last entry, compared with the previous ones. Much of Catherine's petulance on this occasion may have been due to physical weariness; but it is difficult to avoid the conclusion that quite unconsciously Catherine suffered under the spectacle of Phil's married life and was aged by her loss of him. There are various references in her diary from April 1880 onwards which confirm this view—references to her loss of appetite, to her depression about her music, to the emptiness of life in Carr Foot as compared with that in Leipzig, to the tedium of society functions, and so on. Catherine may well have felt at this time that she was rather *de trop* at Carr Fold in face of the reconciliation of her father and mother; she was also undoubtedly realising the difference between going into society with a handsome and universally beloved

sordid business in order to be the mainstay of his elderly parents. Catherine, intensely irritated by his description of the business of designing cloth as sordid, set him right on this point sharply. Lomas was overjoyed to find this foothold in her interest, and often afterwards brought out of his pocket little scraps of designing paper and showed her what he was working at, or a pattern so that she might see what it looked like when it was made up. Catherine, although she suspected that Lomas really cared nothing for his work—in which she was right, for he had the utmost difficulty to refrain from yawning while he spoke of it—was interested in these specimens in spite of herself, and found it difficult to snub Lomas when they were his subject. In a word, the very generosity and nobility, the loftiness and candour, of Catherine's nature laid her open to impositions and encroachments from anybody who was adroit (or vile) enough to take advantage of her good qualities; and Lomas certainly was adroit enough for anything. Besides, he really wanted her, as we know from the testimony of Sir Charles Gill; he lay awake at night, feverish for Catherine; grew thin for desire of her, and would have grown haggard if he had not employed the actor's means of preserving his complexion. Once he positively turned up at Atack Place with the bloom of his cheeks assisted by art. The occasion was a dinner offered by Phil and Dell to the Eastwoods, on the next Sunday after the anniversary of their wedding. Throughout the meal Cordelia's eyes were fixed suspiciously upon her brother's face, her expression, we may surmise, being rather that of somebody who has discovered a bad smell; and immediately the meal was over she took him aside and tackled him on the subject with her customary vehemence and fury. "That a brother of mine should *demean* himself so!" cried Cordelia in a storm of contempt. Lomas raised his eyebrows, shrugged his shoulders, and turned down the corners of his mouth in a sneering smile; but his cheeks burned with unassisted colour, and the scene probably did not increase his already small love for his sister. What it undoubtedly did increase was his determination to have Catherine. Everything increased that. The establishment in Atack Place was run on a lavish and care-free footing, and every time Lomas crossed his sister's threshold he could not fail to contrast it with Majorca Road, and reflect that such luxury—and more also, far more—could be his if Catherine would but yield to him. How superior he would be to Carr and Cordelia if Catherine were only his wife! We can imagine him becoming almost mad on the subject, clenching his short plump hands and grinding his teeth—his teeth, by the way, were not too good—and determining that he would have Catherine, he would, he would! Nothing should stop him. Poor Annie had a rough time with him this year; her charms were stale and failed to please; he spoke of nothing but luxury and Catherine. He *would* have Catherine!

In pursuance of this plan he haunted her path more assiduously than ever. In May, for example, Catherine laid the foundation stone of the new Carr Foot Chapel. The reader will remember that William Ainsley had promised to give half the money for this erection on condition that the other half was raised by efforts and subscriptions. A very laudable spirit on the part of the congregation had delayed the beginning of the building until every penny of the required fund was in the bank, though the plans had been completed by the architect—Mr. George Newton, son of old Mr. Newton of Atack Place, and father of Bales and young George—some months before. Then a builders' delay of three weeks had still further postponed the stone-laying ceremony from Eastertide until the seventh of May. According to Cordelia, Catherine had never looked more handsome than when, clad in a pale blue glacé silk dress and a hat with a blue feather, she laid the stone duly and truly, with becoming earnestness and a very decided pat from the trowel. The ceremony was on Saturday afternoon, so that everyone should be free and able to be present; and as Catherine raised her eyes from the stone-laying she encountered the fervid, impassioned gaze of Lomas Eastwood, who "seemed to be standing," she wrote in her diary that night, "just at my feet, at the right-hand side of the scaffolding. His hands were clasped, and he was gazing up at me in that exaggerated, theatrical way he has, as though I were the only thing he cared for in the universe. Really I am almost afraid of him, he irritated me so. I nearly dropped the trowel!!" It is perhaps significant that when the present writer consulted Cordelia about this stone-laying, and read to her the above passage from Catherine's diary, she started and seemed much surprised, and declared emphatically that she had no idea her brother was present. "I never saw him there," she repeated with emphasis. "Never!"

On another occasion Lomas had every right to be present, having received a special invitation. This was at Charlie Gill's marriage on June 14th of this year. The wedding took place in St. Stephen's, Denbridge, and seems to have been a very grand affair, for the account of it occupies two columns of the *Hudley News*. "The bride," we read, "was accompanied by six bridesmaids"; and amongst the names of these young ladies is that of Miss Catherine Ainsley. As they wore "gowns of pale blue muslin, flounced to the top," and carried "bouquets of tea roses," one imagines that on this occasion too Catherine must have looked rather nice; but when questioned on the subject Cordelia shook her head dubiously, and implied that flounces did not suit Catherine. But at any rate Catherine looked sufficiently well to arouse a special enthusiasm in her lover, for during the reception which took place after the ceremony in the grounds of Mr. Barker's residence, Denbridge House, she received her first proposal from Lomas. One of the features of Denbridge House is its bank of magnificent rhododendrons; and it was while they were admiring these together—Lomas as usual having skilfully detached Catherine from her friends—that Lomas ventured definitely to ask her to marry him. The look of horror and surprise on Catherine's face no doubt wounded his vanity to the core. He coloured to the roots of his hair with mortification; and, says Catherine, "tears actually stood in his eyes." Without pausing to think of what he would say, he stammered in uneven and bitter tones: "I know I'm outside the paddock."

"How do you mean?" queried Catherine, genuinely perplexed.

"I know I'm outside the paddock," repeated Lomas, almost weeping. Seeing that she still really did not understand him, he threw out in a choked angry voice: "I'm not a gentleman, I mean."

It was now Catherine's turn to colour. She drew herself up, and said in her stateliest tones: "Such petty social considerations have no weight with me, I assure you, Mr. Eastwood."

"Then why——" began Lomas, brightening and looking interrogative.

"Oh, it's quite impossible, quite," said Catherine hastily, descending from her stateliness with a rush. "I beg you never to think of it again."

Lomas had now recovered himself, and was able to say: "That is quite impossible too, Miss Ainsley," in a suitably lofty and dignified tone. "I shall always think of you," he added, throwing back his head and looking down his nose in his most impressive manner. "No other woman can ever be to me what you are."

Catherine was wretched. On the one hand she felt insulted in every shred of womanly pride she possessed by the fact that Lomas was the first man to ask her to marry him. Lomas! The detestable, insincere, rhetorical Lomas, whom everyone disliked, even his own sister. Her only lover! Something within her sobbed out "Phil" and mourned that she should be brought so low. For perhaps the first time in her life Catherine felt genuinely sorry for herself. A wave of self-pity rushed over her; she remembered how fine life had seemed that evening before the Carr Foot concert, and how stale and dull it seemed now; tears filled her prominent eyes, and her heavy mouth trembled. Then by a transition impossible to many, but so natural to Catherine's high and generous nature, she reflected that Lomas must be feeling just the same as she was; and she was sorry for him. If Lomas had been of her own class, it would have been so much easier for Catherine to repulse him! As it was, Catherine, who hated snobbery with a deep hate implanted in her by George Eliot and Miss Thompson, could not bring herself to speak as decisively as she felt.

"It's quite impossible, Mr. Eastwood," she stammered again in a vague and distressed tone, turning away her head; and Lomas, seeing her trouble, no doubt rejoiced.

But Phil and Dell were approaching across the grass. "May I beg," pleaded Lomas swiftly in a low mournful tone, "that you will keep my hopeless passion a secret, Miss Ainsley? I should not like my sister and your cousin to be troubled by it."

This was certainly very skilful. It was essential to Lomas that Mr. Ainsley should be kept ignorant of his aspirations until they had secured Catherine's assent; and to secure this, and appear to be actuated by a generous and delicate sentiment towards Phil—of whom Catherine was so fond —all in the same sentence, was indeed a master stroke. Naturally Catherine replied at once: "Of course, of course," and to escape Cordelia's observation interested herself in the rhododendrons. Lomas drew back and simulated politely repressed boredom, and as soon as it was practicable withdrew.

That he did not desist from his insidious pursuit after this repulse we know from that letter of Fräulein Kirchner's which was mentioned in the Preface (see p. viii). The letter is dated July 1881, and after commenting on various incidents of public and private interest—the South African situation, Adelaide's improved health, Herr Kirchner's illness, the growth of young Hammond Carr, Minna's own approaching marriage with Franz Schröter, and so on—continues with remarkable shrewdness as follows:

". . . And now to come to the main point: you have asked my advice in a very delicate matter. Without wishing to be in the least unfair to Mr. Eastwood, I must candidly confess that I cannot at all approve of his behaviour. If I were you, I should tell Uncle William everything. Believe me, dear Catherine, Mr. Eastwood has not given up his designs on you, and I suspect that you have more sympathy with his fate than can be reconciled with your peace of mind.

"You are still very inexperienced in these matters: do not take it amiss if I, as your friend, open your eyes a little. Your hatred of him, your detestation, your indignation are perhaps after all due to quite a different reason from what you suspect. Perhaps it would be best for you to go away and not to see him at all for a time.

"If, as you say, Uncle is really going with the Commission, could you accompany him? What parts of Germany are they to visit? It would indeed be delightful if they were to come to Leipzig. Then you might come to see us.

"Best love to Aunt Adelaide.

"By the way, how is Didymus getting on?

"Write again soon: you may depend upon my discretion.

"With my fondest love.

"Don't be too annoyed with my frankness.

"Yours very affectionately

"MINNA."

It is interesting to note Catherine's comment on this letter in her diary. "My weekly letter from Minna came to-day," she writes on July 12th. "Dear Minna! How I should like to see her again! But as to what she says on the subject of Mr. Eastwood, *that* is all *nonsense*."

The "Commission" referred to in Fräulein Kirchner's letter was, of course, the Royal Commission to investigate Technical Education which visited France, Belgium and Germany during the winter of 1881–1882. The suggestion that Mr. Ainsley should form one of the textile section of this Commission was already in the air, and there was already discussion at Carr Fold about the arrangement which eventually materialised; namely, that Mr. Ainsley should take his wife with him and that Catherine should cross the Channel with them and proceed to Leipzig for a protracted stay. During their absence Carr and his wife and child were to occupy Carr Fold, chiefly so as to be near the mill, but also to keep the Carr Fold establishment in working order. Accordingly, in November, this transfer took place, and Cordelia found herself mistress of a large establishment, including two gardeners, a coachman, Joshua and his wife, Hammond's nurse, and three other maids; while Carr was left in entire charge of Carr Foot Mills. The young couple embarked gleefully and with pride on these increased responsibilities, but probably the only one of their household who profited at first by the change was Hammond, who breathed a purer air on the terrace of Carr Fold than he did in Atack Place. For Carr and Cordelia now made the discovery that being in charge of anything was very different from being second in command. It was now for the first time that the intensely conscientious Cordelia began to allow her conscientiousness to make her a trifle irritable. She was expecting her second child—Philip Eugene Carr was born in July 1882—and any little disaster which occurred to the Carr Fold linen or silver, any little bickering between the nurse and the formidable wife of Joshua, any little indisposition of Didymus, assumed alarming proportions in her troubled little head, and as often as not brought her to tears. As a matter of fact the linen and the silver had probably never been so well looked after in the course of their existence, for whatever Cordelia set her hand to she did mightily and well; but the well-being of his uncle's silver did not atone to Carr for his distress and unhappiness when he came home and found his wife sobbing in the dark in the elegant library of which she was so proud. Carr too found the responsibility of Carr Foot Mills weigh heavily upon him. It was indeed an immense concern, with many departments, and Carr found himself giving orders to men twice his age, who looked at him dubiously when he spoke as if they thought he was a trifle mad, and made difficulties, and shook their grizzled heads, and altogether did their best to frighten Carr into feeling that perhaps he was wrong after all. On the whole, however, Carr got on with his men very well; he knew his job, and they knew it; it was no use trying to pretend to him that the blame belonged to another department, for he shook his head and threw out the truth—in a merry phrase and with a twinkle in his eye, certainly, but not in a manner which left any loophole for contradiction. Much worse to Phil were Carr Carr and Ainsley's customers, who complained bitterly that piece so-and-so was not up to standard—the weight was wrong, or the dyeing uneven, or it was irretrievably damaged—and forthwith returned it. Carr was obliged to argue with them, to be firm with them, sometimes to be rude to them; and argument and firmness and being rude were entirely foreign to Carr's gentle nature. He hated, as we have noted before, to be at variance with anyone; and when he was obliged to threaten a defaulting merchant with a lawsuit he suffered agonies—ate little, lost his sleep, and allowed lines to worry to mar his fine young face. For now one of Carr's defects of character emerged—he could not resist the onslaughts of worry. He came home worried, he kissed Cordelia with a harassed air, he changed and shaved with a preoccupied and gloomy look; when he saw young Hammond in his mother's arms, or watched the rascal have his bath, his face brightened and he laughed and played heartily with the child, making him chuckle and gurgle and coo—for Hammond was a jolly boy—but no sooner was

Hammond in bed asleep than Carr's merriment dropped from him and he began to worry again. The more Carr worried, the more Cordelia naturally did the same; and when Cordelia wept, Carr's spirits sank still lower. After a few months of this they both settled into their new positions and took life a little more easily; but the few months had aged them both, and they no longer looked, as they had done before, ludicrously young to be married. Catherine's diary vouches for this. Her entry for May 27th, 1882, concludes as follows: "So we reached home at last, at six o'clock in the evening. Phil and Cordelia were standing on the threshold to meet us, with dear old Didymus between them. He rushed at me as soon as I got out of the carriage, and jumped up at me and licked my face—it *was* nice and homely. Carr Fold looks just the same, rather neater than usual perhaps. . . . Phil, I think, does not look very well; he seems thin, and would do with a holiday. Cordelia looks very beautiful, more so than ever, or perhaps I have forgotten the sweetness and purity of her face while I have been away. She too looks older, more matronly; but how it suits her! Baby Hammond is still most beautiful; I saw him asleep in Cordelia's arms as they drove off to Atack Place. Such a lovely rounded forehead! Such a soft clear skin! Such beautiful long eyelashes resting on his plump cheek! His hair, too, so bronze and curly! It is good to be back home again amongst those one loves!"

Catherine's sojourn in Leipzig had evidently done her good. It is interesting to note that while there she had received three letters from Lomas Eastwood. On November 20th she records as follows: "I forgot to mention a few days ago that I received a *very* long letter for my birthday from Mr. Eastwood. I was *very* much annoyed, and burned it." On December 25th, among the list of Christmas presents given and received which Catherine always entered on that date, we find the entry: "Letter, and water-colour sketch of the stream in Carr Dene, from the top of High Carr, from Mr. Eastwood. I do not like the sketch, as it seems to me to represent Yorkshire as romantic people who have never lived there think of it, and the letter was much too sentimental for my taste—all about 'the call of the homeland,' the 'dear old Yorshire vales,' and son on; but of course I was obliged to write him a brief note of thanks. I wrote it as plainly as I possibly could, as a hint that his long words and involved sentences are not in good style; but that perhaps was unkind." *"January 12, 1882.—Another* letter from Mr. Eastwood, asking 'to be allowed to proffer his New Year felicitations.' Dear, dear!"

Curiously enough, although Mr. and Mrs. Ainsley's return had been longed for by both Carr and Dell for months, now that they had actually come they felt a trifle flat. Worn out by the toils of Carr Fold, Dell had yearned for the cosiness of Atack Place; but now it seemed small and incommodious, and there was no nice terrace for Hammond's perambulator. Carr had longed to have his uncle at hand to refer to, but now it seemed a little tiresome to have to keep running to him for every little thing. This phase too, however, passed, and in a few weeks the Carrs had resumed their normal routine of life in Atack Place. Again it fell to Cordelia's lot to wake with a start each morning at half-past four, to lie awake till five, or almost five, when she gently shook the arm that lay protectively across her, and murmured "Phil!" Immediately Carr opened bright startled eyes and demanded the time. If it was a quarter to five, ten to five, five to five, he exclaimed "Pooh!" with affectionate contempt, smiled, drew Cordelia a little nearer, tucked his head into the pillow again and went to sleep, waking promptly as the clock struck the hour. (His faculty for five minutes' sleep never ceased to astonish Cordelia, and Carr himself was rather proud of it.) Again it fell to Carr's lot to walk the four miles from Hudley to Carr Foot at least once every day, and apropos of this a little incident occurred which is of considerable importance. Cordelia thought the walk too much for Carr, and wanted him either to remove to Carr Foot—there was Hough Hall standing empty, a most suitable residence for that important young person Mrs. Philip Carr—or else set up a horse or trap. Carr did not seem inclined to do either of these things, and one Sunday in June Cordelia discovered why.

On her return from Carr Fold Cordelia had decided to "go through" her cupboards and drawers, so long left without her supervision. This morning she had come back from church and changed her dress, and dinner was not yet ready; it seemed a suitable opportunity to consult Phil about his drawers, and get a general statement from him as to what might be thrown away. Idly opening a drawer in the chest which by custom was allotted to him, her eye fell upon a mass of papers stuffed away at the back behind his excellent ties and his admirable silk handkerchiefs. Cordelia was a woman; she examined the papers; and the next moment Carr, who was smoking a cigar in the drawing-room and nursing Hammond and feeling exceedingly well pleased with life in general, was horrified by the sudden appearance of his wife in the guise of a fury. She stormed into the room, her rich hair dishevelled, her blue eyes flaming through her tears, her whole form quivering with rage, and thrust at him the wretched papers, which, as Carr was well aware, consisted of unpaid bills. There was the doctor's bill for Cordelia's first confinement, there was the bill for Hammond's superb pram; there were several bills for Cordelia's clothes—one or two of them marked "account rendered"—there was also a municipal rate from the Corporation, the lettering of which indicated the last stage of indignation because it had not been paid before. An unpaid bill was a thing simply unheard-of in the house of that upright citizen Taylor Eastwood—if Lomas had any he concealed them—and not to pay your way seemed to Cordelia a crime, a crime indeed of appalling magnitude. She stormed outrageously at Carr, who stood abashed and miserable, mechanically smoothing Hammond's curls. The situation was indeed very largely of Cordelia's own making. The step from the comparative poverty and small notions of Majorca Road to the comparative affluence and large ideas of Atack Place had seemed to her so immense that she fondly imagined a two-sixteenths share in Carr Carr and Ainsley meant money enough for anything. She liked the best of everything, and habitually and instinctively chose it; and it was as impossible to the indulgent Carr to stop her then as it was for him to reproach her with it now. Cordelia was shrewd enough to realise both these facts well enough, and they added greatly to her distress. But what vexed her beyond anything was her unpaid milliner's bill. To think that she had walked in and out of Mrs. Wright's for the last twelve months with a lofty, haughty, disdainful air, and all the time owed the woman money! No wonder Cordelia sobbed, crimson with rage and shame.

"I shall never be able to hold up my head again!" she wailed. "Never! How could you, Phil! How could you! You're just like your father! Running off with other people's money!" At this Carr exclaimed, but Cordelia went on furiously: "Everyone knows he stole Mrs. Hallas's money. Father said you would be the same, but I didn't believe him, but now I do, I do!" Finding that Carr made no reply, she stopped sobbing long enough to glare up at him, and saw him looking extremely pale. He was, in fact trying to appear insulted and haughty, but he could not; he felt instinctively and utterly convinced that Cordelia was right and his father *had* stolen Mrs. Hallas's money, and the shame of it was too much for him. His sensitive mouth quivered, and his brown eyes became suspiciously bright. "No, no!" cried Cordelia, throwing her arms about his neck: "Of course you aren't in the least like him, not in the least! But how could you! Oh, Phil, how could you!"

She wept upon his breast; Carr's free arm closed about her and he implored her to remember her condition and not agitate herself; Hammond, sitting on his other arm, wept too, and perhaps Carr himself was not guiltless of this unmanly form of emotion. At any rate a good deal of anguish and remorse was experienced by that little trio on the drawing-room hearthrug that Sunday morning. Dinner too was wretched; Cordelia wept into the cauliflower, and Carr could not eat any of the cup puddings which were his especial favourites. After this uncomfortable meal Cordelia retired to weep more vehemently upstairs, and came down at tea-time looking very firm and determined. She did not throw the faults of Hammond Carr (senior) in her husband's face again; but it seemed to be established now that these faults were recognised by both of them. "After all," went on Cordelia firmly—and quite correctly: "small things lead to large ones." The implication that he could ever be guilty of dishonesty touched Carr to the quick; deeply wounded, he asked if

Cordelia thought him capable of that. His wife replied "No, never," with conviction; but added rather wistfully: "But you're careless about money, Phil, aren't you?" Carr was surprised at this view of his case, but on reflection admitted that he was.

"Things will have to be arranged quite differently," said Cordelia, setting her small mouth firmly.

To close this part of the subject now, it may as well be related that Cordelia next day consulted her father about the matter. Taylor shook his head and pursed his mouth just as Cordelia had done.

"It's only what I expected," he told her. "I reckon his father was just the same. But Phil's a fine lad, and you must just get the money into your own hands and keep it straight. He won't grudge it you."

Taylor was perfectly right in his estimate of Carr's character; and from that day onwards it was Cordelia who administered their income. She did this with a conscientious earnestness which was really admirable; nor were there ever any more unpaid bills to be discovered in their establishment—a circumstance which was of inestimable value to Carr later, at the crisis of his career.

Philip Eugene Carr was born on Sunday, July 2nd, 1882, between one and two o'clock in the morning, under somewhat flustering circumstances. The doctor arrived only in the nick of time, and the nurse was still being rattled furiously along the Hudley roads by Carr in a borrowed trap. The child thus ushered rather prematurely into the world was very different, different in fact in almost every possible way, from his elder brother. From his earliest days Hammond Carr had the robust limbs, the sparkling blue eyes, the glowing complexion, the thick waving bronze hair, the perfect health and the cheerful, pugnacious disposition which distinguished him for the first forty years of his life. Eugene, on the contrary—the name was the romantic Cordelia's choice, and though Carr did not like it he could refuse Cordelia nothing—was long and quiet and slender; his hair was black and straight, his face thin and sallow, his eyes brown and soft except when under the influence of anger, when they blazed. It is amusing to observe how plainly the contrast between the two brothers appears even so early as in the photograph—the first of the Carr "family groups"—taken in the autumn of this year. In this Cordelia is, for some occult Victorian reason, standing, with Eugene in her arms, while Carr is seated, with young Hammond tottering against one of his legs. The background is one of palms and flowers, certainly not indigenous to the Hudleian scene; Carr's chair is massive, carved, upholstered in velvet, and fringed. The portrait of Carr is good and attractive. Leaning forward on one arm of the chair, he seems to be looking eagerly at some object on the left. He wears a black braided coat, striped dark trousers, and buttoned boots; his hair shows less curl than in any other of his portraits, but a slight hint of whisker decorates his right cheek. The poise of the fine long head, the half-smile, the bright eagerness of the dark eyes, the manifest tenderness of the hand which supports Hammond, make it a speaking likeness. Hammond, extremely correct in spotless white frock and knickers, with a tartan sash and strap shoes, is also gazing at the unseen object on the left, and seems ready to leap in pursuit of it the moment his father's restraining hand is removed. The wavy bronze hair is much in evidence; his cheeks are round, his legs substantial; in one firm hand he clutches a striped whip, and altogether looks a healthy young person who would stand no nonsense from anyone. Eugene, on the contrary, who is supported by Cordelia in an awkward position between the horizontal and vertical—no doubt so as to make his face visible in spite of the photographer's apparent decree against it—looks aloof and bored, bored perhaps by his long clothes, which sweep down below Cordelia's waist. His tiny hands and thin arms are held in an attitude which somehow suggests helpless irritation; his broad little head, with its patches of dark down, lolls uncomfortably to one side against his mother's arm, and the expression of his face seems to indicate that he found the world distinctly not worth all this bother—his eyebrows look just as though he were raising them in disdain, his mouth has its characteristic pout, and his brown eyes are scornful. Cordelia looks less beautiful here than in any other of her portraits. Her hair is dressed high up on her head, in plaits which do not suit her; her rich black silk dress, pleated and ruched, with its bodice embroidered all over in a gold network design, and a high collar of gathered white lace, is rather too rich and overpowering for Cordelia's simple charm; and her expression, as she gazes down at Eugene, is anxious, severe, even a little cross. This is perhaps not to be wondered at, for as a baby Eugene was fretful and difficult. Cordelia had nursed Hammond herself, but she was not able to do this for Eugene; and many were the diets tried and rejected before one was found which suited Eugene's awkward digestion. Many, too, were the hours of sleep of which he robbed his parents; he cried for hours on many nights, screwing up his thin little face sardonically and beating the air with one clenched fist. (On these occasions Cordelia saw a resemblance between him and Lomas which she never mentioned to Carr.) The first few months of his life were indeed so wearing to his mother that she became quite run down and out of sorts, and the doctor advised a change of air. This, however, Cordelia firmly resisted, ostensibly on the ground that she did not need it, but really on account of the expense, for long-unpaid bills somehow take a lot of paying, and Eugene was expensive; and she grew progressively more run down in consequence, becoming nervous and hysterical, and more than usual liable to sudden bouts of temper or of tears.

This state culminated in a scene in the Carr Fold dining-room on Saturday, November 18th. It was Catherine's twenty-fourth birthday, and the Carrs had been asked to dinner to celebrate it. The party were going to Hudley afterwards to hear W. Kingsley's Royal Hand-bell Ringers, fresh from a command performance. Eugene's digestion was not at all satisfactory just then, and had kept Cordelia awake the greater part of the previous night; she was feeling harassed and out of key with the festive character of the occasion, and moreover, had a suspicion that Phil thought the gloves she had bought for Catherine's birthday present not quite good enough. Like all hysterically inclined subjects she always felt worse during meals—the constraint, the feeling that she was held there by all the force of convention and bound to keep erect and smiling until the last course should have been served, always acted powerfully on her nerves. Mr. Ainsley had already teased her about a letter on the everlasting Bradlaugh-oath question in that day's *Hudley News,* signed "A Lover of Fair Play," but obviously from the hand of her father; and now Adelaide began unfortunately to skirmish about the subject of lace collars. Cordelia was not wearing a lace collar. Cordelia did not wish to wear a lace collar in the evening, thought herself superior to lace collars in the evening, considered Catherine as marked down to dowdiness because

doorway and rush fiercely to her seat as usual, that her breast would remain tremulous and her eyes cast down for an hour or so, and that after that she would recover, and be very good and quiet and sweet all evening, like a child that has had a fright and wants petting. It was several minutes, then, before the Ainsleys took alarm; but when the joint had been removed, and sweets come in and vanished, and the dessert been placed on the table, without the Carrs, Mr. Ainsley allowed himself to express his irritation in a few hasty sentences, and Catherine promptly went in search of the missing pair.

She found them in the library on the horsehair sofa. Carr, his face strained and unhappy, was supporting Cordelia, who lay back in his arms looking white and exhausted. Her lips and cheeks had lost so much of their usual rich colour that Catherine was alarmed, and called her parents. Brandy was administered, and the doctor sent for; Cordelia soon regained her normal hue and professed herself recovered; but the doctor spoke of nervous tension and lack of sleep, and prescribed a holiday away from the children.

Accordingly, by November 28th we find Adelaide, Catherine and Cordelia established in comfortable lodgings in Blenheim Terrace in Scarborough, while Mrs. Eastwood superintends the babies in Atack Place. "Papa," writes Catherine a few days earlier, "is most anxious for us to take Cordelia to the sea and not bring her back till she is well again." We may surmise that William Ainsley knew too well what misery a nervous, ailing wife could bring upon a man to want another of that kind in the family. Since Cordelia went at Adelaide's invitation we may surmise, too, that the little matter of the bills and the financial situation of the Carrs generally had emerged between uncle and nephew in the course of their discussion on Cordelia's health, and that Adelaide was furnished with money by her husband to pay Cordelia's bills in Blenheim Terrace. Catherine does not say so in her diary, it is true; but then at this period of her life Catherine never noticed anything about money. She always had more than she needed, and would have considered herself degraded by any allusion to it—an attitude foreign alike to Cordelia and to Adelaide.

In view of the tragedy which was now so soon to fall upon the unfortunate Catherine, it would be pleasant to be able to relate that during these days at Scarborough she advanced considerably in Cordelia's friendship; but that such was not the case is clearly shown by the following letter, which is interesting in many ways, and especially precious to us as the earliest letter of Carr's which has been preserved. It owes its preservation to the address it gives; Cordelia, having read it, slipped it into her address book, meaning to copy Miss Gill's London address therein, and continued to intend doing this for so long that the letter acquired even in her practical eyes a sentimental historical value, and she could not bring herself to tear it up.

4, Atack Place,
Hudley,
December 9th, 1882.

"My own darling Dell" (writes Carr in his bold flowing hand, with a certain rather attractive lack of punctuation),

"Hammond and Eugene are now comfortably asleep upstairs and your mother is the same or at least I hope so, at any rate she went upstairs an hour or so ago with a hot-water bottle and a jug of linseed for her cold, so I imagine she was going to bed and not out gallivanting along the roofs. Which reminds me, Cherry has got a sore paw and your father is upset about it. I am writing to-night instead of to-morrow because I have promised to go to Charlie Gill's for the day, which I shall *not* like although of course I shall pretend to, for as you know some ladies are not favourites of mine. Besides, Charlie is quarrelling with old Enoch Barker about their new tentering machine, I don't understand the ins and outs of it but it must be very uncomfortable I should think quarrelling with your wife's relations. I am very glad the bazaar cushion is going on so well but I wish you would not work so hard, for we all miss you very much here and shall be glad when you are back. Hammond is always looking round for you. But still, my darling Dell, I don't want you to come home until you are quite better.

"I am sorry you find your present company not quite what you would wish. Between you and me I have always wondered how Uncle William and Aunt Adelaide came to make a match of it. She seems to me a very moderate sort of woman, not his equal in any way, and then I don't like her mouth—it is too thin and tight, like Amelia Barker's, though of course she can't help that, poor thing. But Catherine is pure gold all through. Having known her as an infant in arms, as you might say, I cannot think she is haughty and cold. People often think she is lofty when she is only day-dreaming about some extraordinary thing or other; she is above my head but we ought not to grudge her that. I think it must be a bit dull for her at Carr Fold with only two old things and Didymus, and we really ought to try to make things brighter for her, especially as Uncle William is so good to us. She has a lot of money but money isn't everything. Well, here I have nearly filled this big sheet with stuff and nonsense as usual and not told you anything of importance. Your family are all well except for Mrs. Eastwood having a slight cold and Cherry having a bandage round his off fore-paw. Uncle William is very well, though rather cross because the builders are three weeks behind their contract with the chapel. Joshua is middling. Young James[1] is driving for us just now, as his father has got a very bad throat and has to stay indoors. George Newton *is* engaged to that girl from Nottingham he met in Keswick two years ago, as you thought, and Emily Gill has gone to stay with an aunt in London. Her address is c/o Mrs. Wallas Swaine, 121 Highbury New Park, London, and will you please write to her soon, Mrs. Gill says. Last night I had supper with Nicholas Whiteley; his wife is the best cook I have ever met on this mortal coil, a very dark woman, graceful and dangerous-looking like a cat. However if Nicholas likes her I suppose it doesn't matter. You see I am having quite a round of bachelor gaieties while you are away, but I am not enjoying them. To sit on one side of the hearth with you on the other and the boys asleep upstairs is the best kind of evening for

"Your loving husband

x PHILIP JOSEPH CARR. x

(*anglice* Phil)

"I may come over to see you and get a breath of Scarborough air next Saturday."

Cordelia was, however, destined to see her husband earlier than that, and on a different errand. On Thursday, December 14th, as the three ladies were break-

[1] James Illingworth, old Joshua's grandson, who performed at the Carr Foot concert where Carr first met Cordelia.

fasting in their comfortable room overlooking the sea, the door was suddenly thrown open, and Carr appeared. He was greeted with exclamations of delight, and Cordelia, stirred out of her customary austere restraint, jumped up and threw her arms round his neck. He held her closely for a moment, and his kiss was passionate, but Cordelia has related that she had a foreboding that something was wrong immediately she heard the strong rapid beat of his heart. She drew back a little and looked into his face, and her suspicions were confirmed; but the question on her lips was stilled by a quick pleading glance from her husband and a warning pressure from his hand. Perplexed but mute, she drew Carr down to the table beside her, her hand in his. The other two ladies began to ply him with jocular questions. Had he come so early for the week-end? Did he call Thursday the week-end? Was business at Carr Foot so slack that he could leave it thus? Could he not bear separation from Cordelia any longer? And why had he not brought Mr. Ainsley with him? At this last question Carr's pulse leaped beneath Cordelia's fingers so distressfully that she hastily interposed, and began aloud to pity him for his breakfastless condition and the incredible earliness of his train. The bell was rung, and more breakfast commanded; it was brought, and Carr made a pitiful pretence of eating. It was now observed that he looked pale and haggard, and as though he had spent a sleepless night. Adelaide pressed a few inquiries, and from Carr's manner of evading them both she and Catherine jumped to the conclusion that he had bad news for Cordelia; her mother perhaps was suffering, as she did sometimes of late, from a bad attack of asthma; or her father had perhaps had losses; or that detestable brother had done something peculiarly awful. Or perhaps——

"Are the children all right?" cried Adelaide in a sudden flutter lest Carr's trouble might be due to them.

At this Catherine exclaimed in alarm: "Oh, Phil!" and Cordelia started and gazed at her husband reproachfully. But Phil replied: "Oh, yes, they're all right," with a casualness which was convincing.

"Come out on the front with me a minute, Dell," he begged in a low tone a moment later, suddenly abandoning the pretence of eating.

Adelaide and Catherine, smiling tactfully, affected not to hear this, and conversed artificially with Carr while Cordelia slipped away. In a moment she returned in the sealskin, and took her husband's arm; the two passed out of the house together, and, as Adelaide and Catherine could see, walked briskly down the front and turned to the right sharply.

The moment they were out of the Ainsley's sight they fell apart and faced each other.

"What is it, Phil?" demanded Cordelia unevenly, her small face sharp with fear. "Oh, what's the matter?"

The matter was, to put it bluntly, that William Ainsley lay dead at Carr Fold.

This terrible fatality had occurred as follows. The delay in the completion of the new Carr Foot Chapel, which was now a month behind contract and seemed likely to be a month more, annoyed Mr. Ainsley, and he had lately formed the habit of driving round in that direction at least once a day to see how the work was getting on. On the afternoon of December 13th he left Carr Fold about half-past two—for now that Carr was able to take complete charge of affairs at the mill he allowed himself a little more leisure—in the trap, as usual, and commanded young James Illingworth to drive him round by the chapel before proceeding to the mill, as had for the last few weeks been his custom. James Illingworth did so, and drew up in front of the chapel. As it chanced, the architect, Mr. Newton, was on the spot, consulting about some detail with the master mason; but just as the trap drew up he disappeared round the corner of the building. Mr. Ainsley thereupon took the reins himself and bade young James seek the architect out and ask him to call at Carr Foot before returning to Hudley. The lad dismounted to obey; but hardly had he gone three or four steps when a wild shout of warning rang through the air. Horribly startled, the lad looked up, and had a brief awful glimpse of something hurtling downwards; but before he had time to stir from the spot the tragedy had occurred. A huge stone which was being placed in position on the parapet of the decorative frontage of the chapel had slipped and crashed to earth, pinning William Ainsley fatally beneath its huge mass. The mare was also caught by the hindquarters, and the screams of the wretched animal made the air hideous as the builders' men, directed by the horrified Mr. Newton, hastily rigged up a simple apparatus to raise the stone. Life was, however, completely extinct in Mr. Ainsley's shattered body; the bulk of the stone was such that his death must have occurred at the instant it struck him. The terrified James, shaking in every limb and hardly able to speak from shock, stumbled off to the mill and fetched Carr; the doctor was summoned; Mr. Ainsley's remains were conveyed to Carr Fold and decently arranged; the mare was shot; the wreckage of the trap removed; the necessary authorities informed. As soon as the dreadful news spread through Carr Foot Mills the men ceased work, and the machinery was stopped; all through the evening they stood about the lanes in groups, discussing in hushed and awestruck voices the curious workings of Providence, which had spared young James Illingworth and struck down William Ainsley. With the coping stone of a chapel he had helped to build, too! They wondered, also, seriously and at length, what would happen to Carr Foot Mills, and marked the strangeness of young Phil Carr, coming thus to rule in the mill which bore his name. But all their wonderings, all their discussions, all their musings on the inscrutable ways of Providence, ended up in one universal lament: poor Catherine! Over Mrs. Ainsley the Carr Foot workmen shook their heads, turned down the corners of their mouths, and opined that she would soon console herself; but Catherine—as they all frankly called her—nay! poor thing! Lost her lover, and now her father gone! It was a pity for her! It only needed Didymus to be carried off to make the thing complete! A hush of sympathy fell upon each group as they thought of Catherine; a hush which dissolved after a moment into ejaculations of thankfulness that they hadn't the task of breaking the news to her.

Carr unfortunately had this task, and as the reader has already seen he shirked it. Mr. Whiteley (senior), whom Carr immediately summoned to Carr Fold as Mr. Ainsley's solicitor and friend, urged him to send a preparatory telegram to Mrs. Ainsley saying that her husband was ill. But somehow Carr could not bring himself to do this; he had a feeling, vague but strong, that he ought to be near Catherine when the news began to break on her. After a hundred different schemes had bemused his harassed brain, he called in at Majorca Road and consulted Taylor Eastwood. "Go yourself, lad," advised Taylor. "It's your plain duty." Carr immediately drove to Hudley station and started. It was by then after ten o'clock, and he was advised that he could not get through to Scarborough that night; but he could not bear the thought of twelve hours' inaction, and feared besides that some local paper might thrust the terrible news on Catherine next morning before he reached her if he delayed further, so he began the complicated cross-country journey. The night was stormy; a south-westerly gale howled over Yorkshire, and rain beat insistently upon the carriage windows. Carr, plodding miserably through the dark wild landscape in a maddeningly slow train, pacing small gloomy unknown stations, or trying to get a little sleep in draughty fireless waiting-rooms, did not have an enviable time of it; and it is little wonder that when he at last reached Blenheim Terrace on the following morning he did not feel equal to the task he had taken upon himself, and allowed it to devolve instead upon his wife. For, of course, it was the loving and warm-hearted Cordelia who, with tears streaming from her beautiful eyes, went straight to Catherine and drew her head down upon her breast, and saying, "My poor, poor girl!" told her in broken tones that she had lost her father. Catherine, relates Cordelia, turned deathly white, and as Cordelia and Carr began to tell her gently the dreadful details of her loss, gazed at them each in turn with the sick, horror-struck, doubting look of a trapped animal. When all was at last clear to her she gave a slight shiver, and forthwith fell into a fit of shuddering so violent that her teeth chattered and she could hardly stand. Cordelia led her away to her room to lie down till the first shock of her grief should be over, and with true delicacy left her alone. There remained Adelaide to be told, for she had not been in the room at the moment of Catherine's enlightenment. Carr, however, accomplished this himself, knocking at her bedroom door and breaking the news to her as she stood in front of the mirror putting on a hat to go out. Mrs. Ainsley received his story with alarm, with horror, with tears, with questions, finally with hysterical prostration. Her grief was distressing, but it did not lie on Carr's heart with the leaden anguished heaviness of Catherine's, and Adelaide was soon sufficiently calm to be able to discuss the necessary funeral arrangements.

At the conclusion of the entry in Catherine's diary for December 13th there is this pathetic note, written on a separate line, in an uneven, emotional hand: "To-day at three o'clock poor Papa was killed, and I did not know it." The next entry in the diary runs as follows: *"December 16th.*—Poor Papa's funeral." After that there is a gap of several pages, and the date of the next entry is May 15th, 1883.

The reader may, perhaps, be interested in the account of William Ainsley's funeral given in the *Hudley News* for December 23rd. It occupies a column headed "Funeral of Mr. William Ainsley," and runs as follows:

"The remains of the late Mr. William Ainsley of Carr Foot, an account of the shocking fatality to whom was given in our last week's issue, were interred yesterday in the cemetery of Carr Foot Wesleyan Chapel amid general sorrow. It will be remembered that the Carr Foot Wesleyan Chapel was destroyed by fire in 1879. The deceased gentleman, whose family have always been noted for their liberality and public spirit, had given half the necessary funds for the reconstruction of the building on condition that the other half was raised by the congregation. This was achieved and the building begun early in 1881, Miss Catherine Ainsley, daughter of the deceased, laying the foundation stone on that occasion. It was while inspecting the progress of the building a week last Wednesday that

Mr. Ainsley met his end. As our readers will remember, a coping stone fell upon him, crushing him instantly, his coachman escaping by a matter of a few feet alone. For the past three years the members of the Carr Foot Wesleyan congregation have been meeting in a large empty room at Carr Foot Mills lent by Mr. Ainsley for the purpose, and although very kind offers as regards the funeral service were received by the family both from the vicar at Carr Foot and from the Wesleyan minister at Hough Lane, it was felt by all concerned that the service could be held in no more suitable place than the room in Mr. Ainsley's own mill, and accordingly it was so decided. The rest of the extensive works of the firm, and all the shops and places of business in Carr Foot village, were closed, and the inhabitants testified to their sympathy and respect by drawing down the blinds as the procession passed. As the time for starting approached, large crowds of villagers thronged the line of route from the gates of Carr Fold, the late Mr. Ainsley's residence, down to Carr Foot Mills in the valley. Shortly after eleven o'clock the procession left for the mill, where it was received by the Reverend T. Mellor, who conducted the service. Upon entering the room the impressive strains of Mendelssohn's *O rest in the Lord* were sung by the choir unaccompanied, and was *(sic)* followed by the hymn *O God, our help in ages past*, a great favourite with the deceased. As the coffin was borne from the mill the choir rendered *I know that my Redeemer liveth* with great effect, and at the graveside too the choir took part in the service. Amongst the large number of ladies and gentlemen present were:—Mrs. Ainsley (widow), Miss Catherine Ainsley (daughter), Mr. P. J. Carr (nephew), Mrs. P. J. Carr, Charles Balmforth, Esq., M.P., the Mayor and Mayoress of Hudley, Councillor and Mrs. Enoch Barker,

Mr. and Mrs. Taylor Eastwood, Mr. Lomas Eastwood, Mr. and Mrs. Newton, the Reverend Humphrey and Mrs. Gill, Mr. and Mrs. Charles Gill, Mr. Nicholas Whiteley, Mr. and Mrs. Nicholas L. Whiteley, Miss J. Gill, Miss E. Gill; together with representatives of the Governors of Hudley Grammar School, the Hudley Royal Infirmary, the Hudley Literary and Philosophical Society, the Carr Foot Rural District Council, the Hudley Liberal Association, the Hough Lane Charity, the Hudley Chamber of Commerce, etc, etc. Six of the Carr Foot Mills workmen acted as coffin-bearers, and a large number followed as mourners. The coffin, which was of polished oak, with heavy brass mountings, was covered with beautiful wreaths of white flowers, and as it was lowered into the Ainsley vault, numerous other floral emblems of affection were placed upon it by the members of the family. We understand that Miss Ainsley, Mrs. Ainsley and Mr. P. J. Carr are the principal beneficiaries under the will of the deceased, but that considerable legacies have been bequeathed to local charities, notably a thousand pounds to the Hudley Royal Infirmary, a thousand to the Hough Lane Charity, and two thousand to found a scholarship at the Hudley Grammar School, to be called the Ainsley Bequest, open to natives of Hudley and district by competitive examination, and tenable for three years at Oxford University. We feel sure that the sympathy of all will be extended to the late Mr. Ainsley's widow and daughter in their terrible and sudden bereavement."

Terrible indeed. Poor Catherine! Lomas had some cards specially printed so as to be able to send her one marked "With deepest sympathy."

It may perhaps be mentioned here, as a detail not without interest, that Joshua, at his own urgent request, drove the hearse containing Mr. Ainsley's remains from Carr Fold to Carr Foot Mills, and thence to the chapel burying-ground. After returning home on this occasion he never took reins in his hands again; his heart was broken—he had got the idea into his poor muddled old head, to the great grief and exasperation and pain of his grandson, that if he had been driving William Ainsley on that fatal day the accident would never have happened—and he did not survive the winter.

VI

RESIDENCE AT HOUGH HALL (1883–1886)

THERE now began for Carr a period of great prosperity. He owned a quarter share in that large and flourishing business Carr Carr and Ainsley, and, moreover, drew a salary as manager thereof as well. This salary was less than Cordelia thought it ought to be, but more than Adelaide thought it ought to be; as it was fixed after a thorough discussion of the matter between Mr. Nicholas Whiteley (senior), who was William Ainsley's sole executor, and Carr, and as each party had previously taken expert advice on the matter—Mr. Whiteley from Enoch Barker and Carr from Charlie Gill—it is probable that the sum was reasonable, but erred if anything in the Ainsleys' favour. When his own advantage was concerned Carr was of a yielding disposition always, whereas Mr. Nicholas Whiteley, an astute, extremely able and experienced man of good family and many sound investments, dark, square, solid, with heavy features and beetling brows, a connoisseur in china and an excellent linguist, was not accustomed to yield on any question to anybody. Mr. Whiteley administered William Ainsley's estate with perfect integrity and admirable firmness; he listened patiently, his hands clasped across his massive chest, to Adelaide's maunderings, curbed Catherine's philanthropical impulses when they became too outrageous, and occasionally uttered a sharp word of advice to Carr. On his side Carr, at first inclined to fall overwhelmed by the weight of responsibility which rested on his shoulders, soon became used to being the head and supreme authority at Carr Foot Mills; after all he had done it before, last winter, to his uncle's complete satisfaction, so he supposed he could do it again now.

It was, however, necessary that he should be nearer to the mill than Atack Place, and with Cordelia's approval he decided to move to Carr Foot. Unfortunately Hough Hall had been sold only a month or two ago, but by a piece of good fortune for the Carrs the buyer, who was a widower, shortly after his purchase became engaged to a lady who objected to living in the country. He was therefore glad to let Hough Hall to Carr on a five-year lease with an option of purchase. Early in 1883, therefore, the Carrs moved into Hough Hall, which was, as has been said, a large, square, solid house, interesting chiefly—apart from its earlier connection with the Ainsleys—on account of its situation. It stood, as has been stated elsewhere, on the main road from Hudley into Lancashire, about a mile on the Hudley side of Carr Foot. A traveller coming along this road from Burnley or Rochdale finds himself, on leaving Carr Foot, faced with a long steady hill, not as steep as that leaving on the left to Carr Fold and High Carr, but sufficiently trying to horses or motor engines. At the top of this hill the road takes, or rather used to take, a very sharp turn to the left; and in the triangle formed by this bend and a steep wooded bluff stood Hough Hall. The house faced across the valley in the direction of Hudley and Denbridge Vale, but from its back windows there was a clear view of Carr Foot, and especially of Carr Foot Mills. The side of the house was close to the road, and the small piece of ground at the back was occupied by the stables; but in front a sandy drive wound round a quite considerable lawn flanked by laurels and rhododendrons, and emerged on to the road through a pair of impressive iron gates. The great feature of the Hough Hall grounds was a large "monkey-puzzle" tree which stood in the centre of the front lawn. The present writer remembers being shown this tree at an early age, and, being struck by something sinister in its aspect—it seemed, even to a youthful eye, so strangely different from other trees—weeping bitterly and demanding to be taken away, greatly to the disgust of her father.

For to Hammond and Eugene, as to Carr and Cordelia, the years at Hough Hall were some of the happiest of their lives, and everything connected with Hough Hall was delightful. Carr Carr and Ainsley prospered, and enriched its partners. The option on Hough Hall was taken up, and the title-deeds were presented to Cordelia. Carr kept a smart dog-cart for his own use, and a smart brougham for Cordelia's—young James Illingworth drove them, and did the Hough Hall garden in his spare time, for poor Catherine could not bear the sight of him. Cordelia's dresses became austerely magnificent, and Carr was able to indulge his bent for generous giving; altogether the handsome, rich, intelligent young couple, with their fine babies and their well-run house and their admirable notions of duty and generosity, were extremely well-thought-of in the district. At Carr Fold, of course, they had always been welcome, but gradually, from being there a nephew and his wife whom one had to be kind to, Carr and Cordelia rose into the position of superior, modish, reliable persons whose advice one asked on everything. Whereas in the old days any menu which chanced to be going was more than good enough for them, now Adelaide would go into the kitchen and exhort the cook to make a special effort that night, for Mr. and Mrs. Carr were coming to dinner. All official papers were saved up to show to Carr; all questions about repairs to the house, all suggestions of alterations to the garden, all indispositions of the horses, all indiscretions of the servants, were referred to him; while Cordelia was consulted about bonnets and mantles, about flowers, linen, china, and invitations to parties. Whenever any question of any kind, indeed, came up at Carr Fold, Adelaide, after discussing it for hours with Catherine, would say fretfully: "I wish I knew what Phil thought. He hasn't been to see me for a *long* time. I think we'll send down to the mill and ask him to call in this evening." It fell to Catherine's lot to dissuade her mother from these too frequent calls on Carr's time; for as Carr became more important to Adelaide, by a natural law Adelaide became less important to Carr. An invitation to Carr Fold, formerly an honour, now gradually became a mere duty, a duty which one fulfilled punctilously, of course, but still on the whole rather a tedious affair. Even the children were inclined to make a *moue* when informed that the afternoon's programme contained a visit to Carr Fold.

For of course the two babies were now growing into boys, persons, with individual minds of their own. The country air did wonders for Eugene, and his digestion became less troublesome, though he never enjoyed the glowing, sparkling health of Hammond. The differences between the two became more marked as they grew older. Hammond was plump and solid and bonny, Eugene long and ungracefully thin. Hammond was a cheerful, lively, sociable child, full of noise and laughter; Eugene's disposition, on the contrary, varied between the passionately affectionate and the gloomily misanthropic, and one could never tell beforehand—so at least says Cordelia—which mood he was likely to be in. Hammond had an almost preternatural memory, being able throughout his life to repeat without a mistake enormous strings of words which he had heard only once; he liked mathematics, was good with his hands, could perform wonders with a saw, but took only a tepid schoolboyish interest in lessons generally. Eugene, on the contrary, had no memory to speak of, or perhaps scorned to compete with his brother in this respect; he never tried to understand mathematics and scorned the tool-box, but was a reader of a quite alarmingly omnivorous type. The word "scorned" has occurred twice in the previous sentence, and perhaps this is a good indication of Eugene's character; he was a great scorner. His thin, sometimes intensely eager but more often sulky face, with its sombre brown eyes and pouting lips, formed the strongest possible contrast to the clear, round, sunny, rosy countenance of his brother. The only characteristic, in fact, which the two boys appeared to share in common was one which had descended to them from both parents: a natural and instinctive integrity, an innate shrinking from anything mean or base. Being in other respects so different, the two boys naturally quarrelled fiercely with each other on almost every possible occasion; but were at heart—without having any sentimentally passionate family notions—thoroughly devoted to each other in a sensible brotherly way. At any rate their childhood formed a very happy memory to both of them; for the monkey-puzzle tree, interwoven as it was inextricably with all their childish play, remained throughout their lives the object of their jocular but deep affection. In the mornings one of the vicar's daughters, who seems to have been a surprisingly well-informed girl, came out from Carr Foot to teach them; in the afternoons they walked upon the surrounding hills, or ran along to Carr Fold, or went to look at Grandpa Eastwood's printing works in Hudley; in the evenings they watched for their father from the nursery window—the nursery was at the back of the house—fell upon him with shouts of joy when he arrived, pulled him into the nursery and had a tremendous romp with him. He taught them to joke, to dance, to play draughts and ludo, to sing old songs about buying a fiddle for eighteenpence, to love their mother, be fond of animals, and laugh heartily at their own mistakes; their moral and religious instruction was thoroughly well attended to, as may be imagined, by Cordelia, who inculcated truth and duty with a vehemence almost alarming. In fact everyone at Hough Hall was very happy—there were troubles, of course; Hammond, for instance, fell down the cellar steps and in the heat of the fall accused Eugene of pushing him, which insult the grieved and guiltless Eugene could never quite forget; they both had whooping-cough rather badly; Eugene's fierce bouts of temper were disconcerting, while Hammond too often appeared headstrong and wilful; Carr was sometimes worried about business, or upset by some sharp comment from Mr. Whiteley; Cordelia occasionally felt the cares of life, of Hough Hall, three maids, James Illingworth, a husband and two children too much for her, and shed a tear or two; she had, also, in 1885 the grief of losing Mrs. Eastwood—but on the whole everyone at Hough Hall was very happy.

The same cannot, of course, be said for Carr Fold. Paradoxically enough, during the first year or so of her intensest grief Catherine was not as unhappy as she became later on. At first existence was an agony to her, she grieved for her father passionately, rebelliously, almost madly; she could not sleep or eat or turn her mind to other things; every moment of her life was dark with anguish. But as time went on she found that there are worse things in life than an intensity of grief, for grief is a noble passion: in grief one suffers, but one's heart is soft; in grief one has the sympathy of one's fellow-men; in grief life seems tragic but not sordid or base or mean; in grief, while one truly mourns, the claims of self are not importunate. But later, when in spite of herself her sorrow, always present, became dulled by time, Catherine grew very wretched. There seemed no earthly reason for continuing to live. Her mother did not need her, indeed found her presence irksome; for after the prescribed period of mourning was over Adelaide became very cheerful, went out into the world, entertained quite largely, in a word enjoyed life, and was irritated by what she was pleased to term Catherine's long face. Various little vulgarities of thought and point of view which Adelaide had repressed all her married life out of deference to her husband were now allowed to emerge; from being silent, she became a great talker, and chattered endlessly on such subjects as social precedence and people's clothes. Catherine's mind was starved of all that made life interesting; nobody spoke to her of music or of books; and from being the first consideration of that important man William Ainsley she became a person whom nobody seemed to care about at all, in spite of her money. Carr, of course, was still fond of her, but he was much fonder of Cordelia and his boys, and Catherine saw well enough that coming to Carr Fold bored him. Cordelia was not intimate with Catherine somehow; and of other friends the girl had literally none. When Catherine reached this point in her reflections she always rebuked herself, reminded herself that she was wealthy and had power to do as she chose, and must set about finding something worth doing at once. She roused herself, took violin lessons from an expensive master, did social work as far as the Victorian conventions allowed Miss Catherine Ainsley to do social work, attended a course or two of lectures on first aid, toyed with the idea of being a nurse and was rebuked tearfully for it by her mother, tried to make a friend of Emily Gill and to some extent succeeded—but found poor Emily woefully dismal and boring—tried to make Phil's children her great interest but found that this attitude was not welcome to Cordelia, tried to plunge into a gay social life but was humiliated and thwarted by everyone's lack of interest in her, gave all these attempts up and relapsed into solitary walks with Didymus, then roused herself anew and tried everything afresh, only to fail once more. The fact was that Catherine's outlook on life was different from that of most of her Hudley contemporaries, and the more she tried to be like them the more clearly the difference emerged. In the course of a year or two of this she grew very wretched. A few quotations from her diary will show the trend of her life at this time. It must be mentioned, to make the entries clear, that Catherine never set foot inside the new Carr Foot Chapel. She confided to Carr that she simply could not bear to do so; he passed this on to Adelaide, who was only too glad of an excuse to become Anglican and attend the Carr Foot Church. Catherine, however, was shocked by this unfaithfulness on the mother's part; it seemed to her an insult to her father's memory, and she would not encourage or accompany Adelaide in it, so she took to attending the Hough Lane Chapel, which stood on the main road to Hudley, two or three hundred yards or so beyond Hough Hall, and tried to be friendly with the then minister, the Rev. J. G. Shoesmith, and his family of daughters. The Carrs, of course, attended church at Carr Foot, so the field was clear for Lomas. The present writer ascertained by oral inquiry that these visits of his were entirely unknown to Cordelia, so that he certainly did not go to Hough Hall for his dinner, and the strength of his determination to win Catherine may be gauged by his thus taking the trouble to walk the three miles to Hough Lane and back in order to hear a service which can have interested him but very slightly.

"*1883. May 20th.*—To chapel. Mr. Eastwood there again. After the service he asked if he might walk a little way with me. Thinking he would be going to Hough Hall, I told him I was going home through the fields,[1] hoping thus to avoid him; but unfortunately he came with me, and as we met scarcely anyone all the way, I felt very much at his mercy. He told me it was his birthday. I was obliged to wish him many happy returns, and did so; and to keep the conversation on a light note asked him if he had had any nice birthday presents." (This was, of course, really a straight lead to intimacy, and it is characteristic of Catherine's misunderstanding of the ordinary usages of society that she did not perceive it.) "He at once bent towards me, fixing his large light eyes upon my face in a very disagreeable way, and said in an emotional tone: 'There is only *one* present which can make me truly happy, Miss Ainsley.' Terribly disconcerted, I said nothing, and turned my head aside; but he bent more towards me and

[1] A path ran from part way up the higher portion of Hough Lane across the flank of the hill, skirting the side of the Hough Hall grounds, and striking Carr Bank just above Carr Fold. A rough stile led to the Hough Hall back yard from this path, but the front entrance was not accessible by this route except through the house.

exclaimed: 'You know what that is, Miss Ainsley.' He breathed so deeply that I was quite alarmed, and stuttered very stupidly: 'No, I don't.' 'It's yourself!' he exclaimed dramatically. 'If only I could win your love, Miss Ainsley, I should count myself the happiest of men.' Why is it that he always uses these melodramatic hackneyed phrases? I always want to laugh at them, and yet I 'squirm,' as Phil says, at the same time. I told him very firmly that it was no use him speaking to me in that way, and that in any case he ought not to mention such subjects to me while I was in mourning. At this his whole face lighted up, and he exclaimed: 'Then I may speak to you again after your year of mourning is over?' 'No, no!' I cried. He then became very dejected and mournful, and tried to make out that I had withdrawn my word. Altogether it was most unpleasant, and I was truly relieved when dear old Didymus came bounding over the wall to meet me. I turned to Mr. Eastwood then and told him firmly that he need not come any further with me. He coloured and looked perfectly furious; turned on his heel abruptly and made off at a great pace. Dear, dear! Phil and Cordelia and the children came to tea in the afternoon, and I wondered whether to mention her brother to Cordelia, but somehow I could not—it would be so difficult to explain to her that I hate him without hurting her feelings."

"*June 15th.*—To chapel. Mr. Eastwood there *again*. Came home with the Shoesmiths and so avoided him. I shall not go to Hough Lane for a week or two, I think."

"*June 22nd.*—Did not go to chapel because of Mr. Eastwood. A long, rainy, very very dreary day. Phil and Cordelia did not come in to tea, as they had promised, which made Mamma cross. Phil, however, called in on his way to church in the evening, to tell us that Eugene had a temperature, and that was why they had not come. He also told us that the youngest Shoesmith girl is engaged. Mamma made this the occasion for a long lecture to me when Phil had gone, saying that it is time I married, I am nearly twenty-five, quite an old maid, I do not make the best of myself in society, I talk about the wrong things, I wear the wrong clothes, men do not like clever girls, and so on. I asked her—rather bitterly, I am afraid—why she was so anxious to get rid of me, whereupon she cried and said she was not thinking of herself, but of me. I cannot understand why life is so terribly dull and profitless to me nowadays; at school and in Germany every little thing seemed full of interest. I should like to go and spend a week with Mrs. Whitaker, but what would Mamma do without me? Mamma says she would like to go to Scarborough for a month or two, but I cannot bear the idea. Scarborough! Oh, no, never!"

(The Ainsleys, in fact, spent the whole of this summer in Bournemouth.)

"*September 19th.*—Home again. It is good to see Carr Fold once more. Perhaps I shall be happier after all here than away from home."

"*October 15th.*—7 p.m. First lecture on sick-room nursing. Very interesting, but I am afraid I shall never be very good at it. But I *must* learn to do something useful with my life, instead of frittering it away as I do now."

"*November 18th.*—My twenty-fifth birthday. To think that I have lived a quarter of a century! To think also—which is much worse—that I have another quarter of a century, perhaps even two, to live yet! How shall I fill in all that vast space of time?"

The next few entries belong to 1884.

"*May 20th.*—In the afternoon Mamma drove into Hudley

to pay her compliments to Mrs. Nicholas Whiteley, who is receiving for the first time to-day after the birth of her little girl. I made my cold an excuse, and did not go. Almost immediately she had left the house Lomas Eastwood was ushered in—to see *me,* if you please! I said to him at once: 'Your sister is not here, Mr. Eastwood.' He coloured, and mumbled something about knowing that, and said that he had serious business with me. Rather alarmed, I was obliged to ask him to sit down; to my horror he plumped himself down on the couch next to me, and seizing my hand, promptly asked me to marry him. It is his birthday, he says, and he asked me on this date last year, and I said he might speak to me again when I was out of mourning! This is not true, and I told him so. His clear pink face grew quite dark at this, and those horrid bold eyes of his were so angry that I was quite upset, but I remembered that I was in my own house—for Mr. Whiteley says that Carr Fold *is* my own house, and I can do as I like with it [1]—and took courage, and spoke sharply to him. So then he almost cried, and seized my hand and kissed it, and said he knew he was infinitely beneath me, and that his love was hopeless but would last for ever, and his life would always be a lonely one, and so on; but if only I would allow him the privilege of my friendship he would try to be brave and continue to live. Although the touch of his horrid little fat hand on mine gave me real *nausea,* I could not help feeling sorry for him when he said he was lonely, for I understand what that means so well; so instead of continuing to speak in a haughty, Miss-Ainsley-ish sort of voice, I talked to him very sincerely, saying that I could

[1] This probably refers to Mrs. Ainsley's desire to take down the old Carr Fold gates. Catherine, of course, opposed her on this matter; it was brought to the notice of Mr. Whiteley, who made the statement referred to here.

never care for him, and that it was a pity for him to waste his life in an unrequited attachment. 'You have a useful and honourable career before you,' I said, and he said: 'If ever I am successful in the world, Miss Ainsley, it will all be due to you.' I did not see any sense in that *at all,* and said so, whereat he sighed, and putting his head on one side looked tenderly into my eyes. It was *most* uncomfortable. I said that I must forbid him to mention the subject to me again; whereat he threw up his chin in a manner that reminded me oddly of Cordelia, and said he must beg leave to make an exception to that: every time May 20th came round he should do himself the honour of speaking to me. I was on tenterhooks lest Mamma should return before he went, but fortunately I got rid of him in time. Dear me! It was an odd scene! I laugh whenever I think of it, and at the same time I want to cry. Mamma came home very full of Mrs. Whiteley's new French robe for her baby; she is to be called Suzanne. A pretty name. If I were *really* my own mistress, as Mr. Whiteley says, I think I should adopt a little girl."

Hitherto the conduct of Lomas, as revealed by our available sources, may have seemed to the reader hardly to justify the strictures which have from time to time been passed upon it. The fact is that evidence of an acceptable degree of veracity on Lomas's thought and activities at this time is somewhat lacking. But we have indisputable evidence of his duplicity to Catherine here, for the very day before he was thus speaking to her of his "loneliness," he moved out of 39, Majorca Road into bachelor lodgings in Prince's Road for a very unsavoury reason, namely, that two days previously Taylor Eastwood had caught him in some incident with regard to Annie Hallas which laid him open to the very worst possible suspicions. What exactly this incident was cannot be stated; Cordelia declined to give its particulars, but vouched for the fact. Taylor Eastwood, furious with his son both for the suggestion of immorality itself and for the violation of the laws of hospitality which it involved, had a terrific scene with Lomas, who simply stood silent, looked lofty, and sneered, beneath his father's accusations, which he occasionally took the trouble to deny in a languid and weary tone. Taylor concluded by saying that either Annie or Lomas must leave the house, and as he had not the slightest intention of turning an orphan girl out upon the world it had better be Lomas. Lomas welcomed this opportunity for a freer life eagerly, and at once sought rooms in Prince's Road. These rooms were slightly nearer his work in Denbridge Vale than Majorca Road, certainly; but their chief attraction in Lomas's eyes was probably that they were a good mile nearer Carr Foot than his old home had been. The usually mild, meek, slow Annie was driven almost distracted by his removal, and accused Taylor violently, with many tears and wild exclaimings, of harshness and cruelty. Mrs. Eastwood's grief was quieter, but probably just as poignant; indeed she drooped visibly under it, and her death in the following February was no doubt largely caused by her loss of Lomas. Her son could, of course, have gone to see her regularly, for Taylor had not forbidden him the house; but Lomas had other fish to fry and was temporarily tired of Annie, and his visits to Majorca Road soon became rare.

Three more extracts from Catherine's diary will bring us to 1885.

"*June 4th*. . . . An argument with Mamma about my notion of adopting a child. . . ."

"*June 13th*. . . . Another argument with Mamma about

my adoption scheme in the carriage on the way to Hudley. She was much vexed. . . . We went in to see Mr. Whiteley, and to my annoyance Mamma suddenly broke out and told him all about it. He looked quite horrified, and said there would be time enough for that in twenty years, by which I suppose he means that it will not be settled till then whether I am to be lucky (?) enough to find a husband or not. Mamma also said that to adopt a child would not be fair to Phil. Mr. Whiteley was quite cross at this, and said it was all nonsense; but he advised me strongly not to think of adopting a child for another ten years at least—said I was too young to think of it. But I am older than Cordelia, and not much younger than Mrs. Charlie Gill and Mrs. N. L. Whiteley. I suppose I must give it up, however; I should not like to harm Phil and his children."

"*October 12th.*—I have been much irritated to-day. Mamma did not go to church this morning, as it was very wet, but it turned fine later. I went to chapel as usual, and as usual Lomas Eastwood was there and walked back across the fields with me. Just as we emerged into Carr Bank, Mamma came out of the gates with Didymus, evidently to meet me; she saw Mr. Eastwood, of course, and spoke to him, and to my intense annoyance asked him to stay and have Sunday midday dinner with us. He seemed very pleased, and all through dinner flattered Mamma in the most outrageous manner. I was intentionally very curt to him, and would not admire the sketches of High Carr he had brought folded in his pocket for me to see, though they were really rather clever. We did not get rid of him till after three o'clock—on the slightest hint I believe he would have stayed to tea. After he had gone I expressed to Mamma my regret that she had asked him into the house. She was cross, and said: 'He's Cordelia's brother.

How could I help it?' 'Let him go to Hough Hall for his dinner, then,' said I. Mamma gave a kind of angry exclamation at this, and said in a rather bitter tone: 'Well, Catherine, I understand *perfectly now* why you have not married.' I was rather hurt at this, and said nothing, and Mamma went on: 'You were so *rude* to poor Mr. Eastwood, you *snubbed* him so—if you behave to other men like that, it's no wonder you're still a spinster.' I wondered whether to tell Mamma my real reason for snubbing Mr. Eastwood, but if I did she would talk about it endlessly, and I could not bear that, so I said nothing. But I wonder if she is right about my manner to other men? I have got so into the way of thinking that I talked too much to poor Phil and wearied him that perhaps now I am too cold and silent."

The reader must judge for himself whether or not Catherine is here tacitly admitting her regret at having lost her cousin.

The uncomfortable—and extremely unwise—policy followed by Catherine, of concealing Lomas Eastwood's advances from her relations, was put an end to in the following year. Mrs. Eastwood, as has been stated, died in the February of 1885, from bronchial pneumonia. Her yielding, timid, gentle personality has not, perhaps, received in these pages the consideration it deserves; she has been obscured here, as in real life, by Taylor and by Cordelia. But she was a loving if simple soul; a devoted wife and mother, a very dearly loved grandmother; one of those who understand rather with the heart than with the head, who give rather than exact affection. There were many, including perhaps her children, who under-valued her, but Taylor Eastwood mourned her very truly, and was much aged by her passing. Hammond too declined to eat when he heard of her death. The Carrs were at the breakfast-table when Lomas came in with the news, and Hammond, standing beside his father's chair, was just about to eat the piece of buttered toast which Phil gave him every morning from his own plate as the titbit of his repast. On hearing what his uncle had to say the child threw down the morsel and silently and stolidly walked out of the room. Cordelia was naturally much touched by this, and promptly burst into tears, though previously her feeling had been chiefly one of relief, for Mrs. Eastwood's ordeal had been long and trying. (It must just be noticed here that in Cordelia's inclination to hysteria and her over-quick response to emotion in others with an emotion of her own which was thus secondary, sentimental, and not in any deep sense genuine, there was a slight hint of that element of the histrionic which reached such detestable heights in Lomas.) The question now arose of Taylor Eastwood's future household arrangements. Cordelia did not like the idea of her father living alone with Annie Hallas—whether from jealousy or from a distrust of Annie's housekeeping is not quite clear. She urged her father to let Annie go to one of her married brothers, and to come himself to Hough Hall. Carr, though naturally he would have preferred to keep his house to himself, cordially seconded this invitation. But Taylor had too much sense and independence to accept, and he had a different solution of the matter to propose. Lomas was astounded and considerably annoyed to find his father waiting for him in his rooms one evening. He was still more annoyed when his father expounded the purpose of his visit. In rather nervous and pathetic tones Taylor set forth his own loneliness and Annie's, and the foolishness of running two households when one would suffice, and concluded by asking his son outright why he did not marry Annie and come back to live in Majorca Road. At this Lomas started back, and his smooth face expressed a sneering disgust.

"Me marry Annie!" he exclaimed with a brutal inflexion. "Not likely!" He then saw what a splendid opportunity was offered him for a dramatic sentimental declaration. Drawing himself up he announced in his most genteel and fervid tones: "Father, I shall never marry any woman but Miss Ainsley."

The horrified Taylor exclaimed: "What! You're mad, boy!"

"I know my love for her is not likely to be crowned with success," pursued Lomas, no doubt thoroughly enjoying himself, "but I shall never give up hope. It is useless to try to persuade me to enter into any other matrimonial scheme."

"Good God!" exclaimed his father, distracted to the verge of incoherency. "You're a heartless adventurer, Lomas. You're after her money. That I should have to say it to any child of mine! Do you want to ruin your sister? And Annie? What about Annie? She loves you—little though you deserve it. You're a heartless rascal, sir. You don't care an 'em' for Miss Ainsley. Poor sad thing that she is. You're after her money and her carriage and Carr Fold."

A gleam of triumph may have shot through Lomas's grey eyes at this enumeration of Catherine's possessions; at any rate his sneering smile became more pronounced as he observed with tremendous dignity: "I can't stop you from making these wild accusation, father, but I beg that you will not distress Miss Ainsley by letting her hear them."

"But I shall, you scoundrel, I shall!" cried Taylor furiously. "I'll take good care she knows the kind of rascal you are."

"What can you tell her?" cried Lomas, forgetting his rhetoric, angry in his turn. "You've nothing against me."

"And what about that time with Annie?" demanded his father.

"Oh, rubbish!" threw out Lomas, turning aside irritably. Remembering his pose in time, he added with an air of injured innocence: "Of course, if you wish to ruin me with Mr. Barker and Miss Ainsley by false accusations you must do so, father; but I beg you to consider first what very slight grounds you have for them. I am not aware," he concluded loftily, "of having done anything which makes me unfit to be Miss Ainsley's husband."

Taylor, somewhat taken aback by this direct negative, stood silent for a minute, and then said in a doubtful tone: "Well, I shall tell Cordelia."

Lomas gave an impatient exclamation, but went on smoothly: "I suppose I can rely on your sense of justice to tell Cordelia what I *say* as well as what you *think*."

Taylor grunted an uncomfortable affirmative, and went away very uneasy. Although it was a wild wet night and the hour was late he at once took one of the new steam trams out to Hough Lane, and frightened the Carrs by bursting in upon them, wet and excited, as they sat by the dying drawing-room fire.

"Have they let him in after all?" cried Carr—referring of course to Bradlaugh, who in the January of this year had been declared incapable of taking an oath in law.

"No—no," stammered Taylor, sheepishly, even in this moment of anxiety understanding his son-in-law's allusion "Though they'll have to do it yet. It's not that—it's Lomas. Cordelia, I'd like a word with you."

Cordelia took him into another room, and Taylor poured out the whole story to her. Cordelia, deeply troubled, called Carr in and told him. Carr was inexpressibly shocked and horrified, and the two spent a wretched night. Next morning Cordelia drove with her husband down to Carr Foot Mills, as they had decided; she thus arrived very early at Carr Fold, and demanded a private interview with Catherine.

Of this interview we have no detailed account. Cordelia, whose pride must have suffered enormously in thus having to vilify her brother to Catherine, could never be prevailed on to speak of it to the present writer; and the entry in Catherine's diary is brief. "This morning early," it runs, "I had a very painful interview with poor Cordelia, who has discovered her brother's affection for me, and is very much troubled by it. She came, she said, to warn me. She told me that he is unworthy of me in every way, and begged me never to consider marrying him. She seemed really relieved to find that I had known of it for a long time, and refused him several times already. Although I am sure," adds Catherine the generous, "that Cordelia is right about her brother, I cannot help feeling sorry for poor Mr. Eastwood, who seems to have everyone against him. Cordelia spoke so *very* scornfully of his music and his sketching that I was almost moved to defend him."

It is a sad comment on human ineptitude that actions designed to produce one set of effects often result in their exact opposite. The action of Taylor Eastwood, straightforward and honourable like all his actions, was intended to protect Catherine from Lomas, and make it impossible for his passion for her to come to any fruition. What it really effected, however, was to legalise Lomas's ambitions.

All the circle of Catherine's relatives and acquaintances now knew that Lomas Eastwood was in love with Miss Ainsley—for Mrs. Ainsley was, of course, informed of it by Cordelia, and her tongue did not cease to embroider the subject—and that Miss Ainsley had already refused him three times. The antiquity of the attachment seemed to make it respectable; for a persevering hopeless love indicates a certain amount of solidity and determination in a man's character, while a persistent refusal on a woman's part gives her a dignified reputation for knowing her own mind. At first there were, of course, exclamations of Lomas's audacity, and cynical remarks to the effect that he knew which side his bread was buttered; while men who knew Lomas observed with some force: "I should think she *did* refuse him!" But as time went on Lomas's attachment became one of the accepted facts of life; after all he was Mrs. Philip Carr's brother, and had lately been made head of a department at Enoch Barker's. Enoch Barker was doing extraordinarily well just now—rather too well, in fact, for Carr's satisfaction—and while some said it was due to Charlie Gill's extraordinary driving power, others hinted that their designs were exceptionally good, and that this was due to Lomas Eastwood. Some people indeed went so far as to say that it would be a good thing for Carr Carr and Ainsley if Catherine *did* marry Lomas Eastwood and thus draw him to the firm; and that this idea was understood by Charlie Gill is shown by the fact that from this time he began to invite Lomas very frequently to his house in Denbridge. On these occasions the youngest Miss Barker, Charlotte by name, was always present; and Lottie, as she was familiarly called, showed herself by no means unwilling to become Mrs. Lomas Eastwood if she were asked. But she was not asked. At balls and parties Lomas paid her the decent amount of attention which might reasonably be expected by his employer's daughter and his friend's sister-in-law, but the full flower of his attention was always kept for Catherine. His programme was always empty until he had put her name upon it, for he kept it free on the chance that Catherine might be disengaged—as indeed she so often was, poor girl. At concerts and lectures he bowed and smiled charmingly to Lottie, but he devoted the intervals to Catherine; and was always hovering round the door when the Ainsley's carriage was called. Some cynics, observing the difference in his attitude to the two girls, said that Lottie Barker hadn't enough for him, for Mr. Barker had four daughters and was only middle-aged, while Catherine owned three-quarters of Carr Carr and Ainsley now, together with Carr Fold and a really large sum of money well invested, and a certainty of more at her mother's death; but on the whole Lomas's faithful hopeless clinging to Catherine, when a quite sufficiently bright marriage lay at his feet, was favourably noted. The comment of Hudley was the more favourable perhaps because Lottie Barker was some six or seven years younger than Catherine; and while Catherine's grief and sadness had dimmed her never very bright complexion, and fixed her heavy face in rather mournful lines, Lomas had contrived to keep his thin smooth face as clear as ever—except occasionally for some dark pouches beneath the eyes—and his small neat figure as slender, so that he now looked nearer Miss Barker's age than Catherine's. Nobody knew better than Lomas, however, as he occasionally confided to Charlie Gill, that his good looks were of the type that collapses suddenly and irretrievably in the thirties; he already wore corsets and put belladonna in his eyes; and in keeping up his pursuit of Catherine for so long without result he was playing a dangerous game. The stakes were, however, in Lomas's opinion evidently worth it.

As to what Annie Hallas thought of the general assumption that Lomas would marry Catherine Ainsley or nobody, we cannot of course say for certain, but it is probable that almost from the first she accepted Lomas's decision as inevitably right. When Taylor Eastwood told her one March evening—probably with more directness than tact—of Lomas's declaration of love for Catherine to him a few nights previously, Annie threw her apron over her head, and sinking down on the floor rocked herself violently backwards and forwards in anguish, moaning the while. Taylor, horrified by this outburst from the mild Annie, went to her and tried to soothe her, laying a hand on her large shoulder, but she twisted away from him, and throwing down the apron turned up a hot wild face and screamed violently at him that it was all his fault for sending Lomas out of the house. "You shouldn't have sent him away! You shouldn't have sent him away!" she wailed loudly again and again, her face crimson, her heavy lips pouting with grief like a child's, her thick fingers clutching at her pale dishevelled hair. But the rebellion of this meek and helpless creature against fate was soon over; she descended from screams to tears, from accusations to moans; by next morning she was mild and gentle again, and though she fretted quietly to herself for a long time over Lomas's desertion, she took a kind of pride in his high marriage, which she regarded as entirely fixed. She constantly irritated Taylor, who thought she ought to have tried to regain Lomas's affection, by questioning him about Catherine, and on the rare occasions when Lomas came to Majorca Road she listened with the keenest interest to all he had to say about the Ainsleys and

Carr Fold. She even, to Taylor's fury, occasionally gave Lomas advice on how to win Catherine—though Lomas was much too wise to take it. When Taylor expostulated with her and told her his own opinion on the matter, namely, that Lomas cared for nothing about Catherine Ainsley but her money, poor Annie shook her head and pointed out that she, Annie, was five years older than Lomas and not a lady. This last item, of course, infuriated Taylor and usually sent him off into one of his political tirades; long before he reached the end of it he had forgotten everything but "the lad," as Bradlaugh's workingmen supporters called him, and was explaining to Annie for the hundredth time the exact course of events—trials, bills, appeals—since Bradlaugh's election in 1880. Annie, unlike Cordelia, was capable of listening placidly to all this and enjoying it without in the least attempting to understand it; so perhaps the old man and the young woman were not too unhappy, in spite of their respective losses, as they sat facing one another across the kitchen hearth—for to Cordelia's disgust Taylor and Annie now lived chiefly in the kitchen.

The mention of Bradlaugh leads us on, curiously enough, to the next event of interest in the life of Carr. There had been a General Election in November 1885, at which Bradlaugh had again been elected for Northampton with Mr. Labouchere, and on January 13th, 1886, the new Speaker, Mr. Peel, permitted Bradlaugh to take the oath, refusing to allow any interference. On January 13th, 1886, therefore, "the lad" at last legally took his seat; and at Hough Hall, on that same date, Carr's third and last child was born. Carr, driving his new sleigh into Hudley on the afternoon of Thursday, January 14th to tell Mr. Eastwood the news, met Taylor coming out in a fever of excitement to discuss with Carr *his* news. Taylor was in the steam tram, but seeing Carr he jumped vigorously out, and crunching hastily through the snow to the smart sleigh cried exultantly: "Well, you see! He's in! He's in! He's taken his seat! He's beaten you! I knew he would."

"Well, it won't break *my* heart," cried Carr cheerily. "Jump up and take a seat yourself."

At this James Illingworth promptly dismounted from his position beside Carr and went into the back of the sleigh, Taylor scrambled up, and Carr turned the horse towards Hough Hall.

"Well, we've got our youngster down at home," he then told his father-in-law with great satisfaction.

Taylor was surprised, as the event had not been expected for another fortnight. He congratulated Carr and inquired after Cordelia, then after musing a little space suddenly exclaimed: "Was it to-day or yesterday?"

"Last night at six minutes to twelve," replied Carr with exactness.

Taylor clutched his son-in-law's arm with both hands. "Now call him Charles," he begged—this being, of course, the name of his beloved Bradlaugh. "Do, Phil, do!"

At this Carr laughed heartily, and shaking his head, said in a teasing tone: "Nay, we can't do that, I'm afraid, Grandpa."

"Aye, but do!" pleaded Taylor. "It's a right name enough, and born on the very day and all. Now do, Phil! Will you?"

At this Carr threw back his head and laughed more heartily than before. "Why, you silly old atheist," he cried affectionately, poking Taylor in the ribs with the butt end of his smart whip: "It's a girl!"

VII

RESIDENCE AT HOUGH HALL (1887–1891)

BETWEEN 1886 and 1890 no large event in the history of the Carr and Ainsley families falls to be recorded, but a series of small ones occurred which have their places and their significance in this biography.

Catherine found life more and more desiccated and uninteresting as the years went on. Every year on May 20th Lomas Eastwood asked her to marry him; every year she wearily refused. (On these occasions, as we know from Sir Charles Gill, Lomas used to return to his work at Denbridge Vale trembling with anger, the veins throbbing in his temples, his smooth brows knit, his grey eyes darting furious malice at anyone who crossed his path, his mouth sullen and pouting, his clear complexion mottled with rage. It was literally not safe to speak to him until the passage of time had somewhat soothed his disappointment; for he once threw a heavy bottle of ink at an unfortunate lad who spoke to him on the afternoon of his yearly visit to Carr Fold, and cut open his cheek.) At Christmas 1886 Lomas sent Catherine a present of some music for which he had heard her express a wish, which she thus hardly knew how to refuse; and in successive years he kept up the custom thus established. Perhaps, therefore, the reader will not be unduly surprised to find, on June 17th, 1887, the following extremely important and significant, not to say fatal, entry in Catherine's diary. "Finished *The*

Woodlanders.[1] How fond Mr. Hardy is of showing girls wrongly despising honest faithful lovers who are considered socially beneath them! I hope I am not like that in refusing L. E. I have heard Mr. Gill say he is one of the best designers in the West Riding." This, unfortunately, marks a turning-point in Catherine's life; in 1888, 1889 and 1890 her refusal of Lomas still remained firm, but it is probable that from this date she began to toy mentally with the idea of marrying him, to palter with it, to regard it rather as a noble and unconventional act of generosity than as the moral impossibility it should have been. That nothing could well be less like Hardy's "honest faithful lovers who are considered socially beneath" the woman of their choice than Lomas Eastwood, Catherine's essential goodness and simplicity prevented her from seeing; and the Victorian squeamishness of Carr and Cordelia kept her from enlightenment on the point. We must, therefore, unfortunately regard the years from 1887 to 1890 as a period during which Lomas's long-continued pressure on Catherine began to make itself felt.

During this period Mrs. Ainsley's health became more firmly established than ever; so much so, indeed, that Hammond and Eugene always regarded her as a wiry, tough, thoroughly healthy though white-haired lady, and were astonished when they heard of her early delicacy. James Illingworth married. Cherry the cat died, to Mr. Eastwood's grief, and a new kitten, likewise called Cherry, took up the task of consoling him. The firm of Carr Carr and Ainsley continued to flourish; and though the competition of Enoch Barker became a factor to be reckoned with, Carr's superior textile instinct, his tried

[1] *The Woodlanders* was published in three volumes by Messrs. Macmillan on Tuesday, March 15th, 1887.

integrity and the still valuable prestige of William Ainsley stood him in good stead. Two events, however, connected with Mr. Barker's firm, which occurred during this period, must be noted, as they have an important bearing on Carr's life. They are as follows. In 1887 Mr. Enoch Barker became a widower. In 1888 he had a violent quarrel with Charlie Gill which reached the proportions of a Hudley scandal. The exact cause of the quarrel, which had something to do with the faulty dyeing of a piece, is not known; but Mr. Barker, after threatening to dissolve partnership with his son-in-law, to throw him out of the business altogether and have nothing more to do with him, was somehow obliged to give in; and the affair resulted in a new deed of partnership which enormously increased Gill's share in and control over the firm, and included his name in its official designation.

In 1887, 1888 and the December of 1889 Carr and Cordelia went to London for the first nights of *Ruddigore, The Yoemen of the Guard* and *The Gondoliers* respectively; they regarded this as a celebration of their honeymoon, and regretted that circumstances—the birth of Hammond, the delicacy of Eugene, the death of Mrs. Eastwood—had prevented them from keeping this pleasant ceremony for the four earlier Gilbert-and-Sullivans which had come out since their marriage. A detail about the last of these three visits must be recorded. While listening, with every fibre a-quiver with enjoyment, to the delightful first act, Carr suddenly had a mental pang. The crowded theatre, the Venetian back-cloth, the jolly rows of gondolieri and contadini, Cordelia by his side in a new opera cloak of fawn cloth lined with primrose silk, all seemed to fade away, and for a moment he was standing on the Carr Fold terrace, in the light of the moon, on a spring evening ten years ago. Catherine was by his side, uttering noble sentiments in fervid language, and he, teasing her, said something about how all over the world people were eating and drinking and loving and laughing. That was it, of course! That clever gondoliere up there had just sung about "loving and laughing and quipping and quaffing"—that was just the difference, thought Carr sagely, with the essential sane humility of his nature, between his own mind and that of a man like Gilbert; he, Carr, could think of eating and drinking and loving and laughing, but Gilbert came along and put it in a phrase that could never be forgotten. Well! For a moment he could feel the ivy of the terrace parapet beneath his fingers; he saw the silvery moon and the dark blue sky and the Carr Foot chimneys, and heard Catherine's heavy, earnest voice in his ear. Well! That night he had met Cordelia, and after that everything had seemed to *be* Cordelia, somehow. It was clear enough to him now, though he had never seen it at the time, that of course Mr. Ainsley had meant him to carry Catherine, had hoped perhaps that they would be engaged that very night. Carr involuntarily moved his shoulders at the thought, and drew nearer to Cordelia. His wife, her beautiful little face sparkling with enjoyment, gave him a swift caressing look and turned to the stage again. Carr sighed with relief to think that he was not married to Catherine; he had his Dell, and his two grand little boys sound asleep at Hough Hall this minute, and his darling brown-eyed Baby Meg. The remembrance of all he had made his heart soft, and he thought with a pang of how little Catherine had. Her life must be wretchedly dull, out there with that chattering Mrs. Ainsley. Pity she had never married! Now she was thirty-one he supposed she never would. It is characteristic of his limited but essentially loving and generous nature that he resolved forthwith to take her home some especially beautiful Christmas present, and this resolve was, curiously enough, probably the means of preserving to us Catherine's diary, as the following entry will show.

"December 25th, 1889.—Phil and Dell and the children to dinner at one o'clock. We had a Christmas tree in the library; Phil dressed up as Father Christmas and handed us our presents from the tree. . . ." (Here follows an account of all the presents given, concluding:) "Dear Phil gave me the most charming present imaginable! He took a large square parcel from the tree, and holding it in his hands asked me if I remembered the night of his twenty-first birthday. As though I could ever forget it! It was the night we first saw Cordelia. Phil asked me if I remembered talking to him on the terrace about what was going on in the world. As though I should ever forget that night! For a moment I was rather painfully affected, and Eugene, who was watching me, exclaimed suddenly in a rather rough tone, throwing himself down on the couch: 'She couldn't forget; she's got it all down in her diary!' Phil seemed rather vexed at this, and called Eugene a young rascal for giving away the secret so soon, but I cannot help feeling that Eugene said it to relieve me—he is a curious boy! Phil went on to say something about *The Gondoliers* which I did not quite understand, and then gave me the parcel, which turned out to be a lovely leather case, holding twelve lovely leather-bound books of blank paper, marked 'Diary' on the back. Of course my diary has always been a family joke, but it is a tremendous pleasure to me, and nothing Phil could have given me could have pleased me more. He has had it made specially for me in London. It is just like him! He is always

so good. Dell gave me a beautifully worked linen night-dress case, and the children a new collar for poor old Didymus. It appears this was Hammond's idea; Eugene wanted to give me a book, and they have been quarrelling about it for weeks, as usual. Eugene was sick after tea, which annoyed Mamma. I think I shall perhaps have all my old diaries so far put into the binding of some of the twelve volumes; I think they would go into about five or six. It would be nice to have them all uniform. I asked Phil if he would mind my doing so, and he said not at all. Baby was in silent ecstasies over her doll; would not be parted from it for an instant, and kept stroking its toes and positively *scowling* with pleasure. I wish I saw more of the children."

Catherine's plan about her diaries was carried out. The diaries from 1877 to 1889 occupy six of the substantial volumes; from December 26th, 1889 to January 1892 only two, both of which are incompletely filled; there is then a break in continuity for twenty-five years; the entries from 1917 to 1927 occupy two complete volumes and about a quarter of a third; after March 22nd, 1927, the diary ceases altogether.

Her desire to "see more" of Phil's children had its fulfilment in the summer of 1890, when the Carrs arranged to be absent from home for three weeks during July. The occasion was as follows:—Mrs. Nicholas Whiteley, who was a native of Grenoble, usually spent part of this month at her parents' home, together with her husband and her little girl; and she and Nicholas usually took the opportunity of visiting other places of interest on the Continent, leaving Suzanne in her grandparents' care the while. Mr. Nicholas Whiteley had several times suggested to Carr that he and Cordelia should join them on one of these short tours.

Cordelia was rather timid about going abroad, and she was definitely timid in the presence of the foreign Mrs. Whiteley, but her desire to see the world and improve herself was stronger, at this period of her life, than her timidity, and this year the plan was carried out. The party were to have a delightful holiday in Switzerland; and the three Carr children, with Meg's admirable nurse—a strict person whom Eugene detested—were deposited at Carr Fold for the period of their parents' absence.

Catherine's diary shows that she went through, with regard to them, the three stages customary in the feelings of all kindly adults towards other people's children. To begin with she was overjoyed at the prospect of having them; she told herself and Adelaide innumerable times how much brighter Carr Fold would be with three children about the house; she ran about arranging bedrooms and a nursery for them; she put flowers in their rooms; she received them with intense affection, and on the first day of their stay played with them so vigorously that she quite wore herself out. She then went through a period of disappointment, disillusion and exasperation, when the children declined to be hugged, quarrelled at the breakfast-table, ate untidily and answered back when she reproved them, scoffed at all her plans for their enjoyment, constantly compared Carr Fold to Hough Hall, greatly to the latter's advantage, teased Didymus, worried her mother, and left her not a moment's peace all day long. The climax of this period occurred on one of the nurse's afternoons out, when Hammond set the library curtains on fire during an attempt to make the steam boiler of a miniature yacht work. Protracted screams from Meg, ringing through the quiet Carr Fold air, brought Catherine and Mrs. Ainsley flying to the scene from the drawing-room, where they had been vainly trying to snatch a few minutes' rest. Catherine's heart beat faster, on this occasion, than it had done since her father's death. Fortunately nobody was hurt, not even Hammond, who, however, turned as white as a sheet and had to be revived with brandy. He was very much subdued for the rest of the afternoon, and sat quite still in an armchair by the fire, nursing Meg and playing "Beggar-my-neighbour" with Eugene and Catherine. Catherine's attempts to let him win were clumsy, but Eugene lost with great skill, and even simulated a natural irritation at his own defeat with such admirable art that Catherine was almost shocked—but loved him for it all the same. Somehow this marked the end of the exasperated period; Catherine had now learned the essential lesson that the three children were three individualities, with moods, disappointments and exasperations of their own, not a mere heap of childish attributes from the pages of a Christmas Annual. She had now learned, too, that looking after children is hard and highly skilled work, calling upon all one's resources of tact and character, and not a mere wallowing in sentimental enjoyment. From this time she got on with Hammond and Meg quite well, and developed a genuine and lasting tenderness for Eugene. At this time Eugene was not handsome like the other two children; he was often extremely reserved, almost sullen, in manner; he had an odd way of looking at the world, and he had a positive gift for saying the wrong thing. It may be surmised that all these qualities endeared him to Catherine, who shared them.

However that might be, both Catherine and Mrs. Ainsley felt that the nurse's next afternoon out was a time of peril, and that the children must be guarded at all costs; and Catherine had the inspiration of taking them all to be photographed—partly to keep them safely under her eye for the afternoon, and partly so that their pictured faces might be sent out to Switzerland to comfort Cordelia, who required daily assurances that her children were well. And so we have the third and last portrait of Mary Elizabeth Carr, flanked by her two brothers. She is sitting on a very Victorian chair, the seat of which is so ample that her little feet, neatly encased in white openwork socks and white kid shoes with rosettes and one strap buttoned on the ankle, barely reach the edge of it. She wears a smocked white frock which looks rather large for her, and a large lace collar. Her face is round, chubby, but extremely serious; her brown hair curls about her ears, but is cut in a straight fringe on the forehead; her fine brown eyes are a very striking feature, and the breadth of the forehead is noticeable. (She is said to have been a very loving and imaginative child, passionately fond of dolls and of make-believe.) Hammond, now aged nine, stands erect at her left, looking perfectly charming in a white sailor suit. His delightful bronze curls stick out all round his head (to his own great disgust later); his blue eyes sparkle; and he is smiling all over his jolly round face with a smile which we have seen often before in his father's portraits. Eugene leans against the chair on the right, also in white, but looking somewhat crumpled; his face is chiefly noticeable for its length, its gloom, its heavily marked features and its pouting lips; but an amusing touch is given to his portrait by the fact that his eyes are nearly turned out of his head in his attempt to keep an eye on Meg and yet maintain the attitude which we must suppose the photographer required of him. If this photograph is inspected carefully, it will be seen that both the boys have firm hold—Hammond with his right hand, Eugene with his left—of Meg's dress at the back; this protective brotherly attitude is very charming. Indeed both Hammond and Eugene were passionately devoted to their little sister—the present writer's name indicates this—and even a score of years after their loss of her they could not speak her name without showing that they still felt the pathos of her fate.

For we are now, of course, approaching the series of misfortunes which befell Carr between July 1890 and June 1891. The first misfortune did not appear to be a very great one as far as he was concerned until some months after it occurred, for it was the death of Mr. Nicholas Whiteley, senior. Mr. Whiteley, who, it will be remembered, was Mr. Ainsley's sole executor, had an apoplectic seizure on July 19th. His son was immediately recalled from Switzerland, and although there was some delay in the arrival of the news, he reached Hudley before his father died. Mr. Whiteley did not, however, regain consciousness after his son's return; he had had another seizure shortly before this took place, and passed away on July 27th. By his will his son Nicholas Latham Whiteley was appointed his sole executor, and upon Nicholas Latham Whiteley, therefore, the duties of executorship as regards William Ainsley's estate and trusteeship as regards Mrs. Ainsley automatically devolved. It must be stated here at once, lest a wrong impression be received by the reader, that Mr. N. L. Whiteley performed his duties with perfect integrity and considerable judgment, so that at Mrs. Ainsley's death the principal of which she had been drawing the interest passed to Catherine not only intact but slightly increased from what it had been at the time of her father's death. Mr. Nicholas L. Whiteley had not, however, that authority over Catherine which his father had by reason of his age and his friendship with Mr. Ainsley; nor did he feel able to interfere in her affairs other than monetary.

The second disaster was, as the reader has no doubt already surmised, the loss of the little Mary Elizabeth; and as the third disaster was closely interwoven with it as regards cause and effect, it will perhaps be well to give a consecutive narrative of events during the months of December 1890 and January and February 1891.

Christmas 1890 was, we may gather from Catherine's diary, the beginning of the last phase of her resistance. No present came to her from Lomas, "for which," she notes in her diary, "I am of course truly thankful." (It is curious to note how often the emphatic "of course" gives the lie to the rest of the sentence.) Neither present nor greeting of any kind came to her from Frau Schröter, whose little son was at that time so ill as to engage all her attention. Catherine did not then know of the little boy's illness, and on Christmas Day and for many days afterwards she notes: "No letter again from Minna!" By January 12th this is weighing very seriously on her spirits. "No letter *yet* from Minna! Does she too now not care for me, like everyone else?" she writes despairingly, and adds: "I see Mr. Bradlaugh is ill. Poor Mr. Eastwood will be much distressed. I envy him his power of enthusiasm for that misguided but heroic man. I seem able to love nothing and nobody, alas!"

As every student of the Victorian period knows, Charles Bradlaugh was taken ill on January 10th, 1891; he rallied once and seemed about to recover, but then relapsed. While he lay dying, on January 27th, a resolution was passed in the House of Commons expunging from its records the various resolutions of exclusion passed against him since his election in 1880. On Friday, January 30th he died; and he was buried on February 3rd, next his daughter Alice, in the Brookwood Necropolis. Taylor Eastwood, to whom the month of January had been, as may well be imagined, a period of intense anxiety and grief, insisted on attending this funeral. He was not very well himself at the time, being worn by the suspense of the last few weeks; moreover, he felt that with the death of "the lad" life was over for him, and this conviction showed in his haggard face and undecided step. Cordelia and Annie, therefore, both tried to dissuade him from going; but he put them aside petulantly, and utterly declined to allow either of them even to accompany him. He went alone, and returned on the following day (Wednesday, February 4th) a broken man. As soon as Annie saw him she knew that he was very ill; she put him to bed at once and sent for the doctor, who prescribed rest and brandy, and said he had had a serious seizure. Cordelia had arranged to call at Majorca Road that afternoon to see how her father had fared on his journey. As it was a Wednesday, the half-holiday at the Hudley Grammar School, which Hammond and Eugene had been attending since the previous autumn, the two boys accompanied their mother. Annie was quite sure that Taylor's end was near, so Cordelia took the boys upstairs for their grandfather to see. Hammond and Taylor, who shared Annie's view, were impressed by the historical quality of the scene; Eugene, on the contrary, was obstinately cheerful and would not become pathetic, but fidgeted about the room till at last he roused the old man into an irascible command to sit down. Cordelia, vexed with Eugene, promptly took the boys home, and was met on the stairs by the nurse, carrying Mary Elizabeth wrapped up in a large woollen shawl. The child had had a bad cold for a day or two; it now appeared that she had been fretful all afternoon, so fretful that the nurse had at last taken her temperature, and found it alarmingly high. Eugene has described to the present writer how his heart suddenly sank like a stone at the sight of his little sister's cross, flushed face. James Illingworth was instantly despatched for the doctor, and the child was put to bed. The Hough Lane doctor was away from home, but had left his patients in the care of his colleague at Carr Foot. The latter arrived with comparatively little delay, saw the child, looked rather grave, and diagnosed pleurisy. In the middle of his careful directions the baby—for she was little more—suddenly broke in with the serious inquiry: "And what may I have to eat?" "Nothing but milk and soda-water," replied the doctor. Meg sighed with relief—it appeared she had had a tiff with the nurse over her tea. This slight incident somewhat relieved the tension of the household; but Carr, met at the door of the Carr Foot Mills office by Illingworth with the double tidings of illness, naturally felt wretched.

Next day the situation did not change. The Carr Foot doctor came twice to see Mary Elizabeth, and promised to call in again later; in Hudley the doctor twice visited Taylor Eastwood. It chanced that the Hudley Mayor's Ball—the great social function of the season—was to take place that night. Cordelia had had a very beautiful dress of primrose silk made for her for this occasion, but of course she could not leave Meg; she urged her husband, however, to go. It was important for the prestige of Carr Carr and Ainsley that he should go; the Barkers and Gills would be there in force; his absence would be noticeable; if he went he could explain Cordelia's absence; moreover,

Catherine and Mrs. Ainsley, who were to call for the Carrs in their carriage, were naturally relying upon Phil's escort. With extreme reluctance Carr yielded to her arguments, dressed himself miserably, and joined the Ainsleys' carriage at the turn in the road. They had not heard of the serious nature of Meg's illness, and not wishing to spoil their evening—or perhaps because he was too sick at heart to bear any talk of it—Carr did not at first explain it to them. One would have thought that his harassed face and gloomy pre-occupation would have revealed, to Catherine at least, if not to Mrs. Ainsley, his anxiety; but as a matter of fact it did not do so. Catherine put his gloom down solely to the absence of Cordelia; and the thought that Phil found an evening with her, his once well-loved cousin, so distasteful as to furrow his brow and darken his mind to the state they were in at present maddened her. She felt suddenly that she simply could not bear any more of this useless, unwanted, unutterably dreary life. All her disappointment—unconscious but so real—over her loss of Phil, all her grief for her father, all the ennui of her long, dreary, futile days with Mrs. Ainsley, suddenly seemed to have come to a climax; and the mild, earnest, patient Catherine felt she could bear them no more. Her breast heaved stormily, her eyes filled with tears; she was in a mood to scream with exasperation, to cast herself in front of a railway train or go in for some wild dissipated course of life. She was wearing a new dress of pale blue silk, which did not suit her, and she was so conscious of its deficiencies that, as she reveals in her diary, she could have torn it from her shoulders and thrown it in the road. Mrs. Ainsley's animated chatter raised her exasperation to such a pitch that she could scarcely sit still.

In such moods the three occupants of the carriage reached

the Town Hall and made their official entry into the ball. Lomas Eastwood of course was there—he went everywhere nowadays—and Catherine experienced a positive assuagement when he approached her, his pencilled eyebrows arched, his bold eyes gleaming. He at least, she thought, would not scowl because he had to spend an evening with her, and she felt more disposed to grant him dances than she had ever done in her life. By a curious trick of Fate, however—or perhaps from policy on Lomas's part: it is impossible to tell—he asked her for one dance only, and immediately withdrew. Carr then engaged a certain number of dances with Catherine, all of them in the early part of the evening, for he hoped to leave soon. Nobody else, however, invited the rich Miss Ainsley. It seemed to Catherine a horrible commentary on her own personality, as she records in her diary that night, that not even her money could buy her partners. She spent most of the evening sitting on the red velvet seats beside poor Emily Gill—who always looked so miserably conscious of being an old maid, of having rejected her only chance—and watching Phil and Lomas Eastwood and Mrs. Ainsley dancing with other people. Mrs. Ainsley danced a good deal with Enoch Barker, while Lomas's partner was usually his employer's daughter; and Emily Gill whispered in Catherine's ear that it was rumoured that those two were really going to "make it up" at last. It seemed to Catherine that there was a shade of pity in Emily Gill's tone, and rebellion raged more fiercely in her heavy breast. After a long period of sitting out it was her turn to dance with Lomas, and Catherine tried not to look pleased when he approached her. It is probable, however, that she was not successful, for she records herself that the very way he took hold of her seemed different from his usual grasp;

and instead of agreeing subserviently with everything she said, as he usually did, he lightly but flatly contradicted her on even the most trivial details of every remark she uttered. This was more than Catherine's irritated nerves could stand, and she positively trembled with exasperation. When the dance was over and they were sitting together in one of the draughty corridors she felt that something must really be done or she would burst into tears before his eyes. Making a great effort to control her voice, she said on a light note: "You're very contradictory tonight, Mr. Eastwood."

"Ah, Miss Catherine!" replied Lomas, bending towards her with a languishing look in his artificially brightened eyes. "If only you would agree with me on *one* subject."

(We may remark in passing that he was skillful in this kind of *non sequitur* observation, and that this is the first time we have heard of him addressing Catherine by that name, so that his marked avoidance of her in the earlier part of the evening was probably deliberate and not accidental.)

Catherine hastily swerved into a discussion of *Davy Garrick*, which Mr. Edward Compton had been playing in Hudley in the previous week; but her head ached, her eyes burned, she hardly knew what she said, she felt that she was uttering imbecilities and revealing more and more clearly to Lomas her agitation and lack of self-control. She was unutterably thankful that her next dance was with Phil; he would restore her sanity, rescue her from this awful nightmare where one trembled on the brink of ghastly things, plant her firmly in a pleasant, ordinary world again. She stumbled on from phrase to phrase, while Lomas took the line of pretending to read deep hidden meanings in everything she said, and tormented her by begging her to explain them. At length, however, to Catherine's unspeakable relief, the music for the next dance—a set of lancers—sounded. She immediately rose; as Lomas did the same his face changed, and he said with bitterness—whether real or assumed it is impossible to say—"The evening is over for me now."

"I don't think you quite mean that, Mr. Eastwood," said Catherine quietly, remembering the many dances he had spent with Miss Barker.

"Miss Ainsley," announced Lomas in his best oratorical style, "the whole of my evening is always at your service, but I know it is useless to press you to make use of it." Catherine was too conscious of her long sojourn beside Emily Gill to be able to say anything to this, and Lomas continued: "If I thought I had a chance of spending more time with you, Miss Catherine, I would——" He seized his programme with both hands as though to tear it.

"No, no!" exclaimed Catherine, genuinely alarmed. Acting on a natural impulse, she put out a hand to rescue the programme from destruction. Her fingers encountered those of her companion, and he would not have been Lomas Eastwood if he had not seized them. Even through the white kid which clothed his hand and hers Catherine could feel the heat of his flesh and the passion of his grasp. Involuntarily she trembled, and her eyes sank; she was saved from complete abandon only by the approach of Carr, who now came down the long corridor in search of her, looking harassed and vexed. Lomas, furious, muttered something, bowed, and withdrew, and Catherine turned with intense relief to her cousin.

She was not destined, however, to get much comfort from Carr that night, for he had now been seized with one of those inexplicable presentiments, those curious sinkings of the heart, which do undoubtedly come upon us at times when they are appropriate to some distant and as yet unknown event, explain them how we may. In the middle of the last dance Carr had suddenly felt, though he could not know, that his child was worse, and that he must get home at once; and he was now come to ask Catherine to release him from this next dance. He forgot that he had not told her the serious nature of Meg's illness, and in the simplicity of his heart he had not noticed that she had been something of a wallflower that evening; so he was hurt when she did not acquiesce eagerly.

"Of course I'll stay if you wish it," he said crossly, offering his arm to her in a huff.

"No, no!" exclaimed Catherine for the second time that night, withdrawing from him. "Pray don't do anything of the kind. I'll just go to Mamma."

Mrs. Ainsley was found sitting beside Mr. Enoch Barker; Carr handed Catherine over to her and at once took his leave, somewhat to Mrs. Ainsley's annoyance. It was past the hour for trams, and Carr could not at first find a cab, so with characteristic impatience he gave up the search and walked the whole way home.

As he drew near Hough Hall he saw lights scattered about the house, and his heart sank still further. Full of foreboding, he let himself in, and found Cordelia busy in the kitchen amongst pans and bowls. Her pretty little face was blanched and lined, her bright hair was dishevelled, her eyes were red with weeping, the flannel wrapper she wore was perhaps warm but certainly unsightly; nevertheless to Carr's eyes she was beautiful in the intensity of her maternal solicitude. The doctor, coming in for a last look at Meg about ten o'clock, had looked graver than ever and said he feared she had a small patch of pneumonia. At this dread word Cordelia's heart bounded and stood still. The doctor had promised to fetch a trained nurse at once; she was expected every minute; meanwhile there were to be fomentations. Meg's nurse was sitting with her while Cordelia prepared them. Carr carried up the kettle and the bowl and helped his wife to wring out the hot cloths, his heart sick with fear for that little bundle of his flesh and blood which a dread disease had so unfairly, as it seemed, laid low. He recalled her as she bounded along the hall every afternoon to meet him as he came home from the mill, washed and brushed and clad in a clean pinafore for the occasion, her brown eyes shining, bearing proudly in her hand his slippers. She was learning how to unlace Carr's boots, and the two spent a long time together in the hall each afternoon struggling over this complicated process, which somehow involved a good deal of hugging and laughing and tumbling about. And woe betide Hammond or Eugene if they rashly paused, as they passed by, to give advice on knots or eyelet holes; for Meg was vehement and proud, like her mother; she resented any interference with her prerogative, and had once thrown a boot at her elder brother—an incident which shocked the Hough Hall household, founded as it was on love and self-restraint, from attic to cellar. Now Meg lay flushed and inert on the little bed beside her parents'. Carr hung over her, and, longing to do something, gently felt the lobes of her little ears—this gesture was a joke between him and his children, and now in this hour of pain he did it without thinking. Meg opened her eyes and looked at him seriously, but did not smile. Cordelia, however, had other work for her husband to do; a bed must be put up and equipped for the coming nurse. Carr brought down the frame from the spacious Hough Hall attics, attached the wire mattress, wound it up, and helped his wife to air the necessary linen. It was now time for another fomentation; Cordelia took the child's temperature again, and found it higher than before. Just then the nurse arrived, and an indescribable feeling of relief permeated the Carrs' hearts. Now everything would be all right! Now she would soon be well! The nurse, after the manner of nurses, seemed to regard the case as so commonplace and ordinary that they became quite ashamed of their former fears. The nurse, however, decided to sit up with the child herself, and settled herself in Carr's room. Carr replenished the coal-scuttle, got up a screen, helped Cordelia to prepare the nurse's night meal, and finally, on her advice, went into the boys' room and shared Hammond's bed for a wretched hour, leaving the spare room to Cordelia. As he was throwing off his clothes he heard the sound of carriage wheels; mechanically raising one of the laths of the Venetian blind he saw the Carr Fold carriage passing down the hill.

In spite of his anxiety it probably contained someone who was more to be pitied than he was, for it is at this date, alas! that Fräulein Kirchner's letter, with its shrewd comment on the feelings and designs of Lomas, was found in Catherine's diary. The arguments used by Catherine on that fatal night were probably those used by so many other women in similar circumstances, often with the happiest results. She was thirty-one, she was frightfully lonely; her mother seemed to her morbid fancy to show every sign of marrying Mr. Barker; she longed passionately for some duty, some settled aim, in life, and no less passionately for children of her own. The only man she could ever have loved was happily married. She was debarred by her own wealth from embarking on any profession, and in any case Catherine knew too much about music to be under any illusion about her own talent. Add to all this the essential purity of Catherine's imagination, and her utter incapacity to imagine the evil of which Lomas was capable, and it will be seen how heavily the scales were weighted in his favour. Here was a man who had loved her steadily—as she thought—for nearly ten years; Cordelia's brother; a man with an undoubted feeling for both music and art; a man of a so-called "lower" social standing and comparatively poor—both these facts appealed immensely to Catherine's generous nature, for she felt that she had at least something to offer him, and welcomed the opportunity of showing how little she cared for conventional social ideas. That Carr and Cordelia and most of all her own father disapproved of Lomas, Catherine knew; but when all their disapproval was sifted, what fact against him really emerged? Mr. Ainsley had warned her that Lomas must not be allowed to enter the firm of Carr Carr and Ainsley, but then in those days Lomas was not one of the best designers in the West Riding. In any case Catherine was not proposing to bring him into Carr Carr and Ainsley; he would continue, of course, his own work with Messrs. Gill and Barker. Catherine was enough of a woman, too, to feel perhaps a slight tinge of reforming zeal about Lomas—there were many small points as to his manners and dress on which she could help him. To be able to help somebody, to be of some use in something —what a happy change that would be in Catherine's dreary world! We can imagine her at this point turning to Minna's letter, reading again that sentence: "I suspect that you have more sympathy with his fate than can be reconciled with your peace of mind," and trying to persuade herself that she had really cared for Lomas all the time.

How would she feel, she perhaps asked herself searchingly, if Lomas married another woman—Miss Barker, for instance? She admitted that if he did, life would be drearier than ever. At present she had at least the prestige of owning a devoted though rejected lover; but how would she feel if she had to occupy the position of Emily Gill? Emily had rejected George Newton in the absolute certainty that she didn't want him, and now look at her! A "u.b." as the slang of the day vulgarly denominated her: an unappreciated blessing! And as much in love with George Newton as anyone could wish! Catherine visualised with terror a day when Lomas should be married to Lottie Barker, and she, Catherine, would bitterly regret having lost him! Suppose instead she took her courage in both hands—an action peculiarly attractive to Catherine—and married him? She visualised their life together. They could travel—Mrs. Ainsley was too lazy to travel. She would be independent, her own mistress, not the plaything of her mother's whim; she would have a household of her own to manage; duties in life; a husband who loved her; children. The result of all these cogitations was, unfortunately, the following entries in Catherine's diary. "*February 6th, 1891.*—7.30 a.m. I wish to record here that I have made up my mind to take a decisive step, to enter on a new life, and marry L. E. if he really wishes it. I shall write and ask him to come to see me this afternoon. 11.30 a.m. I have sent Dennis with the note to L. E. God grant it may be for the best!"

(The "Dennis" referred to was the new Carr Fold coachman.)

The hand in which these fatal entries are written is agitated, and no wonder: for Catherine here made not only the greatest mistake of her life, but perhaps the second greatest as well. It was a ghastly blunder on her part to decide to marry Lomas Eastwood, and to give herself no time to change her mind on the point; but to put it into Lomas's power to say that she threw herself into his arms, that she left him no alternative but to marry her, that, in short, she ought to be obliged to him for marrying her, was her crowning folly, and one she probably had cause to regret every day of her married life. Looking back at the event across the years, one cannot see why she should not have waited till May 20th brought round Lomas's customary proposal; but doubtless such a course would have seemed to Catherine a piece of ungenerous chicane, of calculating intrigue. At any rate her note was sent, and Lomas duly arrived at Carr Fold at three o'clock that afternoon. We have two accounts of the extraordinary interview which followed. The first is Catherine's, which on one point shows a reticence perhaps natural, but hitherto foreign to her diary.

"I felt frightfully nervous," she writes, "when I was told L. E. had arrived, and was almost sick with fright as I entered the drawing-room and saw him standing there. He too looked pale and ill at ease, and his eyes somehow looked larger and brighter than ever. However, I commanded myself and asked him to sit down, and then plunged into the thing at once. I said: 'Mr. Eastwood, you have several times done me the honour of asking me to marry you.' He seemed unable to speak, but gulped and nodded. At this point my courage nearly failed me, but I went firmly on: 'If you still have that wish——' Here I stuck altogether. L. E. however, bent towards me and said eagerly: 'Am I to infer that you have changed your mind, Miss Ainsley?' I replied in a silly weak voice: 'Yes.' At this he seemed really beside himself with joy, really in raptures; he turned quite pale and stuttered incoherently and smiled 'all over his face' at first; then he clutched my hand and said I had made him the happiest of men and all that kind of thing. He also said we might have to encounter opposition from my family on account of his inferior social position, to which I replied that I was not bound to take anyone's advice, and should do as I chose. I then went and told Mamma. To my surprise she took it very comfortably, and said she wondered I had not done it long ago. She came in and spoke very kindly to Lomas. I was rather surprised to find how soon we all dropped into our new rôles; L. in particular might have been engaged to me for years, judging from the ease with which he spoke my name and the familiarity which he showed with all my affairs. He begged that the wedding might be on May 20th. Mamma was superstitiously horrified at the thought of a wedding in May, but all that is nonsense, and I rather like L.'s desire to have it on that day. Then, too, as he says, we have reached years of discretion and have nothing to wait for. So we provisionally decided on that date. I am wearing L.'s signet ring until he can bring me another."

The other account is merely a verbal one, and consists of Sir Charles Gill's reminiscences nearly forty years after the event, but it is extremely interesting, as all the accounts of Lomas are from this shrewd and impartial observer. Mr. Gill, as he was then, overtook Lomas as he was entering the mill at Denbridge after his momentous interview with Catherine. He was naturally extremely late, and Mr. Gill, who never minced matters of this kind, demanded with considerable brusqueness what he thought he was about, returning at that hour for the afternoon's work.

"It isn't your birthday to-day, you know," he said

sarcastically, in allusion, of course, to Lomas's yearly visit to Carr Fold.

"That's where you're wrong, my boy!" returned Lomas with a smile of triumph.

"What!" exclaimed Mr. Gill. Jumping at once to the obvious conclusion, he cried: "You don't mean she's accepted you?" Lomas nodded. "Well, the more fool she!" was Gill's comment.

"She sent for me herself and told me she would have me," enlarged Lomas, colouring.

"I don't believe it," said his employer flatly.

"You might as well," said Lomas with a sneer. "It's true. She's wearing my ring, and I've kissed her."

At this Mr. Gill, who saw in the affair simply the probable transference of an excellent designer from his own firm to that of Carr Carr and Ainsley, swore to relieve his vexation. The two men passed into the mill yard together.

"You don't seem particularly elated by your luck, I notice," observed Mr. Gill shrewdly.

"I do, I do!" said Lomas in a peevish tone.

"Well, by God! you ought to be," said Mr. Gill. "It's an astounding piece of luck, Eastwood. She's worth a pretty penny—and," he added, finding suddenly that he disliked Lomas's tone about his betrothed, "there isn't a better woman in the West Riding."

At the mention of Catherine's fortune triumph again lighted Lomas's eyes, but by the end of Gill's speech he was sneering. Sir Charles has a strong impression that he muttered "Woman!"—in reference, probably, to Catherine's age.

"By the way," continued Gill, "how's your father to-day? I hear he was badly yesterday."

Lomas shrugged his shoulders and made an indefinite reply; it was obvious that he knew nothing of his father's illness.

"And what will Phil Carr say to your engagement?" pursued Mr. Gill.

Lomas made an expressive *moue*. "He didn't marry her himself, so he oughtn't to grumble if somebody else does," he suggested cynically.

"He made the biggest mistake of his life when he didn't," said Mr. Gill with emphasis, "And I reckon Catherine Ainsley's made the biggest of *her* life this afternoon."

"Thank you for nothing," said Lomas impertinently.

"And when are you going to give me notice?" demanded his employer roughly. "You'll be lording it down at Carr Foot in another month or two, I suppose."

At this Lomas half closed his eyes and smiled, well pleased, but was discreetly silent.

The impression left on Mr. Gill's mind by this interview and by Lomas's behaviour during the next few weeks was that Lomas, like many another man who has struggled for years to achieve some ambition, found that when it was within his grasp, after the first moment of elation his success gave him little pleasure. He had anticipated it so long in imagination that the reality fell short of his dreams. Then, too, Catherine had fatally cheapened herself to him. Lomas had no intention, of course, of losing his prize now that he had won it; he took prompt measures to circulate the news of his engagement in every quarter of Hudley except Hough Hall and Majorca Road, and was extremely polite and devoted to Catherine; but when he was away from her he became flat, bored and peevish, and only tasted his triumph and enjoyed his prize when some hint of opposition came to heighten its value.

Unfortunately for Catherine there was little effective opposition available. When she called the next morning at Hough Hall to tell her news to Cordelia she was horrified to find the house in all the sad disarray caused by dangerous illness. The two boys had been got off to school, and were to stay dinner there and not return till evening; Cordelia, haggard and with grey threads in her bright hair, came from the sick-room to beg Catherine to fetch them home that afternoon and take them to Carr Fold with her for the week-end. Catherine of course agreed; Cordelia bade the Hough Hall nurse pack up some night things for them; and while Catherine waited for these, and debated whether she could speak of herself and Lomas in such an atmosphere of trouble, a boy from Taylor Eastwood's printing works arrived with a message from Annie—Taylor was very ill, sinking, in fact, if the doctor were to be believed; a nurse had been got in; the heart was not responding to stimulants and he was not expected to live through the day; if Cordelia wanted to see her father alive she must go at once. Cordelia, when this message was whispered to her in the sick-room by Catherine, wrung her hands and did not know what to do. The night nurse was in bed, asleep; the doctor had called once and said something about getting in a day nurse as well, but had arranged nothing definite; Meg could not be left an instant. Catherine offered to say with the child, but Cordelia disregarded this as out of the question. She decided, with tightened lips, that she must, of course, stay by her child; Catherine thereupon offered to drive to Majorca Road and take loving messages. This Cordelia accepted, and soon Catherine found herself in another house weighed down by illness. Taylor was in an uneasy doze, and did not wake while Catherine was there, but for Cordelia's satisfaction—and also perhaps with a feeling that as his future daughter-in-law she had a right to do so—she crept into his room and saw him. To her inexperienced eyes he looked very ill indeed—so much worse than Meg, indeed, that Catherine was reassured about the child. The nurse, however, with whom she had a few words, did not seem to think so badly of Taylor, and when reminded of the doctor's pronouncement merely pulled the corners of her mouth down doubtfully. In point of fact the nurse was right; Taylor Eastwood not only survived that night, but a great many other nights; and although he remained harassingly, dangerously, almost desperately ill for the next fortnight, had a long and trying convalescence, and was never the same man again, he was not destined to follow his idol into death so closely. He recovered, but poor little Mary Elizabeth, in spite of her youth, her two nurses, and Cordelia's watchful and unremitting care, died on February 9th at half-past three in the morning—just on the fatal fifth day from the onset of pneumonia. Cordelia, the nurse and the doctor had been with her all through the night; while Carr sat for hours on the landing outside, silent and motionless, straining his ears to catch any hopeful sound from his little girl. Just before the actual moment of the child's passing the nurse opened the door and beckoned him in. Cordelia was on her knees beside the bed, putting brandy between the child's lips with a most beautiful expression of anxious love in every line of her face and form; but Carr saw at once, from the doctor's look, that her care was unavailing.

There is no need to intrude further upon their grief, except to explain that it was this which made it possible for Lomas to be engaged to Catherine for nearly a fortnight before Carr and Cordelia became really aware of it. Meg's funeral took place on February 11th at Carr Foot Church; and it may perhaps be interesting to note that every sign of sympathy which could possibly be made by the workpeople of Carr Foot Mills was made by them on this occasion. They sent flowers, they paid the tribute of their attendance—not, of course, because they had known Meg particularly well, though doubtless her bonny face and bright eyes were a familiar sight in Carr Foot; but because they knew Carr particularly well, and liked what they knew. Cordelia was so utterly prostrate with grief that she was not fit even to go and see her father, and Taylor, who was not distinctly better, irritably pestered Annie to know why his daughter did not come. Annie unfortunately allowed the sad tidings to escape her, whereupon Taylor suffered a bad relapse. This was on the 13th of February, and there was another week of intense stress and anxiety for Cordelia before Taylor was pronounced out of danger. Lomas, who was desirous of making a good impression on Catherine, visited Majorca Road pretty regularly at this time, but he did not think fit to inform either his father or his sister of his engagement just yet. The news eventually reached the Carrs through Eugene, who inquired thoughtfully at breakfast one day shortly after the boys' return from Carr Fold:

"Will Auntie Catherine be *really* my aunt when she's married to Uncle Lomas?"

"What do you mean, Eugene?" demanded Carr sharply. "Don't talk nonsense."

His nerves were on edge with sorrow, and Eugene was at that stage of his career just a little too apt to embroider his remarks with facts of his own invention. Eugene's face at once clouded, he pouted and was silent; Hammond, however—always a cheerful and persistent boy—made the matter clear. Carr and Cordelia stared at each other aghast across the breakfast-table.

"If it's true," began Carr.

"It *is* true," said Eugene crossly, vexed at being doubted when Hammond was believed. "Auntie Catherine has a ring, and he kisses her."

"Then we're ruined!" burst forth Cordelia with tragic vehemence.

"Now, Dell!" protested Carr in a rather irritable tone. "How can that be?"

But his wife's nerves were not in a state to stand even the mildest remonstrance; she fled from the table in tears. Carr sighed and did not follow her; but he drove round by Carr Fold that morning to remonstrate with Catherine himself. The interview was not a very successful or very happy one. Mrs. Ainsley was present, and Mrs. Ainsley was all for Lomas; she reminded Phil frequently that Lomas was Cordelia's brother, that Catherine was thirty-one, and that everyone knew of the engagement now and it was too late to say anything—think of the scandal if it were broken off! Finally, she hinted that Phil did not want Catherine to marry because he liked to have things all his own way at Carr Foot. This naturally stung Carr to the quick.

"Do you think that, Catherine?" he demanded hotly, turning on her.

Catherine hastened to reassure him, and went on to say soothingly that she was lonely, and that Phil and Dell were so happy in their married life that she had always envied them. Carr, who was still sick and sore with grief for Meg, and irritated by the little scene at his breakfast-table, was in a state of mind and body when all that kind of remark seemed mere silly and sentimental *bachfischerie,* and he exclaimed impatiently.

"I'm sorry you've changed your mind about marriage, Phil," said Mrs. Ainsley with her little air of malice.

"I haven't done anything of the sort," cried Carr, more exasperated than ever. "But I want Catherine to marry a decent honest man, and Lomas isn't one."

At this Catherine threw up her head, and her cheeks became pink as she defended her lover.

"What would your father have said, Catherine?" interrupted Carr gloomily.

Catherine, conscious that here her case was weak, lost her self-control—her nerves too were perhaps on edge with Lomas's gradual encroachments on her maidenly reserve—and said on a shrill despairing note: "I'm my own mistress, and I mean to marry him!"

"Oh, very well!" cried Carr in the sudden fury of the kindly man. "Have it your own way!"

He went out in a temper and banged the door behind him.

Even less successful was Cordelia's honest attempt to deter Catherine from what she felt would be disaster. Catherine was usually so mild, so yielding, that Cordelia had gradually grown into the habit of taking a high tone with her; and as soon as her tears were subdued that morning she walked by the fields to Carr Fold, and tackled Catherine in her usual fundamentally honest but rather sharp and vehement manner. But Catherine was weary of being dictated to by Phil, by Mrs. Ainsley, by Cordelia, and she resented criticisms of her action the more because at the bottom of her heart she had a doubt of it herself; she received Cordelia with a chilling silence, an almost scornful hauteur, which was of all manners the one most calculated to drive her future sister-in-law into fury. Accordingly, Cordelia left Carr Fold in an even angrier mood than her husband, and routed Phil out of the depths of the mill to tell him with furious emphasis: "If Catherine's *determined* to ruin herself, of course we can't *prevent* her." Cordelia had recommended Catherine to hear her father's views on the subject of Lomas, and this one hope now remained to them. It proved, however, quite futile. Now that the secret was out, Lomas requested Catherine, in the genteel phraseology of which he was master, to inform his father herself of their engagement, and as soon as Taylor was fit to receive visitors, Catherine called upon him with this object. She had always liked and respected Taylor, and found no difficulty—comfort rather—in regarding him as her future father. But she found him greatly and pathetically changed. From a vigorous, hale, independent man of original mind and strong character, Bradlaugh's death and his own ensuing illness had changed Taylor into a frail, pitiful, quiet old septuagenarian, living in the past, ready to die, showing only occasional flashes of his former spirit. When Catherine, laying her hands on his—which were now somehow small and crumpled—told him that she was going to marry Lomas, the old man gave a long quavering sigh and then was silent. Presently, however, he turned his small blue eyes—once so keen, but now dim and wandering—upon her, and said in a vague mournful way: "You'll rue it if you do." To this Catherine replied in her heavy sincere tones: "I hope not, Mr. Eastwood." After another pause the old man observed: "Well, I can't stop you if you do." He smiled vaguely at her and seemed almost pleased to think that he was now out of life's battles, helpless, impotent, not called upon to assume responsibility any more. Catherine found him very pathetic, and called to see him rather often, taking a pleasure in enduring tedium with him. When he was as well as he could ever be, and able to move freely about the house, Cordelia became urgent that he should come and live at Hough Hall; but the old man was obstinate in refusing, and Annie and he continued to live in Majorca Road together. The printing business was sold, and Taylor led a narrow existence upon the interest of its purchase money and his savings. Carr began to make him an allowance, which was paid to Annie, but Taylor found this out, and was roused to such fury that they all feared he would have another seizure, and dared not cross him on this point. Cordelia, however, made presents of money and groceries and other amenities of life secretly to Annie as often as she could evade his eye. Thus Taylor, being the mere shadow of his former self, was powerless against his son, and Carr and Cordelia were silenced by pride and that lack of energy which is often the outcome of a sudden bereavement, while to Annie the engagement was no shock—she had never believed that any woman could really refuse her idol. She therefore offered no protest and made no moan, and the preparations for the marriage of Lomas and Catherine went on apace.

Whitsunday fell on May 17th of this year, so that May 20th was a particularly awkward date for a wedding, but Catherine was determined to be married on that day or none. Lomas agreed with Mrs. Ainsley that in view of the inconvenience of the date this was a piece of sentimental silliness, but he rather liked the aristocratic air of being able to indulge one's whims which it lent Catherine, and he decidedly liked the undoubted fact that several important Hudleians were unable to have the trips they had planned for Whitsuntide that year on account of Catherine Ainsley's wedding. That Catherine the reasonable, Catherine the considerable and unselfish, should insist on a date so inconvenient to so many people, is a pathetic indication of her state of mind at this time, which was feverish, excited and uncertain. Her diary reflects her rapid changes of mood; one day she writes: "L. here discussing our life together—I greatly fear I am not suited to be a married woman"; and the next: "In the evening L. sang—I believe a life of great happiness is opening before me." Curiously enough, the weather corresponded to her varying moods; the week before Whitsuntide was so warm as to be almost sultry, but on Whitsunday itself the spirits of all concerned in the wedding were depressed by heavy falls of snow, "which," says the *Hudley News,* "began early in the morning, and continued with intervals till noon. At low elevations the snow melted as it fell, but the hills round Hudley, especially High Carr and Denbridge Moor, were white with the wintry garb, which did not wholly disappear till the middle of the afternoon, when the warm rays of the sun thawed the unseasonable visitor."

By Wednesday the weather had recovered itself and was behaving in a normal spring manner, but the general effect of the wedding, at least according to Eugene, was that of snow in May. Everything seemed slightly out of joint, and as though taken unawares. The flowers were late, the florists having inexplicably mistaken the day of the ceremony; the wedding cake damaged itself by toppling against a doorway as it was being carried through. Carr and Cordelia were not unnaturally cross all day; Mrs. Ainsley all at once seemed less sure that she approved the match, and clung weeping to her daughter; Taylor, when reminded what day it was by Annie and urged to dress for the occasion, suddenly seemed to awake from a long lethargy, and stammered: "What! What!" with an air of consternation.

"You don't mean she's really going to wed him?" he demanded of Annie, aghast. When Annie sadly told him that it was so, he explained "Poor lass! Poor lass!" in a tone of heartfelt sympathy.

"Don't pity me, father," said the gentle Annie. "I know I'm not good enough for him."

"I'm not pitying you," said Taylor irritably. "It's her I'm pitying."

He worked himself into such a state about it that beads of perspiration stood on his forehead; he wanted to start off at once for Carr Fold; and, pale, haggard, with a rug about his knees, tried to stagger from the house. Annie, who had left him for a minute, found him on the doorstep, waving his arms about and muttering unintelligibly. She mildly remonstrated with him, and tried to draw him in, but he turned on her fiercely.

"It's no use you talking like that to me, Annie Hallas," he said with the pathetic, impotent petulance of the sick and aged. "I mun go. I can't let her wed him. What's Dell been thinking of?"

Annie persuaded him, however, to come in and take a little nourishment before setting out; soon he dropped into one of his uneasy dozes, and did not waken till the hour of the wedding was past—for Annie dismissed the carriage sent to fetch them, not sorry, perhaps, of an excuse to miss the ceremony herself.

All through the day Catherine was pale to ghastliness, and wore a pathetic look of surprise; she dropped her bouquet as she descended from the carriage, and her hand shook so violently on Carr's arm as they went up the aisle together—Carr was giving her away—that he feared she was about to faint. She did not faint, however, but went through the ceremony almost inaudibly, and with drooping head. The general opinion of the guests was that she had been crying all night—whether this was so or not we do not know, for her diary simply says: "*May 19th.*—Very busy all day. At night tore up and burned old letters, including Minna's and Phil's. *May 20th.*—My wedding day." Some guests, however, thought that she bent her head to lessen the difference in height between herself and her bridegroom, Lomas being several inches less tall. Lomas himself did not look particularly elated; his frock coat and silk hat and gloves and flower were all such as even Carr could not cavil at, but his fair face was mottled and peevish, and as he waited for Catherine he seemed cross, nervous and bored. With her arrival, however, he somewhat recovered his spirits, seemed to remember that this was his day of triumph, that he was marrying the rich Miss Ainsley; and put the ring upon Catherine's finger with a grace which Annie would no doubt have thought courtly, but which made Carr sick and excited Eugene to mocking imitation. It may perhaps be well to give in full the account of the wedding printed in the *Hudley News* for May 23rd, 1891.

"On Wednesday, at Hough Lane Wesleyan Chapel, near Hudley, by the Reverend J. G. Shoesmith, assisted by the Reverend T. Mellor, the marriage was solemnised of Mr. Lomas Eastwood, only son of Mr. Taylor Eastwood (the well-known follower of Bradlaugh), and Miss Catherine Ainsley, daughter of the late Mr. William Ainsley of the firm of Carr Carr and Ainsley, Carr Foot, and Mrs. Ainsley, of Carr Fold. The bride, who was given away by her cousin, Mr. Philip J. Carr, was attired in a white corded silk dress, with a Court train, and prettily trimmed with old family lace[1] and orange blossom. She wore an embroidered net veil fastened with a pearl and diamond star, the gift of the bridegroom, and carried a sheaf of lilies. The bridesmaids were Miss Emily Gill, Miss Janet Gill, Miss C. Barker and Miss M. Shoesmith. Their dresses were white silk, trimmed with yellow velvet, and they carried sheafs of daffodils. Miss Suzanne Whiteley and Master Eugene Carr (nephew of both bride and bridegroom) acted as train-bearers. Miss Whiteley wore a picture dress, and Master Carr a page-boy dress, of yellow velvet. The happy couple were the recipients of many beautiful presents, among which were a marble timepiece, an old oak dower chest, and a silver tea-set all from the workpeople of Messrs. Carr Carr and Ainsley. The newly-married pair left for London *en route* for Italy for their honeymoon."

Thus occurred the third of the series of misfortunes which befell Carr during the twelve months preceding May 21st, 1891.

[1] Originally the property of that Catherine Carr, Catherine Ainsley's great-grandmother, who married Benjamin Ainsley in 1790 and cemented the firm of Carr Carr and Ainsley.

VIII

DISASTER (1891–1897)

For the next three or four years there is little of outward event or incident to tell of the Carr and Eastwood families. Outwardly their life was smooth and prosperous; but the Carrs had from time to time an uneasy feeling, comparable to that of a traveller on an open road who, whenever he glances over his shoulder, perceives a black and threatening storm cloud rising slowly but surely on the horizon behind him. This storm centre was, of course, the Catherine–Lomas *ménage*. Invitations to Carr Fold did not come very frequently to the Carrs from Mr. and Mrs. Lomas Eastwood, and Cordelia's invitations to Catherine were now refused to an extent which annoyed that little person considerably, and made her very chary of offering them. The Carrs, therefore, saw comparatively little of the newly-married couple, but whenever they saw them at all, their reluctant conviction that trouble was brewing in that direction gained a great deal of ground.

The reader will perhaps recall that the preface to this work states of Catherine's diary: "The entries become irregular the very week after Catherine's marriage, break off altogether a few months later, and when at length resumed in 1917 are in a totally different style." This invaluable source is therefore about to fail us, and the reader would naturally expect to see here, given in full, the last entries which reveal Catherine's life from within. The most part of these entries, however, are of very little value, except in so far as they reveal Catherine's character, with which we are already sufficiently familiar. The entries from May 21st to May 28th consist simply of earnest, detailed, rather over-excited descriptions of the journey from Hudley to Milan and Venice. The references to Lomas, by his initial, are frequent, and, alas! affectionate; he is represented as uttering words of artistic wisdom in Milan Cathedral and St. Mark's, and as conversing with astonishing fluency with the station *facchini*. This suitable honeymoon frame of mind shows a break, however, on May 29th, when we read: "Incident with the German waiter. Alas! it depressed my spirits all day. In the morning to Santa Maria della Salute, which is horrid inside, full of domes. In the afternoon to the Lido. I have no heart to describe it all." What this incident with the waiter was we shall now never know; but in all probability Lomas revealed in it the furious temper and the unbounded egoism which lay beneath his usual smooth and affable manner. There is no further entry in the diary till June 3rd, when this sentence appears, written in a very agitated hand: "Left Venice for Switzerland this morning at ten—I am glad to go; I shall never forget the sound of the bells as long as I live." Again there is a gap; the next entry is dated July 2nd, *i.e.* the day after the Eastwoods' return to Carr Foot, and there is an exceedingly significant fact to be noticed about it. It is this: that although the June 3rd entry occurs at about three-quarters of the way through one of the leather-bound volumes, the rest of that volume—quite a considerable number of pages—is left blank, and the July 2nd entry begins a fresh volume. This alone would not, perhaps, justify our suspicion of Lomas on this point, but taken in conjunction with three slight facts vouched for by Eugene it is sufficiently damning. The facts referred to are as follows. (1) When on the evening of the newly-wedded couple's return home Carr jokingly teased Catherine about the quantity of space her diary in Italy must occupy, Catherine blushed painfully, to her very ears, and replied with a constrained smile that she did not trouble so much about her diary nowadays. Her painful colour remained for several minutes, and she was obviously embarrassed and uneasy, while Lomas looked furious. (2) When, later in the year, one Sunday afternoon when the Carrs were at Carr Fold, some slight dispute arose about the age and birthday of Suzanne Whiteley and Carr said—as he had been wont to say on similar occasions for the last ten years—"Look it up in your diary, Catherine," Catherine again blushed painfully, and tried to turn the subject instead of running eagerly to fetch the appropriate volume as she had been wont to do. (3) A day or two later Catherine called at the Hudley Grammar School with the carriage, to take the two boys home in the afternoon, as she often did if she happened to be in town, and as she put them down at the Hough Hall gates she said to Eugene: "Tell your father that Suzanne Whiteley was born on February 12th, 1884." She coloured as she spoke and seemed to breathe quickly, and the conviction flashed upon Eugene's young mind that Catherine had at some time found Lomas reading her diary, and that she now kept it somewhere out of Carr Fold, for safety.

If all the various items we have enumerated in the last paragraph be taken together, they will be seen to form a body of strong circumstantial evidence in support of

Eugene's theory; later events will confirm it; and there cannot be any reasonable doubt that such was in fact the case. At some time during their stay in Venice, while bells were sounding, Catherine almost certainly entered her room to find her husband reading her diary; and from the day of her return to Carr Fold to that of her death she undoubtedly kept all the volumes referring to the period previous to her marriage, with the leather case given her by Carr, in a safe deposit at the bank of which she was for the time being a client.

This is a sickening commentary on her married life, and although there is no incident recorded in her few remaining erratic entries which reveals the utter wretchedness of her life with Lomas even at this early date, external evidence to this is unfortunately not wanting. Sir Charles Gill, when questioned by the present writer as to the attitude of Lomas on his return from his honeymoon, shrugged his shoulders and replied emphatically: "He was tired of her before they reached Milan." Mr. Nicholas Whiteley confirms this in the informative letter referred to on p. 23. "Mr. Lomas Eastwood was," he says, "during the remainder of the year 1891 irritable, peevish, yet languid; to use the modern word, bored. I think he had forestalled the pleasures of marriage with Miss Ainsley so thoroughly in imagination, that the realisation of his hopes was a disillusionment to him. Moreover, there was still a kind of naïveté, a heavy simplicity, about Mrs. Lomas Eastwood at this time which must have irritated her husband, who was anything but simple, greatly, and her constant references to her cousin undoubtedly exasperated him too. The words 'Dear Phil' and 'I must ask Phil' had always been frequently on her lips, and after her marriage she was not immediately able to break herself of this habit.

I have seen her husband wince and colour at some such remark of hers, which undoubtedly showed her reliance on her cousin's judgment in preference to her husband's. As time went on, however, these references became much less frequent, and I have seen Mrs. Eastwood check herself while uttering Carr's name and glance timidly, like a chidden child, towards her husband, who preserved a smooth and ambiguous expression and did not meet her eyes. They were indeed an ill-assorted pair. *He* needed a constant supply of almost fulsome admiration to keep him on good terms with the world, while *she* was utterly incapable of diverging by a hair's-breadth from the truth. One rather interesting fact about them is the change in their physical appearances which rapidly took place. Very soon after his marriage Mr. Eastwood appeared middle-aged; his hair grew thin: his face, formerly so smooth, sagged into pouches and wrinkles: he lost his fresh clear colour: his figure thickened, and his carriage became less upright. His manners, however, were more genteel, more plausible and more condescending than ever. Mrs. Eastwood, on the contrary, improved very much in appearance. As a girl she was rather heavy and uninteresting; but after her marriage she grew very much thinner, her face seemed refined and spiritualised, possibly by mental suffering, and her eyes became a very striking and expressive feature of her personality. A streak of grey which appeared in the hair over her forehead lent her a striking and distinguished air; and her movements, always slow, took on a kind of pathetic dignity. As a girl, too, Mrs. Eastwood had been wont to utter a good deal of heavy, earnest stuff on metaphysical subjects which was rather tedious in general society; but after her marriage she became very silent and reserved, speaking only at rare intervals, and then in short simple sentences and with a low voice. Her monetary arrangements with regard to her husband—which I as her solicitor of course had to supervise—were of the most generous and delicate nature, especially after Mr. Eastwood left the firm of Gill and Barker."

This latter event took place in the October of 1891, and fortunately we have references in Catherine's diary to shed light upon it. On September 8th Catherine's collie Didymus, who was now very old and almost blind, was run over on the main road between Hudley and Carr Foot by the carriage of Mrs. Charlie Gill, who was apparently on her way to call on Cordelia. Catherine's comments on this incident are as follows. On September 8th: "My poor, poor Dido! Of course it was all his own fault, I am sure; but what shall I do without him?" On September 9th: "L. says he has had high words with Charlie Gill about Didymus, amounting to a quarrel. I am glad L. has so much feeling for poor old Dido, but I do earnestly hope the quarrel will be made up. Phil says . . ." (These last two words are almost illegible, being crossed through many times.) On October 8th: "This morning at breakfast L. suddenly told me that to-day is his last day at Messrs. Gill and Barker's—it seems he gave a month's notice after that quarrel with Charlie Gill about poor Didymus. I am greatly distressed to think that dear Didymus was the cause of this disaster." Catherine's distress was probably misplaced on this occasion; for had Lomas not quarrelled with Charlie Gill about Didymus, he would have quarrelled with him about something else. Subjects for quarrels with Mr. Gill were not at this time very difficult to find, for he was now revealing the masterful, domineering, ruthless side of his character, and his unfortunate father-in-law, Mr. Barker, sank daily into further insignificance and impotence in his own will. That

Lomas chose to quarrel with Charles Gill about his wife's dog is simply an instance of Lomas's skill in intrigue and his eye to effect; for Lomas had not the faintest intention of working as an underling in somebody else's mill while there was Catherine's fortune at hand to live on. When Carr heard that Lomas had left Gill and Barker his heart sank like lead, for he felt the next item would inevitably be Lomas's demand for a position in Carr Foot Mills; and when, one October afternoon, he saw Lomas tripping across the mill yards towards him, he felt sure that the demand was about to be made. To his astonishment, however, Lomas made no such demand; instead, he glibly and suavely explained that he did not intend to make it: he had no aptitude for business matters: he was perfectly satisfied with his brother-in-law's management of Carr Foot Mills. (At this Carr jerked his head, not enjoying commendation from this quarter.) Finally, Lomas thought it unwise for relatives to work for one another. All this was so exactly what Carr felt and wished that he was quite disconcerted; in the simplicity of his heart he took Lomas's words at their face value, went home and related the interview to Cordelia in a tone of astonishment, and began to wonder whether he had not made a mistake about Lomas's character after all. Cordelia, however, soon set him right.

"What it all comes to," she announced with her customary vehemence, drawing a needle swiftly in and out of one of Hammond's football stockings the while, "is that he means never to do a stroke of work again."

This diagnosis, like most of Cordelia's, was, as has already been indicated, accurate in every respect. From that time forth Lomas did no work in the ordinary sense of the word; he contented himself with pottering about Catherine's property, in Carr Foot, supervising the Carr Fold garden and household, improving Carr Fold itself by a little judicious building—in the course of which, by the way, the creeper beneath Catherine's window, presented to her in their childhood by Carr, was removed and destroyed—sketching picturesque spots up and down England, listening to good music, and posing as a gentleman of leisure and patron of the arts generally. As Catherine had no children there was nothing to keep the Eastwoods tied to Carr Fold, and in the two or three years following their marriage they travelled considerably. They also entertained a good deal, and frequently offered hospitality to notable musicians and other artists who visited the West Riding. All this sounds so correct and admirable that it is no wonder that Cordelia, as she admits, had occasional fits of envying Catherine, and of wishing that Phil's share in Carr Carr and Ainsley was as big as his cousin's. She was usually awakened from these moods, however, by some slight incident in the Eastwood household which made her uneasily conscious that Catherine's reserve and restraint might be concealing unpleasant things.

One such incident was the removal of Mrs. Ainsley from Carr Fold, which took place in the January of 1892. By Mr. Ainsley's will Carr Fold, of course, belonged to Catherine; but Catherine and her mother had lived there together since his death without that fact ever being brought home to Mrs. Ainsley's mind, except on the solitary occasion of her squabble with Catherine about the Carr Fold gates, referred to on p. 194. Scarcely had the Eastwoods returned from their honeymoon, however, before Lomas began to say to his acquaintances: "Of course we shall keep Mrs. Ainsley always with us," and "Carr Fold is, of course, Mrs. Ainsley's natural home." The natural upshot of these remarks was that five months after Catherine's marriage Mrs. Ainsley, who had been looking far from well again of late, consulted Nicholas Whiteley about buying a house in Hudley for herself. As it chanced, Number 4, Atack Place shortly fell empty; Catherine bought it and gave it to her mother, and after a few improvements and alterations Mrs. Ainsley moved in. "Mamma," says Catherine's diary on January 23rd, 1892, "moved into Atack Place to-day."

And here the diary breaks off altogether; this is the last entry for twenty-five years; from now until 1917 we can only view Catherine from the outside.

It was noticed by that reliable witness Mr. Nicholas Whiteley that as from the time of Catherine's marriage Mrs. Ainsley's health had sunk progressively, so after her removal to Atack Place she seemed suddenly to become an old and ailing woman, timid, retiring, quite out of date. The Carrs saw little of her, Cordelia paying her a duty call perhaps once or twice a month. On these occasions Mrs. Ainsley always asked very tenderly about Hammond and Eugene, especially Hammond; as the months went on she sometimes even seemed to be mixing Hammond up with Phil, and to be wandering mentally amongst the events of a period thirty or forty years ago. We who know her story fully may perhaps wonder what she thought of as she sat by the hearth in Hammond Carr's house—that very hearth in front of which Taylor Eastwood had accused Hammond of theft. Did she recall her sister, her lover, her husband, now all passed away? Did she reflect on the continuous web of human experience? Did she try to puzzle out the connection between her own young love and Catherine's marriage? On this latter subject she was curiously silent; if Cordelia by chance referred to Lomas, Mrs. Ainsley would give a kind of bridling motion of her head, a tremor would cross her withered features, she would pluck nervously at the many rings on her thin claw-like hands, seem about to speak, change her mind, and at last bid Cordelia take home a seed biscuit for Hammond —who, now a bouncing boy of eleven, thought little of these old-fashioned dainties. Mrs. Ainsley's blue lips indicated only too clearly the dangerous state of her heart at this time; and one cold winter morning towards the end of 1892 she was found by her maid lying dead—she had passed away during the night, presumably while asleep.

The bulk of her property passed to Catherine under Mr. Ainsley's will, being all derived from her husband except the house in Atack Place and some few scanty hundreds of her own savings, both of which items she bequeathed to young Hammond. This bequest gave Catherine pleasure, but annoyed Lomas so much that he positively congratulated Hammond on it with a sneer, during tea one Sunday afternoon on one of the rare occasions when the Eastwoods were at Hough Hall. The boy, flushed, hurt, understanding Lomas's tone though not the cause of it, threw out hotly in a Cordelian manner: "*I* don't want Grandma Ainsley's money, I'm sure."

Lomas permitted himself to smile incredulously; whereon Cordelia exploded.

"Lomas!" she exclaimed furiously. "Kindly behave yourself when you're with my children."

Catherine blushed to the roots of her hair, and murmured timidly: "But if Grandma Ainsley *wants* you to have it, Hammond . . ."

"Pray don't pursue the subject further, my dear," observed Lomas in his light mincing tones: "Phil's wife doesn't like it."

It was now the turn of the Carr family to blush and look

uncomfortable; for though it was not possible for four such lively human beings as Phil, Cordelia, Hammond and Eugene to live together without a certain amount of jarring and friction, so that tiffs did rather more often than occasionally take place between each pair of the four, yet such things as sarcasm and the deliberate intention to wound were simply unknown at Hough Hall, and none of the four had a notion how to deal with them. (An amusing anecdote illustrative both of the lengths to which they carried this and of the quality of their family life generally was often told to the present writer by Eugene. It appears that one Sunday at dinner, which on this day of the week the Carrs ate all together at noon, Carr helped himself to a large piece from the glass of celery, and then passed the glass on to Eugene with the words: "That silly little bit down there will do for your mother." The simple and youthful Eugene, not understanding the nature of celery and his father's joke, turned scarlet and gazed at Carr with horrified eyes, retaining the celery glass in one perplexed hand till Hammond, who as his grandfather's favourite was more conversant with the properties of celery, affectionately told him not to be an ass, as the small bits were the best. Eugene thereupon gave an immense sigh of relief and passed on the glass; and the incident ended in general laughter.)

It was when Lomas said such things as these that Carr and Cordelia had that uneasy premonition, referred to at the beginning of the chapter, of the gradual approach of a storm; and had they but known it, Lomas's reference to his own sister as "Phil's wife" was one of the blackest clouds in the approaching storm. For, if the present writer has read Lomas aright—and this reading alone puts the events which follow on a reasonable footing—Lomas was dissatisfied with his marriage. He had got Catherine's position—he lived in her house, he used her carriage, he spent her money; he did no work, he played with art and music to his heart's content—but still he was dissatisfied, for he had not got Catherine. Two impartial witnesses have told us that Lomas was bored by his wife's society, but still his immense vanity—as that shrewd and experienced lawyer Mr. Whiteley suggests—could not endure that his wife should not admire him. Now Lomas's actions made it impossible for Catherine to admire him—she could not admire a man who read her private papers, who drove her elderly mother from the house by constant bickering, who showed himself mean and tyrannical to his servants, insinuating to his friends, cowardly and fawning to those he considered it would pay to flatter; who thought greed no crime and was false in every fibre of his being. Catherine might be defeated by such a man, subdued, practised on, compelled to his uses; but she could never admire him. By contrast with Lomas the generous, simple, open-hearted Carr must have appeared to Catherine a perfect paragon among men; and this, surely, is the reason why Lomas coloured and winced at his wife's references to "dear Phil," why those references shortly ceased by his command, why he spoke of his sister sarcastically as "Phil's wife," and kept Catherine away from the Carrs as much as possible. Then, too, when the two men were together, Carr's inveterate habit of joking doubtless constantly pricked the bubble of Lomas's carefully sustained pomposity, and put him in a ridiculous light before his wife. There is, for instance, an anecdote told by Hammond, of a night when the four Carrs were the Eastwoods' guests in a box at the opera. (None of the Carrs except Eugene really liked opera, and Lomas knew this.) The principal singers were staying at Carr Fold, and Lomas, who loved nothing so much as posing as a patron of the arts, had been so loftily impressive all evening about the greatness of the occasion and his own services to music that the Carrs, and especially Phil and Hammond, were sick of him. The tenor was just warbling out his passion from a somewhat too obviously cylindrical rock when Carr leaned forward and whispered into his son's ear: "Now I know where that Carr Foot barrel went." The allusion was to a barrel of soap which had mysteriously and unaccountably vanished from the mill yard, and caused a good deal of discussion at Carr Foot and Hough Hall, and some anger at the theft on Phil's part. Naturally Hammond giggled, whereupon Lomas, crimsoning with rage, turned to the boy and whispered savagely: "Be quiet!" This anecdote illustrates admirably the defects of both men—Carr's lack of appreciation of the finer arts and his inability to withhold a jest; Lomas's lack of control over his resentment, and also his essential cowardice, in attacking Hammond rather than his father. Which set of defects Catherine disliked most was probably quite well understood by Lomas when his resentment passed and left his head clear. Lomas needed admiration as a daily food; Catherine could not give it him, but set him infinitely below her cousin; Annie Hallas could give it him abundantly; these are the obscure psychological causes of Carr's ruin. The reader is asked to consider for himself how such a man as Lomas, supposing he had this growing feeling of jealousy towards Carr, would regard the situation at Carr Foot Mills, which practically amounted to this: Carr controlled the greater part of Catherine's money and made the greater part of her income, so that practically every morsel eaten by Lomas was paid for through the agency of Carr. Such a situation must have been poison to Lomas, working slowly but surely through his whole system; and had not events occurred which enabled him to alter the situation in one way, he would surely have decided to alter it in another, would have overcome his distaste for work and demanded a share in the management of the Carr and Ainsley mills.

It will be appropriate here to describe a photograph of Annie Hallas which was taken on her fortieth birthday, that is, on February 29th, 1894. The print gives only the head and shoulders, with the bust fading away into the foreground; but enough of Annie's figure is revealed to show us that she was built on a massive and generous scale. The face is in three-quarter profile, and is shaded by a kind of fuzzy fringe, not unlike a Polish gentleman's topknot, the rest of Annie's soft pale hair being drawn back into a small knob at the back of her short broad head. The ear is large but shapely, the jaw heavy and round, the nose short and blunt, the cheeks plump. The full lips are slightly parted in a placid smile which was habitual with her; the light mild eyes have an expression of simple placid good-nature which was also habitual. Round the base of her thick throat Annie wears two rows of rather large pearl beads, which at the time of writing (January 1929) give her a curiously fashionable air; but the present writer is assured by Cordelia that such beads were not at all fashionable in 1894—she remembers Annie wearing them, and says that she always seemed to wear odd and unfashionable clothing, and was fond of decking herself with cheap jewellery, which "really," says Cordelia indignantly, "made her look not quite right in her head." When we take this in conjunction with other of Cordelia's remarks anent Annie's broad hips, her heavy bosom, the fixed pink of her plump cheeks, her very small and regular teeth, her thick fingers and small feet, her dislike of reading and writing, the almost superhuman efforts she had to make as a girl to learn the simple accompaniments of Lomas's songs, and the bovine placidity of her disposition, we have a fairly complete portrait of a woman belonging to a certain well-defined type, physically very fertile, mentally not very bright; and to this type it is almost certain that Annie Hallas belonged—it must be remembered in this connection that she was the youngest of a family of ten.

On June 25th, 1894, a statue of Bradlaugh was unveiled in Abington Square, Northampton. This event was naturally much canvassed beforehand in the newspapers, and Taylor Eastwood had always some journal beside him, when Catherine called, out of which he begged her to read him a paragraph. Catherine's daughterly visits to Taylor were, we may surmise, one of the pleasantest features of her married life; at any rate she visited him very regularly, and listened to his wandering reminiscences of the past with unfailing sympathy and patience. (This was more than he got from Cordelia, who could not believe that her father was really old and ailing, expected him to be as intelligent as ever, and was constantly being disappointed by his lapses.) In the last three years Catherine and Taylor had discussed many deep political and religious questions together, but now their interviews always took the same form. Taylor would answer Catherine's inquiries about his health listlessly, with a preoccupied air, would then sit silent for a few moments, his withered form bent and motionless, his hands clasped across his knees; then his eyes would wander to the paper, and from thence to Catherine's face; presently his desire became too strong for him, and he would begin nervously to fumble about the folds of the paper with a timid and uncertain hand. At this point Catherine, with a quiet smile, usually asked if she should read to him. At this an enormous relief brightened Taylor's face, and he almost thrust the paper upon her, saying with a sigh of happiness as he did so: "Aye! there's a bit in about t' lad." As the date of the unveiling approached he grew sad and moody, and worried Annie by exacting from her continued repetitions of the exact procedure prescribed for the ceremony. At last one day when Catherine was reading to him as usual he gave a deep sigh, and said wistfully: "I'd like grand to have seen it." As Catherine did not immediately reply, he sighed again, and a tear appeared in each of his dim old eyes. Catherine, much moved, put her hand on his and said:

"Would you really like to go and see it, father?"

"I would that!" said the old man, jerking his head emphatically.

"I'm afraid it would kill you, dear," said Catherine, with that plainness of speech which recommended her to Taylor.

"What if it did? I'm dying now," said Taylor irritably. After a pause he added wistfully: "I'm right fain to see it."

Catherine thereupon determined that he should see it. There was her money to ease his journey and Lomas to escort him and give him a son's care.

"I should have to have Annie with me," murmured Taylor, frightened but eager.

Catherine saw no difficulty in that—there was never any difficulty about Annie. She consulted the doctor, who shrugged his shoulders and said that Taylor had not more than a year or two to live anyway, and the effects of such a journey were in any case doubtful—let the old man go, if he had set his heart on it. Catherine made inquiries about trains, and wrote to a Northampton hotel to secure a room. She then broached the subject to Lomas, who astonished her—for Catherine's knowledge of her husband was not yet complete, owing to her inability to believe so much evil even of him—by saying that the whole thing was ridiculous. *He* was certainly not going to trail off to Northampton on a fool's errand of that sort. "I should look well," he concluded scornfully, "if he died on my hands, in the train." He repeated this filial sentiment as the Carrs and Eastwoods were discussing Taylor outside Carr Foot church after morning service on the third Sunday in June—for it may be noted that Lomas, since his establishment at Carr Fold, had become an Anglican, and rather than argue on the subject Catherine accompanied her husband to church. Hammond and Eugene, who were kicking their heels in the dust beside their elders, awaiting their good pleasure to move on, of course heard him; and Hammond exclaimed energetically: "I'll take Grandpa to see the statue, mother!"

"Don't be silly, Hammond," said Cordelia. She was partly annoyed that this suggestion for Taylor's pleasure had come from Catherine instead of herself, partly angry at Lomas's heartlessness, partly upset by the pathos of her father's state, and so she spoke sharply. Catherine, however, who was always singularly blind to small indications of this sort, did not see her sister-in-law's irritation, and suggested in the mild reserved tone she so often used nowadays: "Perhaps you and Phil would take him, Cordelia?" At this Lomas—according to Eugene, from whose recollections this incident has been taken—started as though he had been stung, exclaimed in a harsh grating tone: "I'll take him!" and turned on his heel towards Carr Fold.

The matter was, therefore, thus arranged; and Taylor,

Annie and Lomas left Hudley on the morning of Sunday, June 24th. Immediately they reached Northampton Taylor went to bed so as to be fresh for the ceremony next day. On the Monday they witnessed the unveiling of the statue, remained in Northampton for the night, and returned next day to Hudley. Taylor took to his bed the day after his return, and never again rose from it; he lingered for some time, but died on the 30th of September. Cordelia, who was recalled by his last illness to thoughts of her early life and her great fondness for her father, blamed Catherine for his death; but it may be questioned whether it was not the old man's sense that all his life's work was now finished and done with, that he had no longer anything left to do in the world, which caused his rapid decline, rather than the physical exertion of his journey. There was again dissension among the Carrs and Eastwoods as to the manner of his burial. Catherine wished the staunch old freethinker to be buried, as was undoubtedly his wish, in unconsecrated ground; Lomas opposed this as scandalous and disreputable; while Carr and Cordelia hovered between the two opinions. Cordelia thought that it would be a disgrace to Hammond and Eugene to have a grandfather buried in an outlandish heathen manner. Carr agreed, but could not bring himself to play a low-down trick on a dead man, and to bury Taylor in consecrated ground appeared to him in that light. When Cordelia argued the point with him he gave a troubled smile, shook his head, and observed on a note of perplexity: "I don't think I can agree to it, Dell." His wife gave a sigh of exasperation, but at the bottom of her heart she knew he was right; and eventually Taylor's remains were accommodated in an appropriate section of the town cemetery. Taylor's favourite, Hammond, was not able to be present at the rather odd secularist funeral; for a few days before his grandfather's death he had begun his first term at Rugby.

Annie continued to live in Majorca Road, maintaining herself comfortably on Taylor's investments, which by a will of recent date he had bequeathed to her, together with her own little share of what Taylor had saved from the Hammond Carr *débâcle* thirty-six years ago. She lived quite alone, declining to have anyone in the house with her, though the claims of several nieces were put forward by her numerous brothers and sisters. Cordelia at first visited her regularly at least once a week, but she so often found her out, obtaining no answer when she rang, that she gradually lost the habit of going to Majorca Road, which in any case was inconveniently far from Hough Hall. Catherine's visits to Majorca Road ceased with Taylor's death. She was not drawn to Annie—indeed the elder woman's placid animal nature repelled her—and it is probable that Lomas found her excellent reasons for leaving Annie alone. For of course all students of Carr's life are familiar with the catastrophe which is now approaching. Towards the end of November Annie suddenly vanished away to Blackpool. Cordelia, astonished to receive a card from there, called on one of Annie's brothers, a certain James Hallas, who was a respectable greengrocer in Prince's Road, to inquire why Annie had thus quietly, almost secretly, gone away. She was met by dubious hesitations from James Hallas, and cryptic remarks in a rather rude tone from his wife. She felt vaguely uneasy, but when Mrs. Hallas concluded roughly: "If *you* don't know why she's gone I'm sure *we* don't," Cordelia flounced out of the house in a fury, convinced that the Hallases were accusing the Eastwoods—and perhaps also Carr—of not making sufficient monetary provision for Annie. When she reported this conversation angrily to Carr, he at once characteristically began to think that probably the Hallases were right, and without saying anything to Cordelia, sent off a cheque for twenty pounds to Blackpool by way of Christmas present. Curiously enough, as he thought, this cheque was neither presented nor acknowledged. When, towards the end of January, he mentioned this to Cordelia, and learned that her gifts of gloves and cake had been acknowledged, they both agreed that Annie was perhaps too stupid to understand the mechanism of banking in another town, and Cordelia wrote off one of her most business-like letters, much underlined, describing exactly the process of signing and cashing. No answer was received to this letter either; and Cordelia, feeling cross at such neglect, impatiently washed her hands of both Annie and the cheque, while Carr forgot all about them. He was destined, however, to receive a reminder of Annie which he would not forget as long as he lived.

Those of my readers who were living in Yorkshire at this period may remember that in the week preceding Christmas Day, 1894, a terrific gale swept the county; chimneys were capsized, hoardings collapsed, the roofs of a row of cottages in Carr Bank were swept off under Eugene's startled eyes[1] like a piece of paper, and several windows at Carr Fold were blown in. This was followed by a tremendous and lengthy frost;[2] pipes froze everywhere, even, in spite of Carr's precautions, at Hough Hall, where water had to be drawn up from the main by one of the mill hoses. Carr flooded a field below Carr Foot

[1] He was standing at the nursery window in Hough Hall at the time. James Illingworth lived in one of these cottages as Catherine's tenant.

[2] Since this passage was first written the cold spell in February, 1929, has recalled this 1895 frost very vividly to England's mind.

Mills, and everyone within a range of ten miles disported themselves on the fine smooth ice. During this period Lomas and Catherine were away on the Riviera. They had intended to remain there till the spring, but Catherine was anxious and uneasy about the damaged Carr Foot cottages and the Carr Fold windows; she wrote to Carr and Nicholas Whiteley many letters, imploring them to attend to the welfare of the inhabitants of the roofless rows; and we may surmise that her feeling for the Carr Foot people and the Carr Foot fabric was so strong that its cumulative pressure overcame Lomas's resistance; at any rate the Eastwoods returned to England in the middle of February.

On the afternoon of Thursday, February 28th, 1895, therefore, Carr was down in the engine-room inspecting one of the gas engines, which had been giving a great deal of trouble and only that morning had injured a man, when a message was brought to him that Mrs. Eastwood was in the office and would like to speak to him. Every detail of that memorable afternoon was so indelibly impressed on Carr's mind by after events, and was so thoroughly canvassed by all the Carrs through many years in their attempts to explain Catherine's later action, that it is possible to give a very detailed account of it. On receiving Catherine's message Carr gave an exasperated sigh; he hated nothing so much as being dragged up out of the depths of the mill to speak to people, who as often as not had come on silly errands or wanted to sell him a new kind of incandescent gas mantle. To do Catherine justice, however, she rarely troubled him at the mill, and as he passed along through the pressing-room, went up the stairs and through the scouring-room and the mending-room, crossed the yard past the boiler, and ran up the steps towards the office, he vaguely wondered, at the same time as he pondered the problem of the gas engine, what she had come for, and hoped it had nothing to do with Lomas. The private office of Messrs. Carr Carr and Ainsley was a very fine and high room, with two large windows giving upon the main road from Hudley into Lancashire. It was extremely well furnished according to the ideas of those days, with a fine Turkey carpet, a solid mahogany desk—at which Carr rarely sat—and table, and several heavy mahogany chairs with red upholstery, including a swing-chair behind the desk. There was a large black fireplace with bands of steel and ormolu, wherein a big bright fire was kept burning almost all the year round; a heavy dark green marble clock with columns picked out in gilt stood impressively on the black marble mantelpiece. Above the mantelpiece hung a portrait in oils of old Benjamin Ainsley, and an enlargement of that photograph of William Ainsley referred to on p. 136 faced it from between the windows. The marble clock struck half-past five as Carr entered the room, closing the door behind him; the bookkeeper had already lighted the gas for Mrs. Eastwood and withdrawn to the outer office. Catherine was sitting in the swing chair behind Carr's desk, and at the mere sight of her Carr's heart sank, for she was obviously in an extremity of trouble. She wore no hat, and her heavy fair hair hung about her face in considerable disorder; she was ghastly pale, and her eyes, darkened by pain like those of some hunted creature, were almost terrifying in their despairing anguish. Her whole appearance was that of a person tormented beyond further endurance; and indeed the limit of Catherine's endurance had been passed. When she saw Carr her brows relaxed, and she exclaimed: "Oh, Phil, Phil!" in a tone of heartrending appeal. Carr, horrified, hastened to her and implored her to tell him what was the matter; she murmured incoherently, but in a tone whose scorn had made itself felt: "My husband . . . that woman." As Carr did not in the least understand what she was talking about, she exclaimed with quivering impatience: "I mean Annie Hallas."

"She's in Blackpool," said Carr blankly, still completely at a loss.

In a burst of grief and anger Catherine made known to him the facts which James Hallas had a few minutes earlier furiously communicated to her: namely, that Annie Hallas had, two days previously, given birth to an illegitimate child at Blackpool, and that her child's father without a shadow of doubt was Lomas. Carr, really stupefied by this news, gave vent to a host of incredulous exclamations, and finished by demanding: "Where *is* Eastwood?"

Catherine replied dryly: "He's away. Mr. Hallas came to look for him."

Even while he had expressed incredulity Carr was conscious that he really believed the story, and he now gave vent to his true opinion by exclaiming with intense conviction: "The blackguard!" He paced about the office. "But it must have been before his father's death!" he cried.

Catherine, her pale lips curving slowly into a bitter smile, told him that it had probably occurred at Northampton.

"Good God!" said Carr. He paced about the room again, and reflected, in one of those curious tangents to the subject in hand so often taken by the human brain, how absurdly his life seemed to be interwoven with Charles Bradlaugh's. There was his marriage, there was little Mary Elizabeth's birth and death, and Catherine's engagement, and now this. (In this, however, Carr was wrong; it was Taylor's life which he had mingled with his own by marrying Cordelia.) He recalled himself to Catherine and her troubles remorsefully. "What a blackguard!" he repeated with all the conviction of his own faithful and loving heart. "That he should have brought you to this!"

"That isn't the worst," said Catherine unexpectedly, looking up at him.

"Not the worst!" cried Carr aghast, pausing by the desk. "What is the worst, then?"

Catherine's lips quivered, her large eyes filled with tears; throwing out her hands in a gesture of despair she said simply:

"Everything!"

Carr, looking down at her in questioning alarm, realised with a shock of horror that she meant that her marriage was a bitter and terrible failure, that every moment of her life with Lomas was misery to her. "Catherine!" he exclaimed haltingly, choked by pity. "Poor girl! Poor girl!" He put an arm about her neck, just as he had done when as a child she grieved over the decapitated geranium, and with his other hand stroked her shoulder in a boyish attempt to soothe her. "Poor girl!" he said again.

He spoke with all the warmth of his generous and loving heart, and Catherine broke down completely. All her suppressed grief for her loss of Phil, all her sorrow for her father, all her long martyrdom of neglect at the hands of her contemporaries, all her loneliness, all the hourly misery of her union with a man morally so terribly her inferior, suddenly rose to the surface of her mind in a dark and bitter flood, and she sobbed wildly in Carr's arms. "Oh, Phil!" she said, turning her tear-stained face up to him piteously: "Oh, Phil!" Carr seated himself upon the arm of her chair, and drawing her head down on his breast, attempted to soothe her by gentle caresses and loving words of sympathy. But now that the barriers of Catherine's reserve were down it was long before she could control herself. The five-thirty buzzer sounded, the throb of machinery died, the workpeople streamed out—at this Carr rose hastily and drew down the blinds, then resumed his position by his unhappy cousin—gates were drawn shut and locks turned, the mill became empty and silent; but still Catherine wept on convulsively. Indeed she had much to weep for. Carr, however, who was becoming stiff and cramped in his uncomfortable position, began to feel that in this as in so many other things Catherine was rather excessive. Presently he thought he heard footsteps in the outer office, and cried sharply: "Who's that?" A voice replied timidly, "It's me, sir"; the door was gently opened, and James Illingworth appeared with a deprecating air on the threshold. Carr remembered that of course James and the horse and trap must have been waiting for him at the mill door for a considerable time. "All right—I'm coming," he threw out shortly, standing up. Catherine—who, it will be remembered, could not bear the sight of James Illingworth because of his connection with her father's death—turned abruptly away from him, and the swing chair probably gave her action more effect than she intended. Young Illingworth retired, and Carr cast an eye towards his hat and overcoat, which were hanging on the massive mahogany hatstand by the door.

"Oh, Phil!" began Catherine again piteously, turning up her blotched and reddened face. "I can't go on living with him. I really can't." As Carr said nothing, merely looking down at her in silent pity, she went on desperately: "He never cared for me—he told me once in poor Mamma's presence he only married me for my money."

"Catherine!" exclaimed Carr in incredulous horror.

"If he'd take the money and leave me alone I should be

glad," went on Catherine recklessly. "Yes, I should be glad. But what about Carr Carr and Ainsley then?"

"That's all nonsense," said Carr soothingly. "He's put himself in the wrong now, and you can get a divorce."

"He'll never let himself be divorced!" exclaimed Catherine with conviction. "Unless," she added more hopefully, "I could bribe him to it."

"He won't be able to help it," said Carr grimly. "Come, we must go now, Catherine."

"I can't go to Carr Fold!" cried Catherine on a sharp note of anguish. "He's expected back to-night—he's due now; he's supposed to be coming from London."

"Of course you can't go to Carr Fold," said Carr rather crossly, buttoning his coat. "You must come back to Hough Hall with me."

"But what will Cordelia say?" demanded Catherine in a broken tone, obediently rising.

"She'll say what every true woman would say," said Carr staunchly. "She'll make you welcome." (At heart, knowing Cordelia's slight tinge of jealousy of Catherine, he was just a little doubtful.) He helped Catherine across the room and down the steps, locked the mill door, put her into the trap, and drove her off with him to Hough Hall.

He went in by the back way to save time. Eugene met them half-way up the drive, and exclaiming: "You *are* late, Papa!" added, as he walked along by the side of the trap: "Mother's crying because she thought there'd been another accident with the gas engine, and you were hurt." This sounded ominous; Carr remembered that Cordelia did not like strangers to be brought into the house by the back way through the kitchen, and began to wish he had driven up to the front door. It was too late for that now, however; he drew up in the back yard, and bidding Eugene run in and tell his mother that Auntie Catherine had come, he helped the wretched Catherine down and almost carried her into the house. He was met at the door of the breakfast-room—a rather dark but cosy apartment under the shadow of the hill, with a window let in by the fireplace whose broad sill, four feet from the floor, formed a seat much beloved of Eugene—by Cordelia in a state of considerable agitation.

"Where *have* you been, Phil?" she demanded vehemently, her voice sharpened by her anxiety. "I thought you were killed! Why *can't* you send a message when you're going to be late?"

At this point she flung her arms round his neck and kissed him. Carr, who was well used to her vehemence but always a little harassed by it, responded warmly to the kiss but said nothing, supporting Catherine on his other arm. Cordelia was surprised to see Catherine, and said so.

"Didn't Eugene tell you?" said Carr, surprised in turn.

"Very likely he did," replied Cordelia, tossing her head. "I didn't take any notice."

Amid injured protestations from Eugene that he *had* told her Cordelia led the way into the breakfast-room and gave Catherine a chair by the fire.

"Be off with you, Eugene," said the harassed Carr. "Your mother and I have something important to talk over."

Eugene, with a toss of his head exactly like his mother's, withdrew in dudgeon.

"What is it, Phil?" demanded Cordelia, alarmed by his serious tone and Catherine's ghastly face.

"It's just this," began the unhappy Carr. "James Hallas

has just been to see Catherine. He went to Blackpool yesterday to see Annie, and it appears she's just had a child."

"It's Lomas's!" cried Cordelia instantly, with terrible conviction.

"Hallas says so," admitted Carr.

The blood rushed to Cordelia's face. "The scoundrel!" she exclaimed intensely. "To think that he's my brother! Poor father! I'm glad he's in his grave."

"Catherine feels that she can't go back to him," continued Carr.

"Go back to him!" exclaimed Cordelia in capitals. "Go back to a man like that? I should think not indeed! Nothing would induce *me* to live with a man who treated me like that, I can tell you. Of course Catherine must stay here."

"The law," murmured Catherine weakly.

"Oh, rubbish!" said Cordelia. "With your money you can get round any law."

At this moment the front-door bell rang vigorously.

"It's he!" cried the wretched Catherine, half rising. "I'm sure it's Lomas."

She trembled so violently that she could not stand without support, but clung to the mantelpiece. Cordelia swung round with a swish of silk and flew from the room; vehemently bidding the alarmed housemaid go back to the kitchen and stay there, she advanced to the front door herself and flung it wide. It was, in fact, Lomas who stood there in his top hat and his coat with the astrakhan collar.

"Well?" demanded Cordelia in a tone of fury. "And what do *you* want?"

"Is Catherine here?" demanded Lomas calmly.

"If she *were* here I shouldn't tell you," replied Cordelia.

"She is here—I know she's here," said her brother, his

calm slightly cracking, "I saw her driving up with your Phil."

"Then what did you ask me for?" demanded Cordelia in a rage.

"Perhaps you'll kindly tell her," lisped Lomas, smooth again but with a vicious glint in his eye, "that her husband is here, waiting to take her home."

"I shall do nothing of the sort," replied Cordelia with fierce decision.

"Then I'll come in and tell her myself," pursued Lomas, making as though to enter the house.

"Indeed you won't!" cried Cordelia loudly, barring his way with outstretched arms. "You've lost the right to enter a decent man's house."

"Good heavens!" exclaimed Lomas in a tone of mild disgust. "What is all this? What mad story have you got hold of? Pray control yourself, Cordelia."

"Lomas," said Cordelia earnestly, leaning forward to him: "do you deny that you are the father of Annie Hallas's child?"

"Most certainly I do," replied Lomas in a tone of injured innocence.

"Then you're a liar!" cried Cordelia in a fury; and stepping back she slammed the door in his face.[1]

Catherine, supported by Carr, now stumbled into the hall.

"Dell," she said pathetically, addressing Cordelia by her pet name for the first and last time in her life: "I feel I ought not to stay here, bringing trouble on you. I have made my bed and I must lie on it."

[1] Eugene, who was standing at his bedroom window upstairs, very disconsolate at being turned out of the breakfast-room, saw Lomas walk off down the drive; his face was crimson with rage, and he gnawed his under lip.

At this Cordelia drew herself up to her full height and replied with emphasis: "If you ever return to that vile man, Catherine, I shall despise you!"

After this there was no more to be said. Catherine was put to bed with every comfort that Cordelia's housewifely care could devise, while downstairs Carr and his wife talked over what was to be done for her further welfare. They decided that next morning Carr should seek out James Hallas, and hear his story at first hand; and then call on Nicholas Whiteley, and lay the affair before him.

This was accordingly done. From James Hallas he did not get much satisfaction. It appeared that none of the Hallases had seen Annie for long enough; her evasions of their visits and refusals of their invitations, coupled with some gossip from her Majorca Road neighbours, at last made them suspicious, and James Hallas had determined in November that if he had to "camp out on the doorstep" he would see his sister. Armed with this resolution he went to the house—to find her flown to Blackpool. From there she evaded her relatives' threatened visits as before; at last James Hallas gathered resolution, travelled to Blackpool and sought out her address. She was not there, but he secured her real address, and to his astonishment found that it was a small private house. He found also that his sister had been passing there as a married woman, and that a female child had been born to her on the previous day. He saw Annie, and was turned out by the nurse for raving at her; stayed the night in Blackpool, saw her again, and demanded the name of the child's father.

"Did she admit it was Eastwood?" cried Carr.

But on this essential point James Hallas had been defeated; Annie had simply smiled sleepily—"She seemed quite pleased with herself," said her indignant brother—

and refused to say. It may as well be stated here that Annie maintained this refusal to the last day of her life; she never confided the secret of her child's paternity to a single soul. This secrecy was no doubt a condition of the liberal provision which the child's father made for her; after a while she returned to Majorca Road, and lived there in comfort till her death. Of the child thus born, who was christened Christabel, we shall have occasion to speak later, and the reader will then have more facts placed before him on which to form an opinion as to Lomas's share in her birth.

Armed with this rather unsatisfactory story, Carr proceeded to Nicholas Whiteley, and there gained even less satisfaction than before. "I was obliged to tell him," writes Mr. Whiteley in the letter before referred to, "that Mrs. Eastwood was in a very unsatisfactory position. The law of divorce at that date required a wife to prove against her husband not only adultery, but either cruelty or desertion as well. I did not think it likely that evidence of cruelty such as would satisfy the court could be procured against Mr. Eastwood, whose disposition was subtle and insinuating rather than bullying; while as to desertion, Mrs. Eastwood had placed herself quite in the wrong by leaving her husband. Moreover, I did not consider that Mr. Eastwood would ever for one moment dream of deserting his wife, for to do so would deprive him of the comfortable income and position which he enjoyed as her husband. As regards the alleged adultery itself, that too would be difficult, though perhaps not impossible, to prove. I requested Carr to ascertain from Mrs. Eastwood the name of the hotel in Northampton where the party had stayed on June 24th and 25th of the previous year, and promised to set inquiries on foot. Any such inquiries were, however, nullified by the letters which I received from Mr. and Mrs. Eastwood the following morning."

Before proceeding to these letters we must conclude our account of the events of this day, March 1st. Carr had an early lunch at Hough Hall before going on to Carr Foot Mills, and of course gave Cordelia a detailed account of the morning's interviews. Cordelia expressed the emphatic opinion that *she* could get the truth out of Annie Hallas, she was sure; and unfortunately, when Carr had gone to the mill, she very characteristically made up her mind to do so forthwith. She ascertained that Catherine, who was still lying silent and motionless in bed, had not the desire—nor as she thought the strength—to get up; gave strict instructions to the maids that if Mr. Lomas Eastwood called he was not to be admitted; then took a tram to the station and went off to Blackpool. Accordingly, when Carr returned from the mill in the evening there was nobody at Hough Hall beside the staff and Eugene; Cordelia had not yet returned, and Catherine, as James Illingworth had hesitatingly told Carr on the way up, had left the house. Very much upset and alarmed by Catherine's departure, Carr stormed into the Hough Hall kitchen in a most unusual rage, and demanded details.

It appeared that a man from Carr Fold had come up to Hough Hall about twenty minutes after Cordelia's departure with a note addressed to Mrs. Lomas Eastwood and marked "Urgent." The maid very naturally took it up to Catherine at once; and half an hour later she was horrified to see Catherine descending the stairs, dressed even to her coat, and with the most ghastly expression of distress and despair on her face that the maid had ever seen in her life. She said in a thick tone which the maid would never have known as hers: "I am going back to Carr Fold. Get me one of your mistress's old hats." The girl obeyed, not without some expostulation as to Catherine's going out alone, and suggestions that she should first have a cup of tea or a glass of wine. Catherine, however, disregarded these, put on the hat—which made the haggard pallor of her face even more noticeable—and left the house by the back door, saying that she was going by the path through the fields. All three maids were now convinced that she was not fit to walk alone; after a hasty consultation they called in James Illingworth from the garden and sent him after her. He overtook her before she had left the Hough Hall grounds, and respectfully suggested that she should return to the house—he would run down and fetch up Mr. Carr from the mill in a trice if she wanted anything. Her bitter smile and slow shake of the head convinced him that she did not mean to return to Hough Hall; he thereupon offered to drive her to Carr Fold. She at first refused, but then murmured something about its being "suitable." James did not understand this, but we may surmise that as he had driven her father on the journey which led to his death, he seemed to Catherine a suitable person to drive her on a journey which led to worse than death. At any rate she agreed to let James drive her to Carr Fold. She returned to the back yard, and sat on a low wall while James hastily put in the horse and the maids whispered. James had deposited her, he assured Carr, safely at the Carr Fold front door, and she had entered the house.

Carr, feeling intensely perplexed, and angry with Cordelia, the maids, James Illingworth and Catherine, mounted the trap again, drove down at a furious pace to the village and up to Carr Fold scarcely more slowly, and gave the Carr Fold bell a tremendous pull into which he put all his feelings about Lomas. The butler—Lomas had introduced a butler—thereupon advanced and gave Carr a piece of information which absolutely stupefied him; namely, that Mr. and Mrs. Eastwood had left Carr Fold about an hour and a half ago to catch the evening Hudley train to London; he understood they were going to proceed from thence either to Devonshire or the Continent. The maids were now busy packing Mrs. Eastwood's things, which were to be sent to a London station to wait till called for. Carr, absolutely dazed with astonishment and perplexity, drove back to Hough Hall and spent the evening pacing up and down the house in a terrible state of worry, thoroughly frightening the impressionable Eugene. Between nine and ten Cordelia arrived, very tired and cross, for she had been quite unsuccessful, and gained nothing but a scolding from Annie's doctor. For once in his life Carr was angry with her; Cordelia at first wept, but afterwards rallied, saying that Catherine was a grown woman and could not be prevented from accomplishing her own ruin if she was determined on it. She also hinted that Carr was making a great deal of fuss about Catherine's welfare. This was one of those jealous little digs which Cordelia could never quite resist; the next moment, however, her upright and loving nature returned to a true view of the case, and she expressed the utmost concern for poor Catherine's future.

"Did you see the child?" demanded Carr, pausing in his feverish pacing.

"Of course I did," replied Cordelia. "She's a dear little thing."

"Is she like Lomas? That's the point," said Carr irritably.

Cordelia very sensibly replied that it was too early to say. On the whole she thought so, but time would show. Carr, with an angry exclamation, began to pace the room again, and unfortunately fell to thinking of William Ainsley. What would he think if he could see poor Catherine's situation now? He communicated this point of view to Cordelia, who said she had been thinking of that all along—it was not in Cordelia's nature to forget benefits conferred.

The next morning there was not a letter from Catherine as they had hoped, but about eleven o'clock a messenger came in hot haste with a note from Nicholas Whiteley. The note was vague, but hinted at bad news, and Carr, after calling in at Hough Hall to tell Cordelia where he was going, drove into Hudley to Whiteley's office in New Pritchard Street with an uneasy heart. When he returned Cordelia and Eugene had nearly finished lunch.[1] The moment he opened the dining-room door Cordelia rose and ran to him with a stifled scream; for the blow had fallen, and Carr no longer looked a young man.

Nicholas Whiteley, limping across his office to greet him that morning, had looked grave and anxious.

"I received two letters this morning," he began in a professional tone as soon as they were seated, "which in view of what you told me yesterday surprised me considerably." He turned over some papers on his table, and avoided Carr's eye. "One is from Mrs. Eastwood," he continued, "and the other from her husband."

"Catherine's written to you and not to me?" exclaimed Carr in astonishment.

For reply Nicholas Whiteley pushed Catherine's letter across the table to him. Carr picked it up, and was transfixed by the first sentence.

[1] There was, as it chanced, a treacle tart upon the table; Eugene, till then, had been very fond of treacle tarts, but from that day he could never bear the sight of one.

"Dear Mr. Whiteley," he read,

"I have decided to withdraw from the firm of Carr Carr and Ainsley. My decision is irrevocable, and I desire no argument, expostulation or correspondence of any kind on the matter. Please communicate this decision to Mr. P. J. Carr at once. I understand that six months' notice is necessary, and I shall expect it to run from this date.

"Yours truly,
"Catherine Eastwood.

"P.S.—You are at liberty to show this letter to Mr. P. J. Carr if you consider it desirable.
"March 1st, 1895."

This extraordinary and fatal document, which has, of course, been carefully preserved by Mr. Whiteley and is still in existence, consists of twelve lines written on a sheet of stamped Carr Fold notepaper in a hand which, though extremely, painfully agitated, is recognisably Catherine's. It is necessary to state this in view of the discussion aroused by its contents, which are indeed hardly credible as coming from her hand. When Carr read it he simply could not believe his eyes; he exclaimed incredulously, he gasped out questions to which Nicholas Whiteley had no answer; he turned hot and fingered the letter with shaking, perspiring hands; he saw in a swift panorama his whole life reeling and falling into ruin; he thought of Cordelia and his boys, Hough Hall, the garden, the horses, William Ainsley, the Carr Foot Mills and Catherine as a child; he then remembered Lomas, a deadly spear seemed to strike right through his heart, he felt sick and numb, and shivered so that his teeth chattered. His handsome face drawn and haggard, his brown eyes wild, he stammered out to Nicholas Whiteley: "But it'll ruin the business! Her father's business! She can't mean it! Why should she? Why?"

"Perhaps this letter will explain it," said Mr. Whiteley gravely, offering him two or three sheets in Lomas's niggardly copperplate hand. Carr gave an impatient exclamation and fidgeted with the sheets irritably—he detested reading letters from his brother-in-law; he knew to his cost that they were always frightfully long-winded and abstruse and full of long latinistic words, with lengthy postscripts which somehow gave a hint of mental deficiency. This one was in the usual Lomasian style, full of phrases like "hereby repel the insinuation" and "no desire to in any way whatsoever exacerbate" and "reputation undeniably at stake" and "no compromise should, however, be effected." Half-way down the third page Carr caught the words "Miss Hallas," and read with more attention. After turning back and forth several times he at last caught the gist of Lomas's letter; it was, in fact, an instruction to Nicholas Whiteley, as his solicitor, to contradict the libellous accusation which had been set on foot concerning Lomas's relations with Miss Hallas, to trace that accusation to its source, and prosecute the utterers of the libel "with the utmost rigour of the law." In vague and cloudy language Lomas hinted that his brother-in-law would probably be found among those thus prosecuted, and stigmatised Carr's action in carrying off Catherine to Hough Hall as "an attempt to separate two loving hearts by a most reprehensible falsehood." When Carr had read so far he threw the sheets down on the table with a contemptuous "Well!" His indignation had made the blood course through his veins again, and his eyes flashed fire.

"What do you make of it?" demanded Nicholas Whiteley.

"He's as false as hell!" exploded Carr. "He's bullied Catherine into writing that letter."

"How could he do that?" queried Mr. Whiteley dubiously. "What means could he employ?"

"God knows! Or rather the devil," returned Carr. "But if she persists in it I'm ruined, and so is the business. Her father's business! Carr Carr and Ainsley! You must make that clear to her, Whiteley."

"Of course I shall remonstrate with her in the strongest terms," said the solicitor. "But you see what she says. You'd better prepare for the worst." The two men looked at each other in silence for a few moments, then Whiteley added thoughtfully: "I'm afraid I shan't be able to continue to act for both of you."

"Are you deserting me too?" cried Carr.

"No, no!" said Whiteley warmly. "But if Mrs. Eastwood persists in this foolish and irrational behaviour . . ." He left the sentence unfinished.

"But you mustn't desert *her,"* said Carr. "Good Heavens! If you do, that fellow'll run through all her fortune and leave her without a penny."

"I don't think so," said the solicitor dryly. "He's not the speculating type. But I advise you to have a personal interview with Mrs. Eastwood at once."

Carr explained that the Eastwoods had gone from Hudley, leaving no address behind, whereat Nicholas Whiteley looked graver than ever. He advised Carr to address a letter of remonstrance to Catherine at Carr Fold, to ascertain her address as soon as possible from the servants, then to follow her, insist on a personal interview, and make a personal appeal. Carr, suddenly feeling sick and numb again, left him and went home to take counsel with his wife.

Before proceeding to describe the effects of Catherine's extraordinary action it will be well for us to investigate, as far as we can, its cause. This remained more or less of a mystery to Carr and Cordelia all the rest of their days. They felt certain, that is, that they had Lomas to thank for it in some obscure way, but they could neither of them imagine how he had managed to coerce Catherine into an action so utterly at variance with the whole tenor of her life. Cordelia eventually decided that Catherine really loved Lomas, and that he had managed to convince her that the Annie Hallas scandal was really an invention of Carr's. Carr, on the contrary, who could not forget Catherine's wretched "Everything!" felt that Lomas had bullied his wife until she had no strength to stand out against him, but simply did as she was told for the sake of peace. At this stage of the argument Cordelia usually remarked that in either case Catherine was a weak-minded fool; Carr then defended her, and the discussion sometimes ended on a rather bitter note. It is possible to-day, however, to approach the matter with more information and in a less prejudiced spirit. Every reader must at once have observed how utterly unlike Catherine's ordinary manner of writing is the style of the fatal letter. It is not Catherine's way to use such high-sounding words as "irrevocable" and "expostulation" and "communicate"; nor would she be likely to speak of a term of notice as "running from" a particular date. The whole letter, in fact—its words, its phrases, its postscript, its tone—bears the unmistakable stamp of having been dictated by Lomas. But that undoubted fact does not shed any light on the cause of Catherine's surrender. Had her withdrawal come at the end of a long period of nagging on the subject from her husband, it could perhaps be understood; but Catherine had escaped from Lomas's clutches, and was safe at Hough Hall—she need not, surely, have returned to him and exposed herself to such nagging if she had reason to dread it. Moreover, she had in her hand a strong weapon against her husband, in the form of James Hallas's accusation. These considerations force us to the conclusion that Lomas's letter to Catherine, delivered to her at Hough Hall during Cordelia's absence on the afternoon of March 1st, must have contained some very strong threat, which caused her to return to him and also to submit to his dictation in the matter of Carr Carr and Ainsley. The compulsion exerted by this threat must have been extraordinarily powerful, considering how much Catherine now disliked her husband and how attached she had always been both to her cousin and to Carr Carr and Ainsley. This attachment to Carr is indeed at the bottom of the whole affair. Twenty-one years later, when Eugene and his wife were spending the last night of one of his brief leaves in a London hotel, they encountered Catherine and her husband. Eugene would hardly have recognised them—Lomas was so stout and bald, Catherine so shrunken and weary—but Catherine addressed him by name, and seemed pathetically anxious to talk to him. The four had coffee together; Lomas poured plausible war-stories into Mrs. Eugene's pretty ears, and Catherine and Eugene had a few moments practically alone. After a few rapid inquiries about Carr and Cordelia, Catherine said hastily, laying her jewelled fingers on Eugene's arm: "That business all those years ago about the mill, Eugene. I want you to know that I did it for your father's good."

"It hadn't that appearance," observed Eugene sardonically.

"It was his domestic happiness or the mill," murmured Catherine with intensity. "One had to go. I want you to believe that."

Lomas's eyes were now roving rather viciously in their direction, and Catherine hastily began to ask Eugene banal questions about Carr Foot. Lomas interrupted her to put one of his own.

"Does James Illingworth still live in Carr Bank?" he drawled.

Eugene said he thought so, and was astonished to see the look of sadness and distress which the apparently harmless question had brought into Catherine's eyes. Now that relations between Eugene and his aunt had been resumed, they were both at some pains to maintain them; Eugene wrote to her from France, Catherine in reply sent him books and tobacco. The first time he was wounded Catherine came to see him in hospital; Lomas left them alone for a while, and on this occasion Catherine again referred to her withdrawal from Carr Carr and Ainsley. An account of the promise she then gave, which as she did not carry it out is not material to the present discussion, will be found in its appropriate place in a later chapter.

The explanation of Catherine's action which the present writer wishes to put forward is based on all the known facts, but especially on Lomas's reference to James Illingworth as given above. The explanation is simply this: that on the afternoon of Thursday, February 28th, 1895, Lomas returned to Carr Fold almost immediately James Hallas and Catherine had left it. He heard of Hallas's presence there, guessed his errand, found that Catherine had gone down to Carr Foot Mills, followed her there, and looking into Carr's office from the road—a perfectly natural and easy thing to do—saw his wife sobbing in Carr's arms. A

neither Catherine's one hundred and twenty thousand nor Carr's forty thousand, though it yielded a good annual return, existed in a realisable form. Messrs. Carr Carr and Ainsley was a very large concern, with large overhead expenses, needing a large amount of material to keep it going; and consequently the Carr and Ainsley money was in bricks and mortar, in machinery, in yarn, in cloth about to be sold, in cloth sold but not paid for. The demand to withdraw such a colossal amount of capital from such a business was just like Shylock's demand for a pound of flesh near the heart; the material to satisfy the demand was indubitably there and in good condition, but in order to be able to hand it over the organism had to undergo changes which meant destruction. The summer of 1895 was therefore the most harassing, tormenting, wretchedly anxious and altogether miserable period of Carr's life, and by the end of it his curly black hair was sprinkled with grey, and a look of harassed perplexity was stamped upon his merry face for ever. He wrote countless letters—he loathed writing business letters. He had countless consultations with Charlie Gill, who made him miserable by suggesting expedients—pretexts for delay, pleas for depreciation, flotation share-jugglings—which Carr did not think quite honourable. He interviewed bank managers. Hitherto bank managers had been extremely affable to the manager and quarter owner of Carr Carr and Ainsley, but now their tone was different, and Carr felt it acutely. There seemed to be a general feeling abroad that the unfortunate Phil Carr had got himself into an awkward hole; and though everybody was sorry—for everybody liked Carr—they all said, or at any rate implied, that he must have made a mistake somewhere or he'd never have got into it. A few of his business rivals even hinted that Mrs. Eastwood would not have withdrawn her money without good cause. These impressions are taken from the recollections of Eugene, upon whose young mind the details of those months were indeed very deeply imprinted. (Hammond was still at Rugby, but provisional notice had been given for him.) There were mornings when Carr remembered cheerfully that after all he had, as it were, always paid Catherine interest on a hundred and twenty thousand pounds, and there was no reason why he should not pay the banks or some shareholders that interest instead. Carr Carr and Ainsley was an extremely flourishing concern, even though his credit was somewhat shaken by his cousin's action—the unsatisfactory gas engine would have to wait a bit longer before being replaced, that was all. On these mornings he laughed and whistled and joked as he had been wont to do in the past; then Cordelia's face grew cheerful, and Eugene felt that the ground was perfectly safe beneath his feet after all. But there were evenings when Carr paced in anguish up and down the room, maddened by his situation and by the stupidity, the utter stupidity and incomprehensibility, of the cause of it. Why on earth could Catherine not see, not understand, that she was doing her best to ruin the village of Carr Foot? Why on earth was she behaving in this mysterious, perplexing, maddening way? The mere bewilderment of the thing nearly drove Carr distracted. On one occasion Eugene, crossing the hall to go to bed—Cordelia was weeping upstairs—heard his father, who was tramping up and down the drawing-room, say in a kind of moan: "But why did she *do* it? *Why* did she do it?" Then Eugene was extremely unhappy, the more so because he really loved Catherine and could not believe that she would do anything wrong. When Hammond came home for the holidays it was rather better for Eugene, for

Cordelia took pity on the boys and sent them out for day-long tramps over the surrounding hills; but the younger lad never forgot the anguish of those summer months.

Time passed on, and the withdrawal of Catherine's capital, from being an incredible and preposterous piece of folly, became a familiar and inexorable task which had to be performed. On September 2nd, 1895, her withdrawal from Carr Carr and Ainsley was an accomplished fact; a notice of dissolution of partnership appeared in the *Hudley News,* and she duly received her money in full. Lomas, with the help of a Torquay solicitor—Nicholas Whiteley had refused to act—made some excellent and varied investments with it, which were still excellent at the time of Carr's death. On Carr's side, in order to complete the stupendous transfer, various crippling, almost killing, sales had to be made, various deplorable papers signed, and various humiliating adjustments effected—for instance, the fabric of Carr Foot Mills became entirely Catherine's, and Carr paid her rent for such parts of it as he from time to time occupied—and at the end of it all P. J. Carr was a mere small under-capitalised manufacturer, struggling, like hundreds of others whose names appear from time to time in the bankruptcy lists, with a concern too big for him, on which the banks had a firm hold—Carr sometimes felt it was a stranglehold.

This situation did not, however, last long. It was concluded in a manner both striking and poignant. On the morning of February 12th, 1896, Cordelia had wakened early, as usual, and called Carr. After he had dressed and gone to the mill she fell into a doze, from which she was abruptly roused by a heavy noise. She lay still for a while, and perhaps dozed again, when suddenly she was startled by the sound of hurrying clogs and loud human voices.

Hough Hall, it will be remembered, lay very near the main road on its south side; so that to Cordelia the clogs and the voices were just to the right below her window. She started up, almost sure she had heard the word "Carr's" called out. The clatter of clogs and voices seemed to continue, and now the mill buzzer seemed to sound upon her ears; decidedly something was going on outside. Cordelia ran to the window and threw it up, and just as she did so she heard distinctly the fearful words: "Aye, it's afire!" With a cry she rushed to the old nursery at the back of the house, colliding on the way with Eugene, whose white frightened face showed that he too had heard the commotion without. The sound of the mill buzzer was now unmistakable though the wind was in the opposite direction. The Venetian blind was down in the nursery; with trembling fingers Cordelia unevenly jerked it up. The sun had not yet risen, and against the wintry dark some of the lighted windows of Carr Foot Mills shone out in regular rows. Only some of them, however; for the middle of the main building—round and above the engine-room—seemed to be in flames. The cord of the blind escaped from Cordelia's fingers and the laths came down with a crash; in a few minutes the whole house was astir, and Cordelia and Eugene were flying, half dressed, down the road to Carr Foot. The remaining history of this fire and its results may, perhaps, be rendered quite adequately by three extracts from the *Hudley News*.

The first extract is from the issue dated February 15th, 1896, and it is headed "Serious Fire at Carr Foot." It runs as follows:

"Shortly after six o'clock on Wednesday morning, a fire broke out in the engine-room of the main building of Carr Foot Mills, at present occupied by the firm of P. J.

Carr, spinners and cloth manufacturers. The fire was caused by an explosion of gas in a gas engine, and it spread until practically the whole building was burned down. Immediately after the explosion the buzzer was sounded, and a man sent on horseback for the Hudley Fire Brigade. The first brigade to arrive, however, was that of Messrs. Gill and Barker, from Denbridge Vale, which rattled along the valley, pushed up the steep incline of Hough Lane and thus gained the main road to Carr Foot in a very vigorous manner. The Hudley Corporation Fire Brigade arrived shortly afterwards, and by 12.30 the fire was got well under, but by that time the main building of the mill had been practically destroyed, the roof having fallen in, and the contents of the upper floors burned or rendered valueless, while the machinery and goods in the cellar were deluged with water. The damage to cloth and machinery is roughly and liberally estimated to amount to £150,000, and that to the building to £5000. It is likely that the main chimney of Carr Foot Mills will have to be felled, as it has been considerably damaged by the fire. Fortunately no one was injured, except two men in the engine-room who were hurt in the original explosion."

The next extract is dated October 8th, 1896, and informs us that the claims "against certain insurance societies" in respect of "the disastrous fire at Carr Foot Mills, on February 12th of this year," have been settled for £96,000. "The original claim," concludes the paragraph, "was, we understand, for £120,000." This settlement requires comment, and it must be stated quite frankly that Carr himself, Cordelia, Nicholas Whiteley, Charlie Gill, and indeed everyone who knew Carr, thought that he ought to have got more out of the insurance companies, that Charlie Gill, for instance, would have got more, and that it was due to some element—or perhaps more to the lack of some element—in Carr's character that he did not get more. "He was too soft-hearted," writes Mr. Gill in a letter on this point, "too ready to see other people's point of view. He never defrauded anybody himself, and could not believe that anybody would defraud or beat down him. He ought to have asked £150,000, and got at least £120,000. I told him so many a time. But on some points he was very obstinate." The fact was that Carr, in spite of all his troubles, somehow never went through that hardening process which seems to assail so many fine young fellows in the early thirties; he remained essentially young in heart, in ideals, and in faith in the essential goodness of humanity, till the day of his death.

The third and last extract from the *Hudley News* on the subject of the fire and its results is eighteen months later than that event, the precise date being June 19th, 1897. The paragraph is reproduced in its entirety below.

"CHIMNEY FELLED AT
CARR FOOT.
Traffic held Up.

"Yesterday afternoon crowds of people waited in the vicinity of Carr Foot Mills, Carr Foot, in anticipation of seeing the chimney felled, to complete the clearing of the premises formerly in the occupation of Messrs. Carr Carr and Ainsley, which were practically burnt out eighteen months ago. About two tons of wood replaced the stones at the foot of the chimney. This was set alight in the early afternoon, and in less than ten minutes the wood was blazing fiercely, the chimney falling in a very short time. The chimney is near the main road between Hudley and Lancashire, and all traffic was stopped, and at 3.30, when the chimney actually fell, quite a number of vehicles were held up. The top portion of the chimney fell across the road, stones rolling against another portion of the premises opposite, but fortunately without doing any damage."

This chimney-felling was witnessed by Cordelia and Eugene from the Hough Hall nursery window—Carr was on the spot giving advice about the operation. Cordelia and her son watched the placing and lighting of the wood stoically through opera glasses; but when the fire had done its work, and the tall slender pencil of the chimney bowed gracefully sideways and collapsed in a sudden roar, by a common impulse they flew into each other's arms and wept.

"It's a shame, a shame!" cried Cordelia with her wonted emphasis, grieving for her poor Phil; and Eugene agreed heartily with it *was* a shame.

Eugene was the first to recover his composure, and he then urgently begged his mother not to cry any more, because, as he said, "it upsets father so." Cordelia, pleased with this unusual display of consideration from her second son, made an effort, controlled herself, and was able to welcome Carr cheerfully when he came home.

"Now it's all over," she told him, "you'll feel better. You must forget about Carr Carr and Ainsley altogether. Put it quite out of your mind."

Her advice was good, for some time before this date the firm of Carr Carr and Ainsley had begun to wind up its affairs, and it had now practically ceased to exist. What with Catherine, the banks, the fire, the insurance company, and Carr's inability to extort his rights by persistence and force, Carr Carr and Ainsley had been obliged to go into liquidation, and Carr was a ruined man. He used the insurance money to pay off the banks, in spite of Charlie Gill's strong urgings to the contrary; and by the middle of 1897 found himself free of all liability, owing no man anything, with a name absolutely honourable, able to hold his head up and look everybody in the face, but owning practically nothing in all the world.

IX

MIDDLE LIFE (1897–1913)

It was now Carr's duty to consider in what fresh way he could best support his wife and family.

Charlie Gill, who was not blind to the worth of a man with Carr's integrity and Carr's technical skill, had already offered him a good post as manager of the dyeing and finishing department in the Denbridge Vale Mills, and Carr, who was sick at heart and utterly weary of the worrying responsibility of carrying on a business for him self, was minded to accept it. But Cordelia would not let him. At first Cordelia had been prostrated by the succession of blows which had fallen upon their prosperity; she wept when anyone spoke to her and did not like to show herself in town. But when Charlie Gill's proposal was put before her by her husband, and it became obvious to her that he was thinking of accepting it, her pride rose up in arms; she rallied staunchly to the fray, and vehemently pointed out to Carr three tremendous objections to his doing any such thing. First there was Charlie Gill himself. Cordelia had perhaps never quite forgiven Charlie Gill for marrying Miss Barker—at any rate she was very bitter against him. He was known, she said, to be ruthless—had he not ousted his father-in-law violently, with a really indecent unkindness, from all participation in the management of what had originally been his own mill? He was known, she said, to be honest only because it paid, to be unforgiving towards the slightest fault in those he employed, to be as hard as stone towards his competitors, to be rough and caustic in manner, to care nothing at all, in fact, for anything or anybody but his own advancement. Carr would be miserable with him, and would soon be obliged either to quarrel with him or to do things of which he could not approve. (At these monstrous allegations Carr smiled sadly, and wondered how Cordelia would have got on if she had married Charlie Gill.) Secondly, there was Carr Foot. The Carr Foot men were out of work, and would with difficulty place themselves elsewhere. Part of Carr Foot Mills still stood, and stood empty. Carr knew the mill, he knew the place, he knew the men; and if Catherine had proved herself unfaithful to her father's memory, that was no reason why Carr should do the same. At Carr Foot P. J. Carr would always be William Ainsley's nephew, and a great man. Cordelia, ever hopeful and vigorous, had visions of Carr starting a new business quite on his own, making a tremendous success of it, collecting a lot of money, and finally buying Carr Fold from Catherine and living in it as lord of all he surveyed. Or if he did not manage this, at least the boys might. And here Cordelia introduced her third and most potent argument, the children's future. Hammond was now sixteen, and Eugene fifteen; they would need to be placed in the world; and where could they be so well placed as in their father's mill? Carr, harassed and perplexed, objected that he had literally no capital with which to begin business again; Cordelia thereupon pointed to the few hundreds which Mrs. Ainsley had left to Hammond. There was also Cordelia's property, Hough Hall, which could be sold. Carr, perplexed and dubious, but guided by his real faith in his wife, kept a hold on some of the Carr Carr and

Ainsley machinery, and evaded the bluff urgencies of Charlie Gill. Cordelia continued to brace and sustain him with her courage and her pride and her sound common sense, and suddenly one morning Carr's spirits revived; he whistled as he shaved, he made two excellent jokes at breakfast, and his mind became active and alert about the future.

This was in the July of 1897, that is to say, just after the completion of Carr Carr and Ainsley's liquidation and the felling of the Carr Foot Mills chimney. Hammond was at home, having now, though only now, left Rugby. Notice for his withdrawal had been given in when Catherine's notice of withdrawal fell upon Hough Hall, but Cordelia had contrived and managed and schemed to evade Carr's orders on this point, so that the lad had in sum been three years away at school. This bright windy morning in July, then—the actual date cannot be ascertained, but it was some Saturday towards the end of the month—Carr called Hammond and bade him come out for a long walk with him. The two set off together by way of the fields to Carr Bank, and thence up the hill to High Carr. We may imagine how Carr, looking at his son as they tramped along together, regarded him perhaps for the first time as a human being, a separate entity, and not as a mere enlarged edition of Cordelia's first baby. When a man has reached his fortieth year he stands on a bridge between the generations; with every further step he takes the preceding generation counts less, and the succeeding generation more. It now becomes necessary, therefore, that we should speak in some detail of Carr's sons, Hammond and Eugene.

While other and more important events in the Carr, Eastwood and Ainsley families were providing material for

Carr's biographer, Hammond and Eugene were passing through all the various stages of boyhood. They went through marbles, kites, canaries, steam engines, birds' eggs, white mice: they learned the rudiments of reading, writing, arithmetic, French and Latin: they acquired bicycles and had several accidents down the steeps of Hough Lane: they learned to skate, to sledge, to swim, to fight: they scaled the Hough Hall trees: they quarrelled and made it up again: they were rude to their father and mother and repented of it: they were occasionally kept in at school and occasionally caned: they could play halma, draughts, nap, comett, Newmarket and whist: their voices broke at the proper time. All these things they did more or less together. But at the risk of wearying the reader it must be recalled to his memory that Hammond had bronze curly hair, bright blue eyes, a brilliantly fair complexion like his mother's, and a merry open disposition like his father's; while Eugene was dark, sallow and saturnine, with rather fine brown eyes and an intensely, almost morbidly sensitive nature he had acquired from goodness knows where. The reader is referred to p. 186 for further particulars of the differences in their dispositions as children. The point to be noted here is, that no sooner did the two boys enter their teens than these differences became rather disconcertingly marked. Hammond was a great footballer, like his father before him; he was also quite a useful bat, and gave a good account of himself at fives. Like his father, too, he loved society and jokes and pretty girls. His interest in lessons other than arithmetic, always tepid, cooled progressively during the years from 1894 to 1897. Eugene, on the contrary, during these years cared for nothing at all but books; he scarcely ever played games, had to be driven out of the house almost by force to take exercise, and was always reading when he ought to have been doing something else. He read in bed at night and went to sleep with the light on; he read when he ought to have been getting dressed, and so was late to breakfast, which made Carr cross; he read during lesson time at school, and so called down upon himself severe remarks in his reports to the effect that his laziness and lack of concentration kept him from taking the place that his abilities deserved. (Cordelia's horror, at finding laziness and lack of concentration in one of *her* children, may be imagined.) In spite of this laziness, however, Eugene was usually a form or two higher than his elder brother; and though this caused Hammond no uneasiness whatever, it was far from good for Eugene. This was the reason for Hammond's departure for Rugby alone. Absolute frankness about Eugene's character is undoubtedly what he himself would have desired; and even at the risk of hurting the feelings of some persons still living it must be stated that he was a source of considerable anxiety to his parents during his teens. During the years from 1895 to 1899 Carr and Cordelia spent some very wretched moments in the fear that their second son was going to turn out like his detested uncle Lomas, and in Cordelia's mind the almost forgotten spectre of Eugene's paternal grandfather rose again and stalked about with a menacing air. During this period Eugene was too often lazy and sullen and dirty; he mooned about looking unhappy and not like a gentleman's son; he said bitter things to Hammond and rude things to his mother, and then appeared very unhappy when his remarks were justly resented. To his father he habitually said nothing, and then would suddenly display a terrible intensity of wounded love and jealousy when Carr took Hammond out somewhere with him and left Eugene at home. Eugene made no friends, but though he seemed to lament his loneliness he was outrageously rude to various lads who tried to break down the barriers of his reserve. He seemed to scorn everybody, and at the same time to feel so conscious of his own defects that he blushed and stuttered and squirmed when anyone spoke to him. All this was very uncomfortable; and then there was a terrible Sunday afternoon when he was discovered by Cordelia telling a substantial lie. He was sent to his bedroom to repent alone; Carr presently came upstairs to rebuke him, but having exclaimed: "That one of *my* children should tell a lie!" in a distress which was obviously heartfelt, he simply could not find anything more to say, and went out again abruptly, his handsome face troubled and perplexed. (That Eugene was really immensely impressed by this scene is shown by the fact that fifteen years later he described it to his own small daughter, who found herself in a similar difficulty.) There are grounds for surmising that Eugene's adolescent imagination was turbid and tumultuous, and tormented him with fevers and desires of which the other three members of the family, simple straightforward creatures all, had no notion. The only member of Eugene's circle who in the least understood him was Mr. Nicholas Whiteley. At this time Mr. Whiteley was one of the Governors of Hudley Grammar School; he told Carr that the lad was clever, had indeed undoubted ability; he counselled patience, and advised sending him away to a different school from Hammond's. While the Carrs were deliberating where to send him the Lomas-Catherine disaster came, and Eugene, rather forgotten amid the crash to Carr's fortunes, stayed at home and continued to attend the Hudley school.

It has been necessary to speak at such length of Eugene because it is, of course, Eugene's recollections and impressions, both written and oral, which provide the material for the next quarter-century of Carr's life. We have now lost the aid of Catherine's invaluable diary, but we have gained in Eugene an observer and recorder possessed of almost the ideal qualities for such a task—that is to say, he was extremely sensitive to impressions, thoughtful, a great reader, devoted to his father, possessed of that imaginative insight which often lies behind and indeed causes shyness, and sufficiently out of harmony with his environment to be able to view it with a detached and impartial eye. His written contribution to the biography of Carr was not begun till the December of 1903; but all through the difficult years from 1895 onwards he was unconsciously noting many incidents and traits which he afterwards jotted down or passed on in conversation and anecdote to the present writer. Thus it has seemed important to indicate his disposition, for it concerns his credibility and status as a witness. It is, however, Hammond who is really in the main line of Carr's history, whose life is, as it were, closely interwoven with his father's and continuous of its main strands; and to Hammond we must now return.

Cordelia regarded the money left by Mrs. Ainsley to Hammond as belonging to the Carr family, to be used for Hammond's good; but Carr had scruples about using it without the lad's full understanding and consent. Carr therefore, as they trudged over the High Carr moors that sunny morning—their cheeks pleasantly reddened by the tearing wind, their spirits lightened by the glorious view of dark rolling hills which lay purring and sleepy in the sunshine but had an underlying hint of grimness and power—explained his situation to his son, and outlined his proposals. He intended to sell Hough Hall—indeed by a piece of great good luck he had already found a prospective purchaser in George Newton[1]—and then to rent a small house in Carr Foot and move there. With the purchase money of Hough Hall and Hammond's few hundreds he thought he could command enough credit to begin business again, this time in dyeing only. Hammond should be his partner, and he thought it would be well to keep up as much of the old name as possible, and call themselves Carr and Carr. As they leaned over the wall of the High Carr reservoir,[2] and watched the small dark waves slapping sharply against the sloping stones, Hammond agreed to this enthusiastically.

"What about Eugene?" he demanded as an afterthought.

"Eugene can come in later—if he wants," replied Carr in the dubious tone he was wont to use about his second son at that time.

There was a pause, then Hammond shook his head, and observed sagely: "I think Eugene'd rather do something else."

"Would *you* rather do something else?" inquired Carr, putting at last the question he had brought Hammond all this way to discuss.

Hammond's blue eyes opened wide in astonishment. "Me?" he exclaimed. "Why, what else could I do?"

Carr hesitatingly mentioned a few of the professions, but was intensely relieved to find that Hammond received them with a really bewildered air.

"Oh no," said the lad when he had done, shaking his head firmly. "I always expected to go into the mill with you, father."

[1] Mr. Newton's first wife had died in the preceding year after a long and painful illness; he was now engaged to Emily Gill. They were married in October 1897 and went to live in Hough Hall.

[2] It will be remembered that Mr. Ainsley was one of the commissioners for this reservoir.

It was therefore so arranged. Hough Hall was sold to Mr. Newton—the trap, the horses, the three maids, James Illingworth and the rest of the Hough Hall establishment had been dispensed with months ago—and the Carr household removed to an odd little house in a Carr Foot side street, which had once been a doctor's. The frontage of Fallingroyd House, as it is called, stands level with the steep, uneven cobbled lane of the same name, and though when the Carrs went there it was by no means old, it had already been so much added to and altered that the original fabric could hardly be discerned. Inside it was a medley of unexpected steps, corners and windows, and the rooms were small; but it was cosy, and though a cottage was tacked on to one side of it and a high wall on to the other it had not the tedium nor the effect of total social eclipse—as Cordelia thought—of a house in a row. It stands on the opposite side of the valley from Hough Hall, and has a good view of the Carr Fold grounds and High Carr. Cordelia, metamorphosed from the rich and fashionable head of a large establishment to a busy and anxious housewife of straitened means, ran it vigorously, at first alone, later with the help of a young maid, Agnes Smith, who was a connection by marriage of James Illingworth's. With the Hough Hall purchase-money and Hammond's legacy a fresh start was made in the business world; the old Carr Foot Mills dye-house was rented by Carr from Catherine, a deed of partnership between Phil and Hammond was duly drawn up, and Messrs. Carr and Carr began their career.

It may perhaps interest the reader to know what became of the rest of Carr Foot Mills. The burnt part was cleared away by a speculative builder, to whom the material and land had been sold by Lomas's direction. He erected several rows of houses and shops there, the district becoming known later as Mill Field. The letting of the standing part of the mill was entrusted to a Hudley solicitor—*not* Nicholas Whiteley, who, as has been said before, did not continue to act for the Eastwoods. Carr rented one portion, and the remaining portions stood empty and desolate, with their windows smashed, for many years, except for occasional unsatisfactory minor tenancies, which never lasted long. From time to time Messrs. Carr and Carr extended their premises and took in another portion of the building.

This, however, is going rather too far ahead; for during the first three or four years Messrs. Carr and Carr had the utmost difficulty to keep going and make a living. Carr, maddened by the thought that he had taken his boy's money to begin this business and seemed likely to lose it all, worked harder than he had ever believed it possible to work; and as he had always been an energetic and vigorous man, swift in execution, it is probable that he worked rather harder than a man in the forties ought to do. Hammond too showed himself a born worker. In a year or two Carr gave up going to the mill before breakfast, and left that duty to Hammond, who fulfilled it punctually and vigorously. At first, of course, Hammond was a mere learner, eager to help but not of much use; then he was found to have a soothing and convincing manner with customers; and presently, by one of those gradual, imperceptible transitions of which life is made up, Carr, whose technical knowledge was of course greatly superior to his son's, got into the way of remaining at Carr Foot to superintend the actual work, while Hammond went up and down the West Riding angling for customers. Hammond was so frank, so open, so obviously genuine and sincere, and withal such a handsome lad with his fine figure and bronze hair and blue eyes, that everybody liked him; moreover, he was able to refer to his father's skill in terms which would have been impossible to Carr himself. At first, however, keeping Messrs. Carr and Carr out of bankruptcy was an unutterably disheartening, sickening, uphill task; the grey in Carr's thick black curls became only too plentiful, and the lines of worry hardened on his merry face, while Hammond too began to look a great deal older and wiser than his years.

In 1900, however, an event occurred which cheered the whole Carr family up wonderfully, and revived their belief that their future would be good. Hitherto Eugene had, as has been stated, been something of a thorn in the family life. From time to time Carr impatiently asked him what he was thinking of making of himself—was he coming into the mill, or not? In any case it was time he gave up going to school—for a great big lad, such as he had grown, to be going to school still was absurd. On these occasions Eugene usually sniffed, turned aside his head, and said nothing, which naturally irritated his father; but when the boy was alone with his mother he always begged earnestly for at least another term. Cordelia, fortified by opinions from the headmaster and Nicholas Whiteley, made the effort and screwed out the necessary fees from somewhere; and in the summer of 1900 her self-sacrifice was rewarded. One afternoon in July, as Carr and Hammond were returning from the mill, they were met by Eugene, who came skipping along the road to meet them with an exceptionally bright face. Carr, glad to see the boy looking happy for once, smiled, and asked why he was so cheerful. Eugene, however, was suddenly smitten with shyness; he blushed, hung his head, smiled foolishly, and would say nothing in reply to his father's questions or to

Hammond's mild teasing. The trio reached Fallingroyd House to find Cordelia in a tremendous state of pride and excitement; and it then transpired that Eugene had won an Ainsley scholarship, and would be able to present himself in Oxford in the following October. By various devices he had kept his attempts on this a secret from his family, and now stood out as quite a hero, with his oddities explained and his purpose in life revealed. Carr's pride and joy were overwhelming. He was immensely pleased, to begin with, that the name of Philip Eugene Carr should figure in the list of Ainsley scholars; then, knowing nothing of these matters himself, he somewhat exaggerated his son's achievement. He took the lad's face affectionately between his hands, and kissing him, exclaimed: "You'll be a great man yet!" Eugene was naturally quite of this opinion; and the cloud of gloom which had been approaching and then hanging over the Carr family since Catherine's marriage to Lomas seemed all at once dissipated. Curiously enough, from that day onwards the fortunes of Messrs. Carr and Carr took an upward turn.

Eugene duly went up to Balliol in October and read modern history. As the time for his departure drew near Carr became rather anxious about him. He reflected on the stories of undergraduates' lives which he had occasionally heard; he though of tailors' bills and tobacconists' daughters. A shy, odd lad like Eugene was, he thought, just the one to fall a victim to such sirens' wiles. In this he judged wrongly, for Eugene was far too much in his element at Oxford to be led astray by such extraneous temptations, but it is extremely fortunate for us that he did so, for it is this anxiety which gave us that charming, that altogether delightful series of his letters, referred to in the Preface. To keep Eugene "straight," to remind him of home influence and preserve him from dangerous blondes, Carr wrote to his son every Saturday morning in term time throughout the three years of Eugene's university career. For a man who disliked letter-writing as much as Carr did this was a real achievement; and the series is one to delight the heart of any biographer. The following four specimens have been chosen as being thoroughly representative of the series, being both characteristic of Carr and full of interesting information about the state of affairs at Carr Foot. It will be remembered that Carr's composition was always rather headlong, allowing him little time for punctuation.

"*Fallingroyd House,*
Carr Foot,
Nov. 24/00.

"My dear Eugene,

"Here it is Saturday again and your poor old father has nothing to say to fill up his usual two sheets. Your Mother is well, Hammond is well, Agnes is well, and I am struggling along moderately well in this vale of tears though why they call it that I can never think—it seems to me to be asking for trouble. We were pleased with your letter on Wednesday, though I notice there is a good deal more in it about walks and the river than about history. But if I were asked to give an account of the work I did every day I daresay I should find it very difficult, so we won't say any more about that except that I hope you will work hard and be a credit to Carr Foot. It is very important that you should be able to make your way in the world, because my dear boy I'm afraid I shall not have anything much to leave you. Somehow or other things don't seem to have gone as they should. I hope you will do better in that way than your father. At the same time Eugene there are things more important than money, and I hope you won't forget those either. I have been thinking about all this because yesterday I went to poor old Enoch Barker's funeral. You won't remember him very well, I think, but in my young days he was a fine upstanding man with very red cheeks and a jolly laugh, who used to give Charlie Gill and myself half-crowns, and it has made me very sad to see him wandering about alone and a bit tipsy, as he has got to doing lately. He used to own the Denbridge Vale Mills before Charlie Gill married his eldest daughter. Well my dear boy I don't want to say anything against Mr. Gill, because I went to school with him and he has been a good friend to me, but all the same if I had all Mr. Gill's money I should feel a bit uncomfortable if I had driven that poor old Barker to drink and misery like he has done. Your Mother is a bit envious of Mrs. Gill's carriage and fine clothes and what-not, but at heart I think she thinks just the same as I do.

"However, I expect you are tired of all this old-fashioned sermonising, so I will just add by way of a lighter touch that your brother Hammond is now carrying on a tremendous affair of the heart with Miss Marian Newton, the eldest of the Hough Hall girls, I mean. But then he is always carrying on a tremendous affair with some girl or other. However I was just the same when I was young so we won't say any more about that. I must say that Hammond always chooses his womenkind with very good taste. I hope you will do the same, and never get friendly with any girl you wouldn't like to introduce to your mother. I think if I sign this rather large now it will fill up the sheet, so here goes.

"Your loving Father,

"P. J. Carr."

The next letter is dated March 25, 1901, but this is probably a mistake for March 24, as Carr speaks in it of the day's being Saturday.

"Fallingroyd House,
Carr Foot,
Yorkshire,
March 25/01.

"My dear Eugene,

"Well my dear boy we have had great doings here this last week, as on Thursday night we went to a party at Hough Hall. I think your Mother was a bit upset when she found herself inside the old place amid all the young people, but however she carried it off very well. There was whist before supper, at which your Father won a prize. Curiously enough it is a brass inkstand, so it won't be much use to me, but it looks very well on the bureau in the dining-room, at least so your Mother says. After supper there was dancing, and I think some of the young ones were a bit surprised to see old Mr. and Mrs. P. J. Carr tripping the light fantastic toe as well as any of them, in fact rather better if the truth be told. Your Mother was always a beautiful dancer, as light as a fairy. I shall never forget the first time I danced with her, I often hum the tune even yet. Of course she weighs rather more than she did in those days, but her foot is as light as ever. Hammond is a very nice dancer too. I thought he would have spent the whole evening dancing with Marian Newton, but it appears that is all quite off, and he seems to have forgotten all about it. Mr. and Mrs. C. Gill and all the little Gills were there—not that they are little, but you know what I mean. Mrs. C. Gill was very resplendent in green velvet, I thought she looked hideous but your Mother says it was a *beautiful* dress and she wishes she had one like it. I don't. But then Mrs. C. Gill was never a favourite of mine. The second Mrs. George Newton, Emily Gill that was, I always liked much better, and she looks very happy since she got her George at last. Some of Mr. C. Gill's daughters looked very nice girls, I thought, and on the way home to Carr Foot I asked Hammond why he didn't make up to one of them. '*Me* marry a Gill,' he said, 'Ha ha!' Or words to that effect. I said they had plenty of money and were quite nice-looking I thought, but Hammond puffed out his cheeks and raised his eyebrows in the way you know, and looked extremely derisive if that is the right word.

"Here is a man come to see me about a piece which he says we dyed wrong but I know the fault is in the weaving, so I must stop and you will have to have short commons this Saturday.

"Your loving Father,

"P. J. Carr."

The next letter has been selected because of its very interesting reference to Suzanne Whiteley. It is written on the business paper of Messrs. Carr and Carr. The "peace" referred to is the peace between England and the Boers, signed at Vereeniging on June 1st, 1902. Jeanie Newton was Mr. George Newton's second daughter.

"Messrs. Carr and Carr, Carr Foot, Yorkshire,
June 7/02.

"My dear Eugene,

"Well, we have got peace signed at last, it seems, and high time too. There are to be thanksgiving services for it all over Hudley to-morrow, and of course in Carr Foot as well. You need not be alarmed about Hammond and Jeanie Newton. He tried Marian and got tired of her, and now he has got tired of Jeanie too, and found quite a new girl from Denbridge Vale. I never knew a young fellow have as many different girls as Hammond has, but when I say anything he simply laughs and says there is safety in numbers, and of course he is right there. The girl I should really like him to marry is little Suzanne Whiteley. Such a pretty demure little thing she is, dark and small and quiet, like a mouse, but how different at the piano! She plays beautifully, I don't know where she finds the strength. And what a pretty pair of eyes! I cannot say that I have ever cared for her mother much, to tell the truth I am rather frightened of her with her French and her rings, but Nicholas Whiteley has always been a friend of mine, and he is a man for whom I have a very great respect. He is both honest and clever, which as you get older my dear Eugene you will find is rather a rare combination. It seems to me that you are likely to be clever, so I hope you won't forget the other quality as well. We are very pleased about your tutor's remarks, though of course we don't quite understand them down here in the wilds of Carr Foot which as you know is not a seat of classical learning. But I have got away from what I was saying, which was re Suzanne Whiteley. When I mentioned her to Hammond he raised his eyebrows and sniffed and said in a tone of great significance 'She wouldn't look at *me*.' Well all I can say is I am sorry, and if I were Hammond I think I should have a shot at her.

"I am not much in the mood for writing letters to-day, as things have been going wrong at the mill a bit this week, and it is rather worrying. Also there is a rumour about in Hudley that Charlie Gill is going to buy Carr Fold from your Aunt Catherine, and this worries me very much indeed and annoys your Mother even more. In fact I can't bear to think of it. But perhaps it won't come off after all. Mind you work hard and try to get up in the world, for the rest of us don't seem to have much luck that way. But of course don't do anything you'd be ashamed of, I would rather see you dead in a ditch than behaving like your Uncle Lomas. Well, good-bye. Perhaps I shall feel more cheerful next week.

"Your loving Father,

"P. J. CARR.

"P.S.—Agnes's engagement to the butcher is broken off, poor girl."

The rumour about Carr Fold was premature. Charlie Gill, who had done exceedingly well out of South African khaki, had, as a matter of fact, approached the Eastwoods' Torquay solicitor with a view to buying it, and Lomas was anxious to sell; but the proposal met with such fierce opposition from Catherine, who roused herself from her apathy to combat it, that it had to be abandoned for the time. The next letter selected from the series is not dated, but it probably belongs to a period soon after the commencement of the Michaelmas Term in 1902.

"Fallingroyd House,
Carr Foot,
Yorkshire.

"MY DEAR EUGENE,

"Saturday again! Well we shall not have many more of these Saturdays when I have to scour round my brains to find something to fill two pages. You will have finished with Oxford by next summer, and I hope you know what you are going to do then, because I don't. But of course as I have said before Carr Foot is a bit of a hole and we don't pretend to know everything there, it would be a poor look-out for the world if we did.

"Your Mother is very anxious for you to put on your thicker flannels during this cold spell, she even hints at a body-belt but I'm sure you won't wear a body-belt, no young man would at least not in my day. But of course you were always rather delicate in your inside, so take care. I remember you often when you were a little chap lying in your cot after you had been sick,[1] looking as white and wan and miserable as you can imagine, and your silly little ears as cold as a stone. But these are the kind of things fathers ought not to say to sons, or at least so I am given to understand, never having seen my own father I am rather at a disadvantage in these matters. I am very glad to hear that you have gone to see Sir Bales Newton's boy as you promised, and also glad to hear he is a nice lad. His father was a very nice fellow indeed, I remember him very well at school, a bit odd and reserved but straight and lively and always getting into trouble for drawing when he should have been doing arithmetic or something like that. He was always rather ugly, but I don't see that that matters much. Fancy him being a sir! Bear in mind your Mother chose *your* name because she thought it would sound well with a title, so you had better see what you can do.

"Hammond doesn't seem to have a girl at all at present, which is a great relief to your Mother, but I am not so sure myself. I should like to see him in love with a really

[1] Note by Eugene on this passage: "One of my earliest recollections of my father was on just such an occasion. I shall never forget the look of serious and loving pity on his handsome face as he bent over me."

nice girl, there is nothing like it for keeping a young fellow straight. Since these last holidays, however, I have a kind of feeling that it is no use advising him to fall in love with Suzanne Whiteley. What do *you* think?

"I am glad to say that Messrs. Carr and Carr are very busy. We have taken in another room and are putting on some more men, and altogether we feel rather pleased with ourselves. Hammond is a tremendous help to me, I don't know what I should do without him. He has a great idea of starting finishing as well as dyeing, but I don't know, I shall have to think it over. Well I have done my Saturday stint, and Hammond is jingling about with the mill keys looking as though he wants to lock up, so I will now sign myself

"Your loving Father,

" P. J. CARR

"and close."

Space forbids further quotation from these charming letters, and indeed a further selection could only reiterate and emphasise the qualities displayed by Carr in the selected four—could only lay further stress, that is, on his essential modesty, humour, gentleness, integrity and affection. It may be stated here that Hammond's idea of adding the "finishing" process to Messrs. Carr and Carr's dyeing was put into practice in time for the autumn season in 1903, and certainly added largely to the firm's clientèle.

Eugene's career at Oxford, while not overpoweringly brilliant, was quite sufficiently successful to make Carr proud of him. He never had any real chance of a first class in the history school, but he got a very good second; he then took the examination for the Home Civil Service and obtained the lowest vacancy. As it chanced that year he just missed the Post Office and found himself in the Public Record Office, where he was very much in his element. The attachment between Eugene and Suzanne Whiteley, slyly hinted at by Carr in the last two letters given above, then rapidly materialised; they became engaged in the summer of 1903, and were married on June 8th, 1904. "Carr," Nicholas Whiteley states on this point in his letter to the present writer, "was quite extraordinarily and boyishly pleased by this marriage. He had for so long been accustomed to thinking of Eugene as the black sheep of the family, as an unbalanced, unstable young man who would be sure to get into hot water over his love affairs, that to find him thus making a perfectly normal and suitable marriage seemed to his father almost incredibly delightful. For my part I was well satisfied. I had long suspected the existence of an attachment to Eugene on Suzanne's part, though in her customary quiet and reserved way she never allowed a hint of it to escape into words; while as for Eugene, I had faith in his abilities and his capacity for work, and felt convinced that he would place Suzanne in a *milieu* agreeable to her. Far from agreeing with Carr that Eugene was unbalanced and unstable, I regarded him rather, at the time of his leaving the university, as a very cool, level-headed and well-informed if rather cynical young man. Eugene was thoughtful, and inclined to question truisms which seemed to him stale, thus naturally alarming the denizens of Carr Foot, but my only objection to the marriage was on the score of age, or rather of youth; Eugene being then but twenty-two and Suzanne twenty. But if I had refused my consent, a very painful period of waiting must have followed for Suzanne, during which she would have had few opportunities for seeing Eugene, living as he did in London. I therefore sacrificed my inclination to keep my daughter by my side to her happiness, and the marriage took place on Wednesday, June 8th, 1904. The wedding was a quiet one, owing to the recent death of my wife's mother; but there was much true happiness felt by both families on that day, Carr being, as usual, the life and soul of the party. I remember too a little mild joking about Hammond's being preceded by his younger brother into the state of matrimony. You ask me whether Eugene and Suzanne went immediately to the house in Hammersmith Terrace where you were born. No, they did not, as the then tenants had had sudden sickness in the house and been obliged unexpectedly to postpone their removal; but I had bought the house some months previously and presented the deeds to Suzanne on her wedding day. Until they could secure this house—which they did in the October of 1904—Eugene and Suzanne lived in a flat in St. Peter's Square, not far away. This explains the discrepancy between the dates of the deeds and those of Suzanne's account, which you mention in your questionnaire."

The references to Suzanne here, and Carr's admirable description in his letter to Eugene, have probably called up a picture of Suzanne sufficiently clear for the small part she plays in Carr's biography, but the reader may like to know that the "pretty pair of eyes" referred to by Carr were large, hazel in colour and shaded by dark lashes; while Suzanne's complexion was of a delicate ivory. She was—and of course still is—an accomplished pianist and a well-read woman; and beneath her quiet and demure exterior there were reserves of energy and passion. Her union with Eugene was extremely happy on both sides; they were admirably suited to each other. Shortly after their wedding they were somewhat embarrassed to receive a present, in the form of a Dutch flower piece with a black background, which contained no indication of its donor. They hung it over the fireplace in the long room overlooking the river on the first floor at Hammersmith Terrace, where it looked extremely well; but they were always a little nervous lest Cordelia should suspect that it came from Catherine, and command it to be returned. This, however, fortunately never occurred.

The year of this marriage brought another event not without interest to the Carrs. On December 10th, 1904, Carr was reading his evening paper by the modest Fallingroyd hearth when he suddenly sat bolt upright and gave a violent exclamation.

"What's the matter?" demanded Cordelia in alarm.

For reply Carr read out the following notice: "Hallas. On December 9th, at her residence 39, Majorca Road, Annie, daughter of the late James Hallas, suddenly after an operation. Funeral cortège leaving the house on Tuesday, December 11th at 11.30 a.m. Friends please accept this (the only) intimation."

"Good Heavens!" exclaimed Cordelia after a pause of consternation. "It's Annie Hallas."

"Do you think your brother will come for it?" inquired Carr, lowering his voice in case Hammond might be within hearing.

This question interested them all evening, and they fell to discussing Catherine and Lomas and old times.

"I wonder what became of that child?" speculated Cordelia. "She'll be nine now."

Carr was inclined to think that she must be dead, as they had heard nothing of her for so long, but Cordelia dismissed this idea scornfully. "We've never heard anything of Catherine or Lomas," she argued. "But *they* aren't dead." Carr sighed, and began once again that unanswerable querying about Catherine's ruinous withdrawal, which had now perplexed him at odd moments for nearly ten years. He mused, too, on Annie Hallas, and began to feel —very characteristically—that perhaps he and Cordelia had been wrong to cut Annie Hallas out of their lives so abruptly. They had never seen her, or indeed any of the Hallas family, since Cordelia's visit to Blackpool on March 1st, 1895. Perhaps they ought to have done more for her and her child.

"What will the little girl have to live on now, I wonder?" he mused mildly.

"Considering Annie had all my father's money," threw out Cordelia with a natural fierceness, "I don't think you need worry about *her*."

"Surely Lomas does something for her too," continued Carr, still troubled.

Cordelia tossed her head and replied with a great air of virtue: "Well, that's not *our* business."

Carr, however, was not satisfied, and he took the trouble to join Annie's modest "cortège" at its entrance to the cemetery gates. He thus saw for himself that Lomas was not present,[1] and he had a glimpse of Annie's child, who remained in his mind chiefly as a gawky little thing in black, with a bunch of fair hair curling down her back, a smooth clear face which certainly reminded him of his brother-in-law's, and rather clumsy boots. He tried to have a word with James Hallas after the funeral, but found himself avoided, concluded that Annie's child was well provided

[1] Those who think this strange must remember that Lomas's only hold over Catherine was his absolute denial of the Hallas accusation, and his counter-accusation against Carr.

for, and returned home with that sad but rather pleasing sense of the passage of time and the touching pathos of mortality which is so often induced by attending other people's funerals. Carr wished his wife to call upon James Hallas and make inquiries about the closing and selling of 39, Majorca Road, which after all had been her father's house, and Cordelia actually started upon this errand; but she turned back midway in a kind of disgust, and could not be prevailed upon to start again. Carr ascertained by inquiry from other sources later that the child was living with James Hallas, was well clothed, seemed in good health, and attended the Hudley Girls' High School; and he thereupon forgot about her. We, however, who are acquainted with the part she plays later in Carr's story, cannot dispose of the Hallas and Eastwood connection quite so easily; and this will, perhaps, be as good a point as any at which to insert an account of the circumstances of Lomas Eastwood and his wife during the period we are now considering.

After the catastrophe which drove Catherine away from Carr Foot for ever, and some eighteen months' wandering among watering-places abroad and at home, Catherine and Lomas eventually settled at Torquay, on the south coast of Devonshire. They bought a large and beautifully situated "mansion"—as Lomas describes it in a letter to his Hudley solicitor—in Lincombe Drive. Those who are familiar with Torquay will have paid many visits to this beautiful road, which winds amid thick woods up and down cliffs commanding a wide expanse of sea. In spring sunshine the white blossom, the glossy and luxuriant green of the trees heightened by the occasional sudden black of a pine or cedar, the reddish cliffs, and the calm clear blue sea, form together a picture of rich beauty perhaps unrivalled in England; while the warm air, heavy with the scent of flowers, invites the passer-by to languorous dreams of bliss rarely induced by the climatic vagaries of our temperate isle. The scene has, of course, been beautifully depicted by Prévost in the "Léa" volume of *Les Vierges Fortes,* to which the reader desirous of a more detailed and glowing description is referred. Catherine's house was white and spacious, with a smooth sloping lawn surrounded by fine cedars and aromatic shrubs; it had a perfect view of wood and cliff and sea, and was richly furnished in the fashion of the 'nineties with specially selected furniture, none of the Carr Fold fittings being used. Amid such surroundings it should seem easy to be happy with a loved companion; but unfortunately Catherine lacked this essential. To what extent it was this deficiency, or the warm relaxing climate—so different from the bracing Yorkshire air—which had such an adverse effect on Catherine's health, cannot quite be ascertained, but she was never well at Torquay. For the first few years after their establishment there she seems to have made a brave effort to adapt herself to her new environment, and build up some sort of life for herself from the ruins of her old affections; but in 1900 she was seriously ill with a kind of enteric fever, and she was never quite herself again. During the fever her hair turned almost completely white, and she lost a great deal of weight; her heart was badly affected, and very soon afterwards she began to stoop and to be unable to walk much except at a very slow speed. Hitherto Catherine had always been an Ainsley in appearance, but now a curious resemblance emerged between herself and her mother. I am told by some Torquay acquaintances—Admiral (retired) Sir Roger and Lady Annam, who had a house half a mile further along the Drive—that at this period she was extraordinarily careless and apathetic about her household arrangements, and often irritated her husband by her laxity in this respect, which sometimes had embarrassing results. The Admiral and his wife regarded Catherine as a decidedly peculiar woman, very preoccupied and abstracted, and only at times emerging from her shell to reveal her really gentle and loving spirit. Lomas, on the other hand, was in great form throughout this period; the place suited him, he began to take an interest in yachts, though he could never be tempted to board one, laid out his grounds very tastefully, sketched the beautiful coast from all points—or at any rate said he did—and constantly regretted aloud, in a mild insinuating pleasant way, his wife's distaste for entertaining. "He was a brisk, pompous little fellow," writes the Admiral of Lomas at this time, "very smooth and agreeable in society, with a silky voice and a lot of interesting anecdotes about the barbarous north, as he called it. He told me that they had left their fine old house at Carr Foot so that he might develop his artistic proclivities in a more congenial sphere.[1] He was rather bald and rather fat, with small hands and feet; and very much disliked physical discomfort of any kind." This description fits in so admirably with what we already know of Lomas that we may feel great confidence in the Admiral's powers of observation, and thus credit fully his account of Catherine, which differs so much from our earlier notions of her. After describing her personal appearance, as given above, the Admiral continues: "Mrs. Eastwood was at this time an odd woman. She always looked as though she was wandering about in a nightmare and could not wake up. She played the violin rather well, but so often broke off in the middle of a piece that it was quite distressing. She

[1] Surely this is a quotation from Lomas himself!

never finished any book she read, and always forgot to hand her visitors the sugar, and so on. Her husband liked to see her wearing rings and jewellery, of which she possessed a fine selection; to please him she wore them, but I think she disliked doing so; for she often left the rings about and lost them in a manner which like the rest of her behaviour was very exasperating. She was, however, very fond of yachting, and when on the sea would become quite another person, agreeable and well informed. I was not in the least surprised to hear of her nervous breakdown, and my wife said she was only surprised it had not happened before."

The breakdown here referred to occurred in the February of 1910. It was a serious one, and the doctors prescribed a complete change of air and scene. Lomas and Catherine therefore went round the world together, occupying about eighteen months with the journey. On their return Catherine's health was found to be much improved; but as soon as she took up residence in her Torquay house her spirits seemed to droop, and disquieting symptoms again showed themselves. The Lincombe Drive was quiet and remote, the house was withdrawn from the road, and there was perhaps an effect of being shut up in it alone with Lomas which wore upon Catherine's nerves. The house was therefore abandoned, and the Eastwoods moved into one of the many excellent residential hotels for which Torquay is noted. At first this change was meant to be temporary, but they both liked it—Lomas no doubt liked the excellent cuisine and the opportunity for endless posing to fresh guests, while Catherine had the opportunity for seeing that there were still decent people in the world—and presently they sold their house and furniture and became permanent residents in the Hôtel Quita.

But this account of the Eastwoods has carried us rather

too far ahead chronologically, and we must return to 1905 to record an event which at the risk of appearing egotistical the present writer is obliged to describe as interesting—namely, the birth of Carr's first grandchild. This event took place on Sunday, December 24th, 1905, at her parents' house in Hammersmith Terrace; and a few weeks later the child was christened Mary Elizabeth Carr, after Eugene's lost little sister. (Catherine again sent a present with no name attached; this time it was an ivory and silver teething ring.) The event is interesting to students of Carr's life because of the extraordinary pleasure Carr took in it. Space will not permit the present writer to record all the gifts of woollen and rubber animals, of dolls, of tea-sets, of skipping-ropes, later of tennis racquets, of fur-lined gloves, of skates and birthday cakes and chocolates, which Carr lavished upon her out of the not very extensive yearly sum devoted to his pleasures. He gave her also the priceless gift of his affection. In her he probably saw again his own little daughter, Mary Elizabeth Carr the first—whom she somewhat resembled—and all his loving heart went out to her. The Christmas holiday was usually divided by Eugene and his family between Hudley and Carr Foot, so that the present writer's early recollections of Carr are chiefly of him smartly clad in beautiful thick dark overcoats with velvet collars, leading her by the hand down Fallingroyd Lane to the mill, swinging her with Hammond's aid over all the icy pools, teaching her to flap her arms in the cabman fashion to keep out the cold, or poring long and earnestly over the diminutive wooden skates which he fitted with his own hands to her little boots. Within the mill he measured her height against the office door, weighed her on the mill weighing-machine, and explained earnestly the whole process of dyeing and the meaning of indigo. As the house in Hammersmith Terrace was much visited by young people with a future in literature or the arts, Eugene's friends, M. E. Carr was a rather precocious child, of the genus known as chatterbox; and Carr delighted in her babble, which he chose curiously enough to describe as "old-fashioned." He delighted also in her letters, and often sent her boxes of gaudy decorated stationery, intensely pleasing to a childish eye, as a hint to continue her correspondence with Carr Foot. The present writer's first literary production—a poem entitled *The Earthquake,* with lurid illustrations embodying a good deal of vermilion and ultramarine from her new paint-box—was given to Carr as a birthday present in 1911; it was found among his papers after his death. An earlier birthday present than this consisted of a large iced bun, which M. E. Carr bought for a penny in Hudley and conveyed by tram to Carr Foot. The date of this is uncertain, but it may have been in 1909, when M. E. Carr's other grandfather, Nicholas Whiteley, had an attack of pleurisy in May, which brought Suzanne home to his side. The bun was consumed by Carr with every appearance of enjoyment. Carr and his granddaughter had a special technique of hugs, which they guarded jealously and permitted no one to imitate; and there was also a special mode of rapping on her bedroom door which he practised, to her infinite glee. This was instituted in 1911, when Suzanne had a somewhat serious miscarriage, and M. E. Carr was sent to Carr Foot to get the country air and be out of the way. This year Carr taught his grand-daughter to skate, and it was probably also this visit that gave the present writer such vivid recollections of Carr waltzing with her in and out of the drawing-room furniture, to teach her, as he said, "how to steer." Later in the year Eugene and Suzanne came north to fetch their daughter, and it was on this occasion that Hammond took a photograph of the family group.

In this Carr and Cordelia are seated side by side on the garden seat at Mr. Whiteley's residence, Low Bank. Carr has his arms folded and his head on one side; his hair is now decidedly flecked with grey and rather less thick, but his eyes are as merry and loving as ever. Indeed he wears a particularly naughty and lively expression, and as far as the present writer's recollection serves he was teasing Hammond about the exquisite polish of his Sunday boots—Hammond was always rather a dandy, as the phrase then went—saying that they dazzled him, that he could not keep his eyes fixed in that direction, and so on. Cordelia is very much stouter than in her previous photographs; her hair is done in a large mass above her forehead which does not suit her; she wears a light striped dress with a high lace collar sustained by bones, and her bosom is decked by a large number of complicated fancy buttons and a gold watch attached to a brooch. Her profile, however, retains much of its youthful purity and sweetness; and she supports her grand-daughter, who—perky and diminutive, with her hair tied up on the top of her head in a little black bow—is leaning against her knee, with one maternal hand. Eugene, dark and lanky, slouches behind in one of his customary negligent but rather distinguished attitudes; he has a pipe in one hand and wears a sardonic but not dissatisfied air. It may be mentioned here, perhaps, that although Eugene would have been very unhappy if he had lived permanently in Hudley or Carr Foot, and although he never from quite early days intended to do so, he yet was extremely fond of his native place, and very much liked to revisit it. He was keenly interested in its local history and topography; he enjoyed lounging about Carr

Foot and High Carr with a pipe, asking the natives he met questions about old times and customs, and explaining to the present writer the significance of the gradual alterations in the appearance of the village. (He was quite distressed, for example, to find on his Christmas visit to Carr Foot in 1913 that the Hough Hall monkey-puzzle tree had been cut down in the preceding autumn.) This was, of course, one of the ways in which he collected the material referred to in the Preface. Eugene as a matter of fact always regarded the West Riding as a kind of colossal joke—grim, formidable, sometimes even deadly, but always amusing and apart from the serious business of life—and consequently as soon as he crossed the boundaries of Yorkshire on his way to Hudley his face always took on a peculiar look of sardonic satisfaction, which was well known to Suzanne and the present writer, who called it his Hudley smile. He is wearing it in this photograph.

It is a pity that Hammond was not included in the group of Carrs described above, which with him would have represented all the family of that blood and name; but the present writer has a very distinct recollection of him as he stood there facing her in the spring sunshine, bending his head over the camera. M. E. Carr was in her youth rather afraid of Hammond, though she admired him very much indeed. He was what was then known as a fine figure of a man; that is to say, he stood six foot one in his stocking feet, had broad shoulders, a massive chest and superb arms and legs. His head also was large, and his bronze hair, which had darkened considerably as he approached his thirtieth birthday, was very thick and curly; in conjunction with this his blue eyes and very fair complexion gave him a decidedly striking appearance. His strength was proportionate to his size, and in manner he was pleasant but very emphatic, like Cordelia; while in the mill he was always very serious and occupied, and had no time for little girls. He loved a joke, and could laugh as heartily as anyone need wish; but he had not that delicate sympathy with the jokee—if one may so describe the person joked upon—which was such an essential characteristic of his father, and in a less degree of Eugene. Hammond was, like Carr, not very fond of books or of what he called the heavier kind of plays and music; his tastes ran to sports and matters military; he was a Territorial; and altogether, as has been said, the M. E. Carr of that time regarded him with an admiration decidedly tempered by awe, and was always rather relieved when the party was without him. He was, however, undoubtedly the mainstay of the firm of Carr and Carr, which during the period from 1900 to 1914 made slow but steady progress. Unfortunately it was always hampered by lack of capital, and in 1912 Hammond turned it into a private limited company, in which both Suzanne and Nicholas Whiteley had shares.

We may describe this period of Carr's life, then, from 1897 to 1913, as one of gradual assuagement after grief, of recovery after disaster, of slow adaptation to new conditions of life. At the beginning of this period Carr had just passed through a tragic experience, was intensely harassed in business matters, anxious about the future of his family, and especially worried as to certain characteristics he thought he saw in Eugene. By the end of it his business, though still lamentably small to one who had controlled Carr Carr and Ainsley, was firmly established and run on sound lines, and in spite of disastrous strikes and the terrible competitive pace of the age, making good headway, thanks to his own technical knowledge and Hammond's administrative skill. Cordelia was almost as beautiful and as vital as ever, and quite as loving and as loved; and both Carr's sons seemed to have turned out well. Eugene was very satisfactorily married, and Carr had a grandchild of whom, though he regretted she could not carry on the name, he was very fond. Cordelia might be and indeed often was envious of Mrs. Charlie Gill's superior luxury, and Carr himself must sometimes have sighed for Hough Hall and Carr Foot Mills and his smart dog-cart and the power of being generous; but if life was not brilliant, neither was it utterly black, and Carr did not carry the analysis any further.

X

THE GREAT WAR (1914–1918)

Of the ghastly fret and fume, the awful toll of lives, the feverish emotions, the frightful anguish, the harassing irritations, the wonderful heroism, the appalling blunders, the submarine campaigns, the air raids, the ration cards, the defeats, the muddles, the suspense and finally the Pyrrhic victory of the Great War it is fortunately not this biographer's business to speak in detail. No attempt can be made here to render the delirious and poignant atmosphere of that terrific event, which has marked the beginning of this century with a deep purple stain and changed the face of Europe; the battles and the captains must be sought in the many lengthy histories devoted to the period. But the Great War affected Carr and his fortunes, as it affected every English man and woman, powerfully and permanently, and the various incidents of it which concerned him must be presented in a clear and continuous narrative, though at the time they appeared more like the incoherent catastrophes of a nightmare. The reader will perhaps pardon the present writer if she does not dwell unduly upon these incidents, necessarily so painful.

At the end of July and the beginning of August 1914, Cordelia, Eugene, Suzanne, the present writer and Mr. Nicholas Whiteley were spending their summer holiday together at Robin Hood's Bay, a small seaside place near Whitby on the east coast of Yorkshire. Mrs. Nicholas

Whiteley had met her death in somewhat tragic circumstances in the early part of June. For some years past she had suffered from a gradual loss of sight. This made the roads dangerous to her, but she was obstinate in going out alone; and on June 13th she was run over by a car in Prince's Road, Hudley, and fatally injured. This family holiday was therefore undertaken really for the benefit of the bereaved Mr. Whiteley. Carr, however, had remained at home in Carr Foot, and was to join the party on August 7th, when Hammond returned from camp; for Hammond was, as has been stated before, a Territorial. He was then a first lieutenant in the 4th Battalion, Duke of Wellington's (West Riding) Regiment.

On July 26th, 1914, the Battalion had gone into camp at Marske-by-the-Sea. On July 28th, as is only too well known, Austria-Hungary declared war on Serbia. As those first blazing days of August passed slowly on it gradually dawned on the little family group at Robin Hood's Bay, anxiously poring over their feverish, excited, declamatory but mysterious newspapers, as on so many other thousands of little family groups poring over their feverish and mysterious newspapers, that war was really at hand; and consequently Cordelia was not really surprised, though frightened, to receive, in the late afternoon of August 3rd, a telegram from Carr which said simply: "Come at once." That day the men of the 4th Battalion had been sent back from camp to their homes, to wait in hourly expectation for orders to mobilise. Carr had therefore wired to Cordelia to return so that she might see Hammond before he left home. She did so, travelling on the fatal fourth of August; and reached home about an hour before the mobilisation order was received. The same night the Battalion (afterwards known as the "first fourth" or 1/4), was concentrated in a neighbouring town, the men sleeping in the Secondary Schools. At this time the Battalion was about 650 strong, and Hammond was in charge of a company. The Battalion left the West Riding next day, but did not actually get to France till April 14th, 1915.

Eugene's participation in the War was not so simple, for he had held strong Pacifist views; after a sharp struggle with his conscience, however, he enlisted in the 10th (S) Battalion (Prince of Wales's Own) West Yorkshire Regiment, in November 1914, and shortly afterwards received a commission. The house in Hammersmith Terrace was given up, and Suzanne and the present writer came to live in Hudley with Mr. Whiteley. This was an admirable arrangement from every point of view; it pleased Mr. Whiteley, it was less desolate for Suzanne, and it enabled Eugene, when on leave, to see both his wife and his parents without waste of time. Eugene went to France for the first time in the July of 1915.

A month or so later the Carrs received news that Hammond had been wounded in action near Ypres, and was lying in a hospital in Glasgow. Cordelia, terribly agitated, at once travelled north, and found Hammond progressing favourably; a piece of shrapnel had been successfully removed from his left leg, and his excellent constitution was serving him well. Cordelia remained about ten days in Glasgow, till Hammond was quite out of danger, and then returned to Carr Foot to look after Carr.

In order to make it clear why Carr needed to be looked after, why he had not been able to accompany Cordelia to Glasgow, and also why the next two events upon our chronological list occurred at all, it will perhaps be well to explain briefly the textile situation in Hudley and Carr Foot at this time. During the War the Government demanded and obtained from the West Riding—at a good price—millions upon millions of yards of khaki, millions of yards of French grey, millions of yards of navy for the W.R.N.S., millions of yards of the odd colour used for W.A.A.C.'s, later millions of yards of Air Force blue. The mills ran day and night, on elderly and diluted labour. Khaki is of all shades the most difficult and exasperating to dye, and though the Government inspectors allowed an enormous latitude—as any memory picture of a detachment of the New Army will remind the reader—there were occasions when even they put down their foot, and the military foot is a heavy one. On one such occasion, for example, Carr found six enormous and unaccountable crates dumped in the mill yard, which when opened were found to contain a huge consignment of soldiers' caps. They had been refused by the authorities, and the refusal had been passed back until it reached the dyer. Carr's sons were in the trenches, and he himself was nearing the sixties. It is impossible to use female labour in work where pieces of cloth some fifty or sixty yards long, each yard interleaved with heavy sheets of "paper," have to be conveyed in and out of presses. This brief description will perhaps suffice to explain how it was that Carr prospered during the years 1914–18, but prospered at the cost of his health. He could hardly leave the mill long enough to eat; the minute he got home and sat down some man came running with a message which demanded his instant attention. Night shifts, as every mill-owner knows, deteriorate machinery, produce bad work, and in general are more trouble than they are worth. When to these customary difficulties is added unskilled labour, it can well be understood how the problem of night shifts drove Carr nearly frantic. No sooner did he get in a manager to help him than the conscription age was moved up to include the manager, and he had to go. In the early stages of the War it was generally believed that to produce the best results everyone ought to work on and on without intermission; it was only gradually that the value of rest pauses, holidays and welfare work began to be understood. This pressed very hardly on Carr's workpeople, but it pressed hardly on him too. He grew cross and irritable; he lost weight; lines furrowed his brow; his head throbbed; his appetite vanished; he lay awake tossing and worrying through the night; if he forgot khaki for an instant he remembered Hammond and Eugene, his heart contracted and he lay still in the grip of a greater anguish. Nevertheless he prospered—in a small way, because his plant was small and he had not the capital, or the daring which would have taken its place, to extend it very largely. Moreover, being only a dyer and finisher and not a manufacturer, he did not get hold of Government contracts direct, but only through the link of his customers. Charlie Gill, on the other hand, was a manufacturer; he had plenty of capital and daring enough for the whole of Yorkshire; he had some influence and knew how to get more; he was extraordinarily efficient and always produced his goods on time; he sat on tribunals, and his eldest son remained in Denbridge Vale till late in 1917. Consequently Charlie Gill flourished enormously, pocketed contract after contract, fulfilled them admirably, and became a great man in the land. He was so useful in producing the essential cloth, in fact, that it began to be rumoured about that he would get a knighthood. In the summer of 1915, therefore, when the rumour was fairly rife, Charlie Gill made a second offer to Mrs. Lomas Eastwood for Carr Fold. Motor-cars had now made the distance from Carr Fold to Denbridge Vale a mere fifteen minutes' run, so that it was not an unsuitable place for the head of Messrs. Gill and Barker to live in. (Denbridge House, Mr. Barker's former residence, was still occupied by three unmarried Miss Barkers, who, with an obstinacy equal to Mr. Gill's own, declined to move out of it.) His offer for Carr Fold was so large that it made Lomas's mouth water. The Eastwoods' income stood pretty much where it did before the War, whereas the price of all commodities was doubled or trebled; so that although Lomas and Catherine were still extremely well off, a certain slight retrenchment had become necessary in their way of life. In these circumstances the opportunity of turning Carr Fold from an expensive incubus into a source of income was one, in Lomas's opinion, which ought to be jumped at. Catherine had opposed the sale of Carr Fold bitterly enough before, but circumstances had now changed, and she might be more amenable.

In the event she proved so. It may be imagined with what anguish Catherine, brought up so largely under German influence, saw the outbreak of war between that country and England. The horror of the event—this information comes from Lady Annam, who, when her husband re-entered active service, went to live at the Hôtel Quita—seemed to waken her out of her preoccupation, to make her come, as it were, to life again. At first Catherine could not believe that her Leipzig friends could really be the monsters which the newspapers and the public imagination pictured them. She argued the point, was looked at rather askance by some of the Quita visitors and staff, and called down upon herself some sneering strictures from her husband. Soon, however, when the Belgian atrocities were established in her mind by the personal testimony of refugees, she formed the habit of regarding the German army as exclusively Prussian, exclusively composed of the dominant military caste, exclusively as it were Kaiserish, and therefore as great a danger to the German people whom she loved as to her own beloved England. Having tuned her mind to that key, she was able to allow her naturally sympathetic and loving nature full play; she rolled bandages, she knitted socks, she did clerical work at local hospitals, she gave money largely, in a word she threw herself vigorously into all the various efforts then being made for the welfare of the army and navy and the maintenance of England. "This reawakening of interest in life," writes Lady Annam in a passage it seems best to quote in full, "had, curiously enough, a beneficial effect on her relations with her husband. I had never regarded the marriage as a happy one—my sympathies, I may say, unlike the Admiral's, were chiefly with Mrs. Eastwood—so that unconsciously I gave a good deal of attention to their mutual behaviour. It seemed to me that I observed in them a phenomenon I had observed in other jarring couples; their common interest in the one absorbing topic of the War drew them together. Then too, if I may say this without offence, Mr. Eastwood did not then seem as different from other men as he did before the War. He was always prone to lengthy outpourings of high-falutin' sentiment which rang false; but now everybody was in a tense state, everybody's emotions were wrought up, everybody said rather sentimental and high-flown things—Mrs. Eastwood herself said them, I said them, we all said them and meant them. Be the cause what it may, Mrs. Eastwood and her husband undoubtedly became friendlier to each other in these War years; Mrs. Eastwood seemed to settle down, to accept life for what it was and her husband for what *he* was; and then too the war work they both undertook was good for them.

Mr. Eastwood used to grumble a good deal at times about the difficulty of adapting pre-war incomes to the present state of affairs, but I never took much notice of this, because it was obvious that they were very wealthy. Mrs. Eastwood's war charities were large. She told me once that there was a question of selling her house in Yorkshire; I advised against it, but she said that as she had no children she thought she perhaps ought to sell it and give much of the money to hospital schemes. We were all so thoroughly imbued with the war spirit at the time that this did not seem to me unreasonable; I saw that Mr. Eastwood approved strongly of the notion, and was not surprised when Mrs. Eastwood told me the house was sold. There was some question, I believe, about family statues and paintings; I think I remember advising her to loan them to some local museum."

Thus on November 16th, 1915, the deeds of Carr Fold were transferred to Charlie Gill. The furniture was sold by auction; some was bought in by Charlie Gill, some by dealers, a few pieces by Carr. The full-size statue of Benjamin Ainsley reclining on a mattress, by Edmund Carr, was presented to the Hudley Museum, together with the Carr Fold library and several valuable paintings. The portrait of Benjamin Ainsley by Lawrence was loaned to the same museum. In 1902, Carr, writing to Eugene, says he "can't bear to think" of Charlie Gill buying Carr Fold; but in 1915 he was so busy with khaki and so anxious about his sons that the sale went by almost without his noticing its significance. This sale of Carr Fold is the first of the two events we mentioned; the second is, of course, the knighthood which was foreshadowed by rumour, of which the reader is already aware. Charlie Gill's name appeared in the New Year's Honours List in 1916.

It was in the spring of this year—on March 22nd, 1916, to be exact—that Eugene, since February a full lieutenant, and Suzanne had that encounter with Lomas and Catherine described on p. 286. The Eastwoods had come to town on the business of some war charity of which Lomas was the local treasurer. It will be remembered how Catherine's reference to her having preserved Carr's domestic happiness at the cost of his worldly wealth, and Lomas's sneering interruption about James Illingworth, gave Eugene and later the present writer a clue as to the real reason for Catherine's withdrawal from Carr Carr and Ainsley. Eugene went on to say that James Illingworth now gardened for Sir Charles Gill, having left the employ of Mr. George Newton of Hough Hall—he had had a row with Mr. Newton over some raspberry canes. Eugene told the story of the row in his own sardonically amusing fashion; but Catherine looked uneasy while he did so, and as soon as he had finished turned the conversation by speaking of Eugene's little daughter.

"I *should* like to see her, Eugene," she said wistfully.

"Yes, we should both like to see her," chimed in Lomas. "When this terrible business is over, my dear fellow, you must all three come and stay with us down in Torquay." He smiled into Suzanne's eyes as he spoke, and the present writer imagines that Eugene must have looked more sardonic than ever. "How well you look in uniform, my dear boy!" pursued Lomas smoothly. (This was not true; the tall, broad Hammond made a fine appearance in uniform, but khaki made Eugene look lankier and sallower than ever. His appearance in his private's uniform had been really atrocious; being at this date a lieutenant he looked rather better, but he was always sensitive on this point.)

"At any rate," said Catherine eagerly, disregarding her husband's conversational padding, "write to me, Eugene."

It has already been related that Eugene did so.

The next year, 1917, contained three events which concerned the Carr family. On July 12th Hammond was gazetted captain. On July 30th Eugene was severely wounded in a mine explosion. Besides other injuries his face was very much torn, and at one time it was feared that he would lose the sight of one eye, but this was averted. He spent a considerable period in St. Thomas's Hospital, and Suzanne came to London to be near him. The house in Hammersmith Terrace had been sold, but the kindly tenant-owners invited her to stay with them during this time of anxiety for her husband, and she gladly accepted. Cordelia and Carr also spent a few days in London, staying with Sir Bales Newton at his pressing invitation; and Cordelia repeated this visit once or twice. Eugene was, however, somewhat astonished, one afternoon in September, to receive Mr. and Mrs. Lomas Eastwood as visitors. He surmised, however, that Lomas was rather fond of visits to London, and glad of any excuse to pay one; and this opinion was strengthened when Lomas, after a few smiles and smoothly uttered patriotic sentiments, waved a valedictory hand and made off down the ward, leaving Catherine and Eugene together. Catherine sat down beside Eugene's bed, and the conversation which followed was extremely important as regards this biography; for in the course of it Eugene told Catherine of the material he was collecting relative to Carr Foot and the Carr, Ainsley and Eastwood families, with a view to writing the official "life" of Carr. Catherine was naturally deeply interested, and drew him out on the subject at some length.

"But I should like to have access to your famous diary, you know, Aunt Cathie," said Eugene laughingly.

Catherine coloured, appeared to hesitate, and then said

in a low tone: "It still exists." She hesitated again, then went on impulsively: "I'll leave it to you in my will. But," she concluded in great agitation, "don't mention it to me again."

She then turned the conversation abruptly to the present writer, who, then aged twelve, was attending the Hudley High School. Eugene always had an exaggerated opinion of his daughter's abilities, and he spoke now of her youthful productions, from *The Earthquake* onwards, with fatherly zeal.

"In fact," he concluded, only half in jest, "you'd better leave the diary to her, Aunt Cathie, failing me." Catherine smiled but said nothing, whereupon Eugene pressed her. "I may never come out of this silly show alive," he said.

Catherine, probably seeing that he was becoming more excited than was good for him, promised that she would do as he wished. They then spoke of other things—including the Dutch flower-piece and the teething ring, which had, as Eugene suspected, come from Catherine; and also the death of Frau Schröter, of which Catherine had by roundabout ways recently heard—but just as Catherine was rising to leave him Eugene reverted to the subject.

"You'd better leave a paper with the diary, Aunt Cathie," he said, holding her fingers loosely in his; "explaining your withdrawal from Carr Carr and Ainsley."

Catherine coloured painfully, and pulling away her hand, seemed to be thinking deeply. At last: "Very well," she said, "I *will* write such a paper and place it in a sealed envelope, not to be opened till after your mother's death." She then kissed Eugene and left him.

On her return to Torquay on the following Tuesday, Catherine, undoubtedly influenced by this conversation with Eugene, resumed the keeping of her diary. As was stated in the Preface, it was not now written in the old flowing detailed form, it is true; but for dates and facts it again becomes very useful. It contains, however, only one statement of personal opinion: this will be recorded at the appropriate chronological point. Her promise to write an explanation of her withdrawal from Carr Carr and Ainsley and leave it by will with the diary was not kept by Catherine. It is highly probable that this paper was once written out, for on September 30th we find in her diary the highly significant remark: "Wrote a note for Eugene." Some students of Carr's life have regarded this merely as concerning a letter written *to* Eugene, but the present writer takes a different view. If Catherine *had* written an explanatory note, as she promised Eugene, in what other way would she record the fact, having regard to Lomas's known proclivities? To confirm this view there is an entry on June 10th, 1918, which runs simply: "Destroyed papers." The present writer's theory is that Catherine wrote an explanation which she meant to will to Eugene, indeed the clause runs "Diary and *other papers* in my safe deposit number E. 572"—but that she could not bring herself to leave this difficult explanation, involving as it probably did a question of Carr's honour and her own, to a child whom she had never seen.

For of course the next event to be recorded is a tragic one, and the fact that these tragedies were commonplace in households all over the world at that time does not make the tragedies any less deep nor the cause of them any less frightful. Eugene recovered from his wounds, went out to France again in the following January, and was killed on May 30th, 1918. He received a machine-gun bullet through his heart as he was coming back from an evening patrol. The news was received by Suzanne at Low Bank through the medium of the customary telegram; and to Mr. Whiteley fell the task of communicating his son's death to Carr. Eugene's daughter was not present at that painful scene, nor has she ever heard any particulars of it. Under the blow Carr's health sank visibly; his hair became entirely silver, and though he remained handsome, he began to look thin and worn and old. Cordelia fretted stormily, wearing herself out with bursts of rebellious tears; and they both brooded, in an ever-increasing tension which they dared not remark to each other, over the safety of Hammond, who was due to arrive on leave within the next few days.

The present writer used perfect frankness when dealing with the difficulties and dissatisfactions of Eugene's teens; and the same must now be employed with regard to his brother. At this time Carr and Cordelia were very much troubled about Hammond's moral welfare. In the early stages of the War Hammond had, as it were, been thoroughly in his element; he enjoyed the training, the open-air life, the sense of adventure; his superb physique was equal to the most exacting demands upon it; and as he had always been a friendly, sociable soul and close association with his fellow-officers and his men was no strain upon him. Eugene, on the other hand, detested the War and everything connected with it; route marches bored him, his mess bored him, the trenches bored him, in fact the whole business bored him unspeakably, and he wanted only to get the job done and finish with it for ever. Both these men had by 1918 passed through three years of the most ghastly, filthy, horrible and heartrending experiences imaginable. Eugene's reflective, realistic, sardonic turn of mind had stood him in good stead; his mental attitude had not changed—except to become slightly more realistic and sardonic than ever—and as a married man with a child he had a moral anchor upon which he rode securely through the stresses and temptations of a soldier's life. Hammond had no such anchor; moreover, the reality of war had shattered his bright dreams of it; and his simple soul became perplexed and disillusioned by the palpable "wranglings," the petty treacheries, the little meannesses which are always present when men gather together to take common action. His mind became at last so full of revolting images that he could not bear to be alone with it; in a word he grew "war-weary," and when on leave plunged into every possible kind of dissipation. The last time he had been in Yorkshire Carr had seen him drunk; Cordelia had not seen it but she guessed it; and they both went in fear of other and more terrible iniquities. Hammond was becoming quite noted in his battalion for a foolhardy and useless daring; and this calculated recklessness lent his handsome face, now brown and rather too lean, a powerful attraction for adventures of a less savoury kind. That their good, simple, loving Hammond should turn out like this was an anguish to Carr and Cordelia; they felt it more, even, the present writer thinks—this is not said in bitterness—than Eugene's death. Eugene had always been a curious and independent creature; he had made his life separate and alone, and would not even join his brother's regiment. That he should die was sad, pathetic, tragic, and they grieved for him truly and lovingly; but to lose Hammond—Hammond who lived at home, who ran the mill, who stood somehow for Carr Foot and William Ainsley—to lose the real Hammond and have only this excitable, reckless, hard-living and hard-drinking stranger left: that was bitter, almost more bitter than they could bear.

Hammond was, as has been said, due to arrive on leave a few days after Eugene's death. The agonising suspense and dread suffered by Carr and Cordelia between these two events proved unnecessary, for Hammond reached home safely on June 7th, the present writer happening to be at Fallingroyd House when he arrived. He was at first much shaken by the news of the loss of his brother, receiving it with blanched cheeks and a spasmodic contraction of the muscles of his face which gave him a painful look of nervous horror. For a day or two he brooded silently about the house, standing for hours in front of the dining-room window, whence he gazed out across the valley to High Carr from wide unseeing eyes, fingering the money in his pockets in a constant maddening jingle the while. To Carr's suggestions that he should come along to the mill and see how things were going he turned a deaf ear and a blank face; nor would he accompany his mother on her errands about the village. He declined flatly to go and see Suzanne. He would not leave the house for any long walks, and when he was not gazing out of the window he was lounging untidily in an armchair, idly and unseeingly turning the pages of some old magazines. He replied to all Cordelia's motherly attempts to rouse him in sulky monosyllables, and winced whenever she mentioned Eugene's name. A letter of condolence on Eugene's death had come from Catherine. It was long, expressing in many rather incoherent pages Catherine's sincere love for Eugene and grief for his death. Cordelia was moved by it to a feeling of kindness for Catherine, but Hammond read it through with a cynical expression and threw it down with a jeer. His parents finally left him alone and watched him in silent misery, torturing themselves by memories of the bright jolly boy he used to be.

Then suddenly one afternoon Hammond went off to Hudley, and did not return till three in the following morning. Carr sat up for him, hovering wretchedly between the fear that he would return drunk and the fear that he would return in the same black mood of grief. When, however, the sound of his key was at last heard, and Carr went nervously out into the little hall to meet him, the Hammond who swung open the door was neither drunk nor depressed; indeed he seemed curiously elated. His eyes sparkled, he smiled cheerfully at his father, slapped him gently on the back and bade him be off to bed at once for a dissipated old fellow. Carr, somewhat disconcerted by this change in their rôles, but pathetically relieved by his son's air of cheerfulness and normality, smiled his loving kindly smile and with bright eyes did as he was told. The next morning Hammond was up betimes, whistled cheerfully about the house and made a good deal of noise in his room. Cordelia, her eyes, we may imagine, wide in that look of innocent perplexity which still kept her face so young and sweet, whispered to Carr that she thought he was packing. This proved to be the case, for at breakfast Hammond announced abruptly that he was going to spend the rest of his leave in London—he was off that morning. Cordelia promptly burst into tears and heaped reproaches on his head, while Carr, looking intensely miserable, continued to serve out the bacon in silence. He could not find it in his heart to try to keep the boy in the dismal atmosphere of Carr Foot when he was hankering after the gaiety of London. After breakfast Carr took up his hat to go to the mill, whereupon Hammond said: "I'll walk down with you." Carr was pleased. The two men walked side by side through the village in silence; from time to time Hammond appeared about to say something, but he reached the mill door with it still unsaid. Carr, who would have given an arm to have Hammond safely inside running the mill again, observed mildly: "I suppose you won't come in?" Hammond, who for some reason seemed suddenly very much moved, shook his head; he wrung Carr's hand, said "Good-bye, father," in a choked tone, and suddenly stooped and kissed his father's cheek. He then made off rapidly in the direction of Fallingroyd Lane, and Carr was left alone at the mill door with a sense of impending disaster.

When Hammond reached home he found Cordelia running up and down the house in a flutter, putting on her best new mourning and giving Agnes a host of instructions about Carr's welfare during the day.

"I'm coming to the Hudley station with you, to see you off," she told her son.

Hammond's expression thereupon changed alarmingly, and he threw out: "You'll do nothing of the kind, mother!" with a vehemence which was characteristically like Cordelia's.

The two had a certain amount of argument on this point, but Cordelia was obliged to give way, and when the taxi ordered by Hammond appeared he drove off in it alone. To yield was always a painful operation to Cordelia; she had by no means recovered from the shock of Eugene's death, and was now having her only surviving child torn from her; we are not surprised, therefore, to hear that she spent the rest of the day in tears, feeling very desolate, and, as she says disconsolately, "very old."

This occurred on Wednesday, June 12th. On June 14th, Mr. Nicholas Whiteley took Suzanne, who was utterly broken by her husband's death, to Whitby for several weeks to re-establish her health. The present writer was, naturally, to have accompanied her there, but she declined. Always an intensely ambitious child, and very responsive to her father's talk about books and Oxford, M. E. Carr even at thirteen years old did not wish to leave school in the middle of an important summer term in order to be mournful with her mother at Whitby. The Whiteleys were, perhaps rightly, shocked by this seeming display of heartlessness; But Cordelia, who had never allowed her own children to be absent from school unless they had a temperature, and thought that her grandchild ought to be brought up on the same lines, supported her, and said that she could stay at Fallingroyd House and attend school from there. There were trams. The child was a Carr, and must be kept free from the sentimental Whiteley notions. Thus with a characteristic toss of her head said or hinted Cordelia, who was probably unconsciously longing to have Eugene's child in her own care. Something of a similar emotion may perhaps have coloured the present writer's eagerness to go to Carr Foot; at any rate the matter was so arranged, and M. E. Carr went to Fallingroyd House after school on Friday, June 14th. It has been necessary to introduce this slight personal detail in order to explain how it was that the present writer was an eye-witness of the scenes about to be described.

On the morning of Monday, June 17th, then, the present writer rose early and ate a solitary breakfast in the Fallingroyd dining-room. She was rather proud of this fact, and of having to leave Carr Foot so early; it made her feel that she was suffering and struggling in learning's cause. The postman came; the child hurried to the door in the hope of finding a letter for herself from her mother. Her hope was realised; there was also a letter with a London postmark addressed to Carr in Hammond's large firm writing. M. E. Carr thereupon called cheerfully up the stairs: "Grandpa! There's a letter for you from Uncle Hammond." Carr, who was shaving, did not hear; but Cordelia did, and with bright expectant eyes came running down in a patched pink dressing-gown, with her still rich though faded hair half done, drooping about her face and neck. She pushed her grandchild before her into the dining-room with an affectionate warning not to let her egg get cold, then took up the letter, glanced at the address, and impatiently opened it. The present writer will not easily forget the really alarming change which came over Cordelia's face as she read the first few sentences. Her complexion became leaden, her lips turned blue, her eyes seemed to start out of her head. She exclaimed, in a voice which cracked with horror: "He's married! Married!" and stared at the present writer without in the least seeing her. She then read another sentence, suddenly screamed wildly: "Phil! Phil!" and running out into the little hall, still clutching the letter, beat upon the banisters with her clenched hands. "Phil!" she cried. "Phil!"

Carr, terrified, rushed from the bathroom, and disengaging Cordelia's hands from the banister, half led and half carried her to a dining-room chair. He was still in his trousers and vest alone, with his braces hanging down behind him and his face half lathered; his hands shook as he seized the fatal letter; his hair, unbrushed, looked thin and grey; altogether it was suddenly borne in upon the present writer that her grandparents were getting old.

"Hammond's married!" wailed Cordelia.

"Good God! Who? Who? Who is she?" cried the wretched Carr.

Cordelia, unable to articulate the fatal name, pointed to the letter; Carr, holding it a long way off—he was in these days very long-sighted and had difficulty in focussing without his glasses—scanned it rapidly through, and exclaimed in a weak high tone: "Why, the silly lad! She's his own cousin!"

"She's the daughter of the man who ruined you!" thundered Cordelia. "And she need never come here, for I won't have her across the doorstep."

At this the present writer, miserably conscious of the noise she was making by crunching toast, inquired timidly: "Who *has* Uncle Hammond married, Grannie?"

"Nobody you know, child," threw out Cordelia fiercely. "Eat your breakfast and be off with you to school."

"She's your son's wife," observed Carr, "and your own niece, Dell, after all."

"I don't care!" said Cordelia in a fury, throwing up her head. "I won't have her here."

"That's nonsense," said Carr sadly, sitting down and turning over the pages of the letter. "We shall have to have her. Hammond asks us to let her live here till he's back from the War."

"He may ask," said Cordelia from between clenched teeth. "But I won't have Annie Hallas's daughter in this house."

"She's your own niece, Dell," said Carr again.

"Don't talk so in front of the child, Phil," his wife rebuked him sharply.

She then turned to her grandchild and hustled her vigorously off to school. The present writer well remembers the mingled feelings of curiosity, alarm and offended *amour propre* with which she left the house that morning, and how at the bottom of her childish heart she even then knew that Cordelia's bark was worse than her bite, that Carr's ideas would prevail and that the new Mrs.

Hammond Carr might shortly be expected at Fallingroyd House.

This, in fact, occurred on the following Saturday. Hammond Carr returned to the front on Friday, June 21st, and the next day his wife Chrissie came to Carr Foot. The present writer had been sent out for a walk so as to be out of the way when Chrissie arrived, and she returned to find this new personality—in whom she was intensely interested—sitting at tea with Carr and Cordelia. Cordelia's face was extremely long, and had that grim closed expression which in a Yorkshire-woman indicates volumes of disapproval; Carr looked hot and unhappy, but kept glancing at his daughter-in-law and brightening every time he glanced.

How their son could have met Christabel Hallas—for Mrs. Hammond Carr was in truth Annie Hallas's daughter—how he could have fallen in love with her, how above all he could have married her, was always something of a mystery to Carr and Cordelia; but the present writer, having had the privilege of Chrissie's confidence, is better informed than they could ever be on this important point, and is able to give an account both of the how of this marriage and its why. Briefly, then, Hammond had met Chrissie Hallas while convalescing from his leg wound in the autumn of 1915, at one of the many dances which during the War were rife in the West Riding as in every other part of the country. He had, in the slang of the day, "picked her up," for in their war-time states of mind they made a tremendous impression on each other. To begin with, they had for each other the attraction of the forbidden thing. Hammond knew well enough that Chrissie was Annie Hallas's child, reputed to be Lomas's, that her existence had ruined his father's life and that at Carr

Foot she was altogether anathema. Similarly Chrissie had been brought up to think of the Carrs, and especially of Cordelia, as haughty proud people who would not condescend to know her mother. A veil of glamour and romance therefore clung to each. (It will be remembered that Hammond had been at school in Rugby during the actual painful Lomas–Annie episode, and therefore had not the same feeling of distress about it as Eugene had.) Hammond was a fine handsome fellow, an officer and a gentleman; he was also a strictly brought up bachelor of thirty-seven, a romantic by temperament, and in a reckless let-us-eat-drink-and-be-merry state of mind. Chrissie in 1915 was twenty years old, in the first bloom of her youth. She had that wonderfully clear, smooth, delicate pink complexion which distinguished her putative father, and its effect was heightened, in her case as in his, by a little mole on her right cheek-bone. She had also quantities of extremely pretty, soft, fair wavy hair, large grey eyes, good teeth, full red lips, and a very white throat. (Indeed her complexion was quite out of the ordinary, almost consumptive in its delicate colouring.) In figure she resembled her mother, being full-bosomed, with rather broad hips. But it was probably her temperament rather than her appearance which really gained Hammond's heart. In Chrissie the vague artistic leanings noticeable in the Eastwood family—discernible perhaps in Taylor, skipping Cordelia and Hammond, but visible in Lomas, in Eugene, and in the present writer—found a fuller expression; for to a beautiful contralto voice Chrissie added undoubted histrionic ability. Neither her voice nor her taste had ever been trained, and she would have made but a poor show amongst professionals; but the present writer has often thrilled to her terrific dramatic effects in such songs as, for instance, *The Enchantress*. She had the temperament which belongs to these gifts; gay, irresponsible, sensual, pleasure-loving, as happy as a child (and in the same way) when anything pleased her, but subject to fits of uncontrollable temper, during which she would raise her voice to a scream, shout violent epithets at any person who annoyed her, and throw inanimate objects about the room. These moods, however, were rare; usually Chrissie gave the impression of being made for love and laughter. She had a nice little income of her own, bequeathed her by her mother and presumably originally coming from Lomas, but if at any time anyone mentioned Lomas to Chrissie, she put her head on one side, smiled at the speaker in her charming childlike way, and finally broke into a musical giggle—the thought of him and his (alleged) odd behaviour to her mother genuinely amused her. Chrissie had not received from the Hallases what Cordelia called "the upbringing of a lady"; but she sometimes for the fun of the thing *acted* the lady, and did it amusingly and well. Altogether Chrissie was rather an odd organism to be planted down in Fallingroyd House with Carr and Cordelia; those two simple souls hardly knew what to make of her, and did not understand her nearly as well as the present writer, to whom she used to confide portions of her life while the child brushed her beautiful hair. Chrissie's marriage to Hammond in 1918 was undoubtedly caused by Eugene's death; spurred on by the thought—so common in those terrible years—that he might never return from France again, Hammond decided to gather his rosebuds while he was yet alive, and so whisked the willing Chrissie off to London and married her.

One of the present writer's most vivid recollections of Chrissie dates from the Saturday following her arrival at

Fallingroyd House. Carr, Cordelia, their daughter-in-law and their grandchild were sitting at their midday meal, and Carr was just cutting a particularly small piece of meat to tempt his grandchild's capricious appetite, and arranging it in a jocular manner on the exact centre of her plate, when Agnes the maid came suddenly in with a white face, bearing a telegram. Everyone started up as their thoughts flew to Hammond; and Cordelia stretched out her hand to take the orange envelope. But Chrissie, crying loudly "Hammond!" snatched it from her fingers, and tore it violently open, sobbing. The disconcerted look on Cordelia's face, at being thus outplayed in her own strong suit of emotion, was amusing even in that poignant moment. Almost immediately Chrissie fell to laughing: "It's all right!" she exclaimed. "It's all right, Father!" (To Cordelia's annoyance she had already developed a habit of calling Carr "Father." "Uncle" she might have endured, but "Father" from Annie Hallas's daughter to Carr was intolerable to Cordelia. Carr also disliked it, but was too kindly to attempt the necessary hint of objection.) She turned from one to the other of Hammond's parents in a reassuring way. "Look!" she said, laughing again and showing her strong white teeth. "See! It's only his arm. It's only his arm, father!"

Hammond had been wounded in the left arm on June 26th, near Vlamertinghe, while under shell fire. Unfortunately his arm did not heal as it should, and after various preliminary operations it had finally to be amputated just above the elbow. Even this did not at first prove satisfactory; the surgeons continued to tinker with him a good deal, and the Armistice was signed before he was eventually invalided out of the Army and able to return for good to Carr Foot. By this time Chrissie had ceased to be an alarming portent at Fallingroyd House—time had performed its wonted task—but her presence wore upon Cordelia's nerves and made her both look and feel much older. In later years she was wont to say, with an angry sigh: "I've never felt the same since Hammond's marriage, never!" Certainly from this period her carriage became slightly less upright, and her look of innocent perplexity deepened to a rather pathetic degree.

The effects of the War from 1914 to 1918 on Carr may, then, be summarised as follows. His elder son was maimed, his younger son killed; he had added considerably to his monetary resources, but was physically and mentally exhausted by the strain.

XI

THE CLOSING YEARS (1918–1927)

REFERENCE has been made to a letter of condolence on Eugene's death received by Carr from Catherine. Carr of course replied to this as soon as he felt able, that is, a day or two before the news of Hammond's marriage to Chrissie reached Carr Foot. A good deal of curiosity was felt by Carr and Cordelia as to Lomas's reception of the news of this marriage, and they debated whether to send any special notice of the event to Catherine. Eventually, however, they decided to leave that to the Hallases—who, by the way, made a good deal of fuss about Hammond's "abduction," as they called it, of their niece. A notice of the wedding duly appeared in the *Hudley News;* and as a sentence or two in Catherine's letter, referring to that paper's obituary of Eugene, had shown Carr that the Eastwoods had the local paper sent to them, he felt that any further notice was unnecessary. Scarcely, however, had Hammond married than he was gazetted as wounded; and Catherine's letter of sympathy covered both events. In this letter she referred to Chrissie as Annie Hallas's daughter only, not in the least as her husband's; and great was the speculation between Carr and Cordelia as to whether Catherine really thought Chrissie was not Lomas's daughter, or whether she only pretended to believe so. A day or two later Carr was immensely startled to receive a letter from Lomas himself. After touching, in his usual long-winded and high-flown manner (which made Carr squirm) on Eugene's death and Hammond's wound, and throwing in a skilful side-reference to Hammond's marriage, Lomas went on to express a hope that bygones were now bygones. After all it was now nearly twenty-four years since "the unfortunate disagreement" which had caused his wife "such pain"; they were all growing old together and nearing their last resting-place—"Damn the fellow!" said Carr at this—and he for his part was quite ready to extend the hand of brotherly reconciliation and good feeling if Carr was prepared to take it. This letter was intended as an olive-branch, he concluded.

"Does he think we don't see through him!" exclaimed Cordelia with contempt on reading this effusion; and even Carr could not but feel that Lomas's letter came rather too near the introduction of Chrissie into the family not to have some connection with it. On inquiry from Chrissie, it appeared—after a series of charming soft giggles—that she had never seen her alleged father; nor had he to her knowledge ever seen her. Cordelia's comment on this was: "Heartless scoundrel!" But Carr shook his silver head over it, and found it in his heart to feel sorry for Lomas. Never to have seen his own child! And he and Catherine had none of their own, of course. Carr reflected on what his own life would have been without his children, shook his head again, and told Cordelia that he thought it was his duty to accept the reconciliation which Lomas offered. Cordelia at first exclaimed: "Never!" But after a night or two's thought she gave in, rather unexpectedly to Carr, and urged him to write in as friendly a tone as he could manage. The plain fact was, of course, that Cordelia had remembered Catherine and Lomas's lack of heirs. There was nobody for all that money to go to, and why should not some of it come to the children of Hammond and Chrissie? "Your grandfather," she told the present writer seriously in later years, "never thinks of that kind of thing, you know." The present writer, who had known that trait of Carr's character since she was four years old, nodded agreement; and Cordelia continued: "But somebody has to think of them." The present writer, not being so sure of this, said nothing.

Carr's first letter to Lomas was rejected by Cordelia on the ground that it revealed too clearly what he thought about Chrissie. Carr was rather cross about this criticism, and sulked mildly for a few days, leaving the letter unanswered. It was his daughter-in-law, who was already fond of Carr in her unconscious, rather animal way, who got him out of the difficulty by suggesting with a giggle that he should write about a very lively quarrel which was then going on between Sir Charles Gill and the Denbridge Vale U.D.C. about a right of way. There had been piquant scenes in the council, and very piquant ultimatums from Sir Charles, and it was rumoured about in Hudley, not without joy, that for once Sir Charles had met his match. Carr, who now as ever loved a joke, brightened at this suggestion, and his brown eyes sparkled; he sat down forthwith and, smiling, with his head on one side, wrote one of his long rambling charming letters to Lomas, only remembering just in time, on the last page, that he was supposed to be replying to a letter of condolence on his son's death. Cordelia was shocked, but in spite of herself enjoyed the letter; it was sent, and apparently had the desired effect, for from this time communication between the Carr and Eastwood families was carried on fairly regularly. Lomas was always telling the Carrs about the beauty of Torquay; not understanding what he was driving at, they were rather irritated by his flowing descriptions of a place obviously so very different from their stern West Riding. In the spring of 1919, however, Lomas showed his hand. Carr had had a mild but lingering attack of bronchitis, from which he did not recover as quickly as Cordelia wished. Naturally the Eastwoods learned of this illness; and Lomas in a letter even vaguer and more flowing than usual suggested that the air of Torquay would do both Carr and Cordelia good. Surely Carr could leave the mill for a week or two now that his son was at home to manage it. (In Lomas's letters Hammond was always "your son"; he never referred to him by name.) Hammond was just settling himself and his wife in a small house (Number 221, Lancashire Road) in a row by the roadside between Carr Foot and Hough Hall; the accommodation was rather meagre, but in those days of housing shortage he could not find anything else. Carr did not want to leave home till Hammond's removal was complete, nor did he quite see himself spending a holiday with Lomas Eastwood; while he dallied over the polite letter of refusal he meant to write, another epistle of enormous length arrived, in the course of which it emerged, first, that the Eastwoods meant the Carrs to be their guests at Torquay, and secondly, that if Hammond cared to accompany them, or come to fetch them, or stay for a week-end, he would be very welcome. At the mill next morning Carr communicated this invitation to Hammond, who promptly blew out his cheeks in the derisive manner of his youth, long since abandoned, and said: "You won't catch *me* going near Uncle Lomas in a hurry. I never could stand him."

"But Chrissie, Hammond?" objected Carr in a serious tone.

At this Hammond laughed, and patting his father soothingly on the back, replied: "I don't see Chrissie going either."

Carr shook his head over this, and announced to Cordelia that evening that he thought they perhaps ought to go to Torquay. Cordelia, who was really intensely curious about Lomas and Catherine and desirous of seeing them again, grumbled a little and made rather a fuss about her need for a new evening frock, but agreed; and on May 8th Hammond saw them both into the through carriage at Bradford. The last thing Cordelia said before the train went out was:

"Well, I shall have it *out* with your uncle about Chrissie!"

She tossed her head as she said this, and spoke with all her wonted vehemence and fire, so that Carr squirmed nervously in his corner. Hammond, noticing his father's uneasiness, said firmly: "For Heaven's sake don't, mother. Let sleeping dogs lie."

Cordelia pursed her lips, and looking her son steadily in the face, repeated with emphasis: "I shall have it *out* with him."

Hammond, who was thoroughly and admiringly familiar with his mother's character—as Eugene with his father's—laughed and shrugged his shoulders, and the train moved out.

The Carrs reached Torquay between six and seven in the evening, and found an admirable car and man waiting to convey them along chestnut-lined roads to the Quita. Lomas, with his unfailing sense of the dramatic, had decreed that their meeting should not take place until just before dinner, and that its site should be the lounge; so that Carr and Cordelia dressed somewhat nervously in the shadow of this coming event. The Quita is an excellent hotel, with broad corridors and a tremendous plate-glass frontage overlooking its own fine gardens and the sea. Carr and Cordelia had somewhat lost the habit of first-class hotels since the crash of Carr Carr and Ainsley, and as they sat in the large and brilliantly lighted lounge waiting for their hosts—for Cordelia's unfailing punctuality did not desert her—they felt excited and a little alarmed. Then a voice said: "Phil! Oh, Phil!" in a thin, quiet tone like an echo of Catherine's; they jumped up and turned, and the Carrs and the Eastwoods were face to face. Carr stood petrified with astonishment. In spite of Eugene's descriptions he had always visualised Lomas as a young man, slender, with smooth fair hair and that wonderfully clear complexion heightened by the little mole on the right cheekbone; and lately his recollections of his brother-in-law were very naturally mixed up with his impressions of Chrissie. But the man before him was short and fat—Carr had forgotten Lomas's lack of height—with a faded, wrinkled, sagging face and small watery eyes. His mouth protruded slightly, his shoulders drooped, his head was almost entirely bald. When he spoke he revealed himself to be a pompous elderly ass, and at the same time far more of a gentleman than Carr's remembrance of him. On one hand he wore a really fine diamond ring, and his clothes were so good that Carr at once became conscious of the shabbiness of his own well-worn dinner jacket. As for Catherine, neither Carr nor Cordelia would have recognised her. She seemed small; she stooped; her hair was white; she was beautifully and fashionably dressed; on thin knotted hands which reminded Carr irresistibly of Mrs. Ainsley's she wore magnificent rings. She spoke rarely, and always in a low voice; only the smile was the old Catherine's, and how rarely one saw her smile! On the Eastwoods' side the impression of change was probably less striking, for in Catherine's diary we have this entry. "*May 8th.*—Phil and Cordelia arrived in time for dinner. Phil's hair is silver, but he is still young. He laughs just as he used, and is still tall. Cordelia rather faded, but still beautiful, and as vivacious as ever. We talked of old times—Didymus, and skating, and the Carr Foot concert. Ah me!"

They went to dinner, and Carr discovered that Lomas was now an authority on wine. The Eastwoods had a splendid table in a window—the kind of table usually allotted to permanent residents who are rich and generous—and almost all the guests who passed by spoke a word of deferential greeting, or at least bowed and smiled. Hotel life was Lomas's natural element; he loved introducing and explaining people in his smooth genteel voice—nowadays rather weak—and marking shades of precedence by his honeyed artificial smile. "*I* enjoyed it," Cordelia was wont to say later defiantly when describing this scene to her granddaughter; and we may imagine how the simple Carrs, excited by the lights and wine, sat erect and tried to keep their end up against the overpowering atmosphere of wealth and prestige diffused by Lomas. They returned to the lounge, and had coffee and liqueurs and excellent cigars; in the intervals of old-time gossip Lomas confided impressive financial anecdotes to Carr, while Catherine talked to Cordelia about Eugene; everything was somehow very bright and rich and glossy, and Fallingroyd House and Carr Foot and the one-armed Hammond and all their West Riding life looked somehow rather dull and small and out of date.

This impression persisted for the next few days. Awkward topics were carefully avoided. Catherine, they learned, always breakfasted in her room; so usually did Lomas.

The Eastwoods pressed their guests to do the same, but the spartan Cordelia was horrified by the suggestion, and the Carrs appeared in the dining-room punctually at nine-fifteen each morning. After this they sat out on the terrace in the brilliant sunshine, surrounded by palms and blossom and pink tulips and blue forget-me-nots and orange wallflowers and Shirley poppies, and a host of other glowing flowers of which the Carrs did not even know the names. At eleven or so Lomas strolled out, very elegant in a light grey suit and spats, and carried them off for a mild walk along lovely elmy lanes to Cockington, or by red cliffs and blue sea to the superb house formerly occupied by the Eastwoods. Catherine, it seemed, never appeared till lunchtime, but Cordelia, who was a fairly acute observer, thought that Catherine and Lomas were now on good terms. This corresponds with the view of Lady Annam, and is probably the truth; the fires of Catherine's nature had burned themselves out in twenty-eight years of suppression and apathy, and long habit had resigned her to her husband. In the afternoon the car came round; they settled themselves into it with a perfectly extraordinary number of rugs and air cushions, and drove away over the bracing slopes of Dartmoor, or down by Slapton Sands to the gentle estuary at Salcombe. On these occasions they always had tea at excellent hotels, and Carr marvelled at Lomas's expert handling of managers and waiters. The soft mild air, heavy with the scent of blossom—so different from the keen Yorkshire breeze—the vivid colouring of the landscape—so different from the sombre black and purple of High Carr—somehow worked upon the Carrs and relaxed their nerves. This was a place obviously meant for pleasure. Awkward topics *could* only be avoided. Even Cordelia's fierce puritanic morals suffered a sea change; she forgot to attend church, and did not observe Lomas with quite such sisterly scorn as formerly. As for Carr, he felt soothed and lulled; his bronchial tubes were clear; always inclined to love and laugh and judge the other fellow leniently for doing the same, he now laughed heartily at all the men's jokes, teased the girls, flattered the old ladies by listening to them with serious attention, and became an enormous favourite with all the inhabitants of the Quita. The only thing that worried him was Cordelia's reiterated determination to "have it out" with Lomas; whenever the name of Hammond was mentioned he sheered off from it in a panic, and was never comfortable when *tête-à-tête* with Catherine for fear of what Cordelia was saying to her brother.

In spite of his precautions Cordelia had her way on the morning of the day before they were to return to Yorkshire. Stimulated by the act of packing—Cordelia always packed twenty-four hours before she left—and the associations of home which it brought her, she emerged purposefully on to the sunlit terrace, where Carr and Lomas were peacefully smoking together, and, sternly commanding her husband to go and fold up his shirts, carried off her brother to a remote part of the garden. They returned late for lunch, and in a state of some agitation; Cordelia had obviously been weeping but looked triumphant: Lomas was pale and in a flutter, and his heavy eyelids twitched. Unfortunately Cordelia has never, from that day to this, been persuaded to give an account of what took place between Lomas and herself on that occasion. When pressed by the present writer to reveal the cardinal fact as regards Chrissie, she took refuge in a simulated Victorian prudery and announced herself shocked by the heartlessness and general lack of propriety of the new generation as evinced by such a question. To Carr, who immediately after lunch that day (Wednesday, May 21st, 1919) eagerly and in some alarm asked what Lomas had said, Cordelia replied firmly:

"There's no need to go into all that—but," she added, and now her triumph was undisguised, "you needn't worry about the future of Hammond's children."

"He hasn't got any children! I don't know what you mean!" cried Carr, flushing painfully.

In spite of this disclaimer he understood perfectly well, however, that any money of Catherine's which came into Lomas's hands would eventually find its way to Chrissie and her heirs. This knowledge spoiled the rest of his holiday for him, and all that last day he was sulky and morose when he was not snappy. Indeed the thought of Chrissie's future wealth probably tainted his whole relations with his daughter-in-law, and confirmed him still more in his predilection for Eugene's child. At any rate these dispositions on his part were more marked after his sojourn in Torquay.

The next day the Carrs left by a morning train. At breakfast there was a general feeling among all the four, or so Cordelia thought, of relief at the coming separation, and a nervous longing for the hour of departure to be past. Carr, in a last attempt to be genial, said: "Well, let us know when you think of coming to Yorkshire, Eastwood." To this Lomas replied sternly: "We shall never return to Yorkshire." There was an awkward silence and everyone again wished that the parting was over. But when they had reached the station and the fuss of boarding the train was past, when the train actually began to move from the platform and the moment of parting was at hand, Cordelia suddenly saw Catherine's face become contorted, and with surprise she found that she herself was weeping. The memory of old times rushed upon her, and she felt suddenly that she had not said half, not a quarter, not a tenth of what she had meant to say to Catherine and her brother. She exclaimed something incoherently. Tears were now pouring down Catherine's face, while Carr exclaimed "Well! Well!" in a nervous, jerky style, and fidgeted with the strap of the window. Suddenly Lomas climbed on to the step and seized Carr's hand. "Good-bye! Good-bye!" he cried, his pale mouth working. Carr wrung his hand and stammered; porters shouted; Cordelia, sobbing, hastily aimed a kiss at her brother's cheek; Lomas was pulled off the step, and the train left the station.

After this touching scene Hammond's welcome at Hudley seemed rather flat and boring; and for some years after this Torquay visit Cordelia was apt to dwell upon the splendours of the Quita and the glories of the Eastwoods, at considerable length and in a rather envious tone. The contrast between the luxurious indolence of Torquay—the fine clothes, the beautiful flowers, the elegant car, the comfortable appointments of the hotel—and the conditions of life prevailing at Fallingroyd House struck Cordelia's practical mind rather too forcibly; she could not help remembering the days when she was the mistress of Hough Hall and Lomas lived in lodgings in Prince's Road, and her opinion of her brother seemed to have improved with his fortunes. Curiously enough, however, this did not have the effect of reconciling Cordelia to Chrissie; indeed she seemed almost to revenge herself, as it were, for being bound to feel obliged to Chrissie, by criticising and despising her on every possible occasion.

Indeed the Hammond–Chrissie *ménage,* for the few months it lasted, was rather an odd one; one never knew, on ringing the front-door bell, whether one would interrupt an almost superhuman happiness or a frightful storm. The present writer had not many opportunities of observing the relations of Hammond and his wife, because both Mr. Nicholas Whiteley and Suzanne were repelled by Chrissie and avoided her; but even on the few occasions when she entered the house she was struck, young as she was, by the passion and intensity which marked every speech and action of the husband and wife. That Hammond and Chrissie were passionately attached to each other cannot be doubted; but Hammond was of a jealous disposition, and this was aggravated by the loss of his arm and the difference in age between himself and his wife, while Chrissie was utterly careless of appearances and loved to tease. She disliked housework, and during her pregnancy preferred to lie on a couch all day in a half-dressed condition, with her beautiful fair hair disordered, reading magazines and eating chocolates. During this period Hammond's meals were very irregular, and his mending was not well done. It may be imagined what the spartan, puritanic, punctual, orderly Cordelia thought of such a wife for her eldest son. Moreover, Carr and Cordelia, simple, essentially decent, and perhaps rather timid souls both, were appalled by the atmosphere of reckless passion which pervaded their son's house. They had not, however, long to suffer it. On August 31st, 1919, as is well known, Chrissie gave birth to two fine healthy boys, who were christened Hammond Taylor and Philip Taylor respectively. For the first three days Chrissie seemed to be recovering nicely, but puerperal fever set in, and before the week was out she was dead.

This tragic and unexpected bereavement left a terrible mark on Hammond. It was years before he even partially recovered from it; and from his loss of Chrissie, and not from his war experiences, dates his extreme reserve, which forms so strong a contrast to his manner in his younger days. Cordelia, of course, expected him to give up his Lancashire Road establishment and bring his children to Fallingroyd House and her care, but this Hammond declined to do. He said, quite justly, that at her present age his mother would feel the strain of two young children very severely indeed; and he did not wish to leave the house where he had lived with Chrissie. The difficulty was solved by his securing the services of James Illingworth's son, at that time a slightly disabled ex-service man, and his wife, who had been trained as a nurse. (By one of those coincidences which often obtain in small provincial towns, where the lives of families criss-cross through the generations, she was the granddaughter of the jocular cabman mentioned on p. 103, who drove Carr and Cordelia from the skating rink on December 27th, 1879.) This pair lived in Hammond's house; the wife brought up—admirably both as regards physique and morals—the two boys, while the husband, with some outside help, performed the household duties.

In connection with Chrissie's death it again becomes necessary to consider the attitude of Lomas. This time Cordelia charged herself with the duty of communicating the news to her brother, and she presently did so by letter. This letter is not extant, but the reader who remembers Cordelia's direct, not to say abrupt, style of correspondence will easily share Carr's belief that Lomas was offended by it. At all events he did not reply to it; nor were the Carrs ever invited to Torquay again. Cordelia lamented this, but Carr was not sorry; he had no desire to be made envious by the sight of his ancient enemy's prosperity, nor was he anxious to divert the stream of the Eastwoods' wealth towards his own family.

For the next three years nothing occurred in Carr's life worthy of report, save that in 1921 Carr and Cordelia, with Suzanne and the present writer, visited Eugene's grave in France—a very sorrowful experience for all of them, in which Hammond declined to participate. Hammond struggled with post-war conditions in the textile world; Carr worried over them; his two grandsons grew and thrived; the present writer was away at boarding-school—where, by the way, Carr addressed to her some very charming letters. One of these, which gives some rather interesting details about Carr Foot life and is besides very characteristically expressed, may be quoted here in full. The heavy formalities of the opening and conclusion are, of course, a joke. May 15th was Carr's birthday, and the Jack Illingworth referred to is James Illingworth's son.

"Fallingroyd House,
Carr Foot,
Tuesday, May 16th, 1922.

"MY DEARLY BELOVED AND ONLY GRANDDAUGHTER,

"Thank you for the nice bright shaving mirror which came to hand yesterday morning. I don't know that I am so particularly anxious to see my face particularly well, for to tell you the truth I am a little tired of it, having had it now for 64 years, which is quite a long time don't you think. Still the mirror looks very well hung up in the corner of the bathroom. I thought of putting it up in the bedroom so I should have a mirror of my own to tie my tie in every morning while your grandmother is doing her hair, but it appears it would spoil the new wallpaper so that idea had to be given up. I am glad you won your cricket match last Saturday, it seems odd to me for young ladies to be playing cricket, but so long as it doesn't interfere with your work why not?

"Well here is a vast sheet of paper waiting to be filled so I suppose I must fill it with something. The only thing that has happened at Carr Foot lately is a funeral, a very grand one with a motor hearse and a long string of cars and flowers galore, to wit Lady Gill's. To tell you the truth Lady Gill was never much of a favourite of mine, too snappy and too keen to know which side of her bread had butter on, but still I have been sorry for her lately, between you and me and the doorpost I don't think Sir Charles is a very easy person to live with, though a better business man never trod the West Riding. If he went to hell he would buy it up and turn it into a limited company with preference and debenture shares and whatnot, for supplying the Esquimaux with heating in the winter. What he will do in the other place remains to be seen.

"The twins have got a dog, a jolly little fox terrier called Jack, after Jack Illingworth, who got it for them. It is as round as a barrel and about six inches long or a bit longer. Young Hammond fell out of a milk-cart the other day and cut his lip. You may well ask what a child of three was doing in a milk-cart, that's what his grandmother wants to know but nobody seems able to tell her. I hear your mother has gone to London, but I daresay you knew that before. Your uncle is quite well, but a good deal worried because business is so bad. Your grandmother is quite well too, she is playing a lot of old tunes to me now which were written long before your father was thought of. She sends her love, and hopes you have settled down by now after the holidays. I think that is all the Carr Foot news. You see we have not got a thousand curly-haired girls here to make life interesting as you have. I will now close, and subscribe myself.

"Your loving and beloved (I hope) Grandfather,

"P. J. Carr."

Later in 1922 an event took place which had a certain effect on the lives both of Carr and Cordelia and of the present writer. Suzanne married again, her second husband being the widowed owner of the house in Hammersmith Terrace presented to her on her first marriage by Mr. Nicholas Whiteley. It will be remembered that this gentleman, with his wife, had given a very warm welcome to Suzanne in the summer of 1917, when she came to London to visit Eugene, who was then lying wounded in St. Thomas's Hospital. Since then each had suffered a bereavement; a mutual sympathy drew them to each other, and their union was the natural consummation of their five years' friendship. Natural and inevitable as this event was, however, it gave Carr, and perhaps even more Cordelia, great pain; Cordelia wrung her hands when she heard of the engagement from Suzanne's lips, and said pitifully: "There'll be nothing left to us soon!" Suzanne, distressed, affectionately tried to console her by reminders of Hammond and his two sons, and promises that the present writer should frequently visit Carr Foot; but these promises were rendered unnecessary by the march of events. The marriage took place in London on September 21st, and Suzanne's daughter spent the Christmas holidays at the house in Hammersmith Terrace. The present writer wishes it to be clearly understood that she has a deep love for her mother, and an affectionate, indeed almost an admiring, regard for her mother's second husband, whose eminence in the literary world is considerable, and whose advice on the preparation and format of this book has been highly valued—that his name does not figure amongst those to whom the writer's thanks are offered in the Preface is due entirely to his own urgently expressed desire. But some deep current of the writer's mind and heart seemed to set towards Hudley and Carr Foot, and the change in her place of residence occasioned her very great distress. She spent part of the Easter holidays in 1923, and a great part of the summer holidays, at Fallingroyd House; and before going up to Oxford in the autumn of 1923 she had decided, and obtained her mother's and grandparents' consent to the plan, to make her headquarters at Carr Foot for the next few years. It may seem strange that a young girl should prefer to bury herself in a West Riding village with two ageing grandparents rather than enjoy the amenities of a London suburb; the present writer can only explain it by the passionate interest she had always felt in Carr's life and surroundings, an interest heightened by Eugene's memorandum on the subject, which after his death came into her possession, an interest which has perhaps found its justification in the present work. Be that as it may, her decision, once made, was adhered to; and she therefore had considerably opportunity of observing Carr during the last four years of his life.

The characteristics of this period were, first, the gradual weakening of Carr's health by repeated attacks of bronchitis, from which in the winter he was hardly ever free; and, second, the gradual increase of his interest in Hammond's two sons. Of these two delightful and most promising boys, by a curious freak of heredity which gave their father and grandfather (and I may add their cousin) very great pleasure, the younger one, Pip, at this time strongly resembled Eugene both in appearance and disposition, while the elder boy, Hammond, was in many ways very like the early portraits of Carr, though lighter in colouring. In later years these resemblances diminished. Both these lively and spirited young gentlemen have very strong wills and a great propensity for harmless mischief; it remains to be seen how life will work upon them, and what threads from the web woven by the previous generations will emerge in their pattern. From 1923 to 1927, that is to say, from the ages of four to eight, they were one of the most pleasing elements in Carr's life. Wheelbarrows, fairy cycles, soldiers, footballs, cricket bats and Meccano sets flowed from Fallingroyd House to Lancashire Road; and it was delightful to see how Carr's loving brown eyes sparkled with merriment and how heartily and boyishly he laughed, when his two grandsons climbed trees or ran along the tops of walls or kicked their football into inaccessible places, or in other ways reminded him of his own joyous youth. Carr was excellent, too, at composing their childish squabbles, for he looked so utterly dismayed when either of the twins complained of the other that they were quite abashed, and made up their quarrel on the spot. On Sunday afternoons Carr and Hammond and the boys often went out for short suitable walks about Carr Foot. Leaning on his stick—he had lately taken to leaning rather heavily on the admirable silver-plated cherry-wood stick presented to him by his employees on the occasion of his fortieth wedding day—Carr with keen enjoyment watched the boys' antics as they frolicked along the road, instead of listening to Hammond's exposition of the financial situation, which was too often unsatisfactory.

On these walks they often encountered Sir Charles Gill, and the two old friends had a chat together. Sir Charles was not above asking Carr's advice on vexing textile questions, and often followed it—so he told the present writer—with great profit to himself. Another old friend who saw a great deal of Carr during this period was Mr. Nicholas Whiteley. At this time Mr. Whiteley was the solicitor for a very large West Riding combine; and the business this brought him, though very lucrative, was also extremely harassing. It was one of his most refreshing forms of recreation to have a quiet smoke and talk with Carr, and the two spent many a pleasant hour together exaggerating the abilities of their granddaughter, who spent the period 1923–26 in keeping terms at Lady Margaret Hall.

In November 1924 Mr. George Newton, who, it will be remembered, now resided at Hough Hall, died; and Carr and Mr. Whiteley attended the funeral together. At this funeral Carr caught a very bad cold, which soon developed into a rather serious attack of bronchitis. When the present writer returned to Carr Foot a few weeks later for the Christmas vacation she was very much struck by the change in his appearance, which, of course, was more obvious to her than to Hammond and Cordelia, who saw him constantly. Scarcely had Carr recovered from this attack than he again caught cold. The widowed Mrs. Newton sold Hough Hall to the Hudley Corporation, and they promptly began to pull it down in order to widen the road. Carr was very much affected by this operation and interested in its progress; he spent hours leaning on his stick by the demolished garden wall, watching the slow destruction of the house where he had spent so many happy days. Cordelia's remonstrances were useless, for Carr pretended that he never caught cold; but the month was February and the corner an exposed one, and soon Carr was again in bed with a really severe attack of bronchitis. So severe indeed was the attack that the present writer was sent for, but the danger was averted and Carr recovered. In the spring he and Cordelia spent two months at Bournemouth, and Carr returned much strengthened. From this time onwards, however, he went but little to the mill, leaving its affairs almost entirely in Hammond's hands; and in this abstention Hammond encouraged him, for the post-war slump made these years an extremely anxious time, and he wished to spare his father as much as possible. "I went down to the mill this morning," wrote Carr to his granddaughter on June 13th, 1925, "but Hammond was quite cross, and packed me straight off back home again. Your grandmother was quite cross with him for being cross, so there we are! When will you be at home again to keep us all in order? Your grandmother has got a new hat, a marvellous affair with an osprey floating about the front. She looks very well in it, but then she always does look well if she would only believe it. Now if she were to have her photograph taken in that I should be quite overshadowed, and a very good thing too."

This reference to a photograph is in response to the present writer's reiterated plea that Carr and Cordelia would have one taken. The present writer could not but feel alarmed by the gradual decline in Carr's health, and was very desirous of possessing a really good likeness of him in his old age, handsome and merry as he still was. She did not, however, succeed in this plan until the August of the following year, when she employed the pretext of securing a group of all those bearing the name of Carr. This appealed to Carr's family pride, and the group was accordingly taken by a good photographer in Leeds. It is pleasant to be able to say that the portraits of Carr and of Cordelia are both excellent. They are seated; Hammond, looking tall and handsome though rather grave, stands behind his mother; the present writer is behind Carr. The two boys, clad in the comfortable woollies of the present day, are cross-legged on the floor at their grandparents' feet. Cordelia, in a dark and well-cut cloth dress with a white collar, her hands clasped primly in her lap, looks really charming; she sits almost fiercely erect, and her eyes are full of life; her hair is simply dressed and suits her, and her profile is as sweet, as innocent, as loving and as pure as in the days of the sealskin coat. Carr has thrown up his head and is gazing straight out of the picture; the photographer has been most happy in securing him just in the midst of a most merry and delightful smile. This is, of course, the last photograph of Carr.

The present writer took her degree in the summer of 1926, and was fortunate in securing a post as history mistress at the Hudley Girls' High School in the following autumn. She was therefore at Fallingroyd House throughout the period of Carr's last illness, which began in February 1927. In spite of his family's remonstrances Carr attended a football match in Hudley on February 5th, and next day he was in bed with a bad cold, which promptly turned to bronchitis. During the next six weeks he put up an energetic fight for life. Time after time he recovered sufficiently to come downstairs, and on returning from school in the afternoon the present writer found him sitting by the fire in a warm woollen dressing-gown, bright and lively as ever in spite of his painfully strained breathing, and full of interest in his granddaughter's doings during the day, on which he would make humorous comments. The picture of him thus, looking round the edge of his chair to greet her with his loving merry smile, while Cordelia fluttered about in the background with an extra rug or one of those invalid dishes which Carr contemptuously designated as "gruel," is very often before the present writer's mind. The next day perhaps he would be stricken down again; but his spirit and his love of fun never deserted him. It is to this period that the following charming anecdote belongs. The present writer returned one day to find him lying in bed, with closed eyes, propped up amidst pillows and breathing alarmingly fast, whereas the day before he had come downstairs and seemed fairly well. She therefore said to him in a jocular tone as she kissed him: "Who told you to start breathing like that again, you naughty old thing?" Carr, opening his eyes just wide enough to allow their twinkle to appear, replied with a smile, though he could not raise his voice above a hoarse whisper: "N. or M."

Towards the middle of March it became apparent to all concerned that this attack was much the worst that Carr had yet sustained, and the services of a night nurse were secured. He was by now very weak, and began to ramble somewhat, the subject of his delirious talk being, curiously enough, usually an umbrella. He was always speaking of this umbrella, asking where it was, whether it had been wrapped up, whether it was paid for, whether its covering was of silk, and so on, much to the perplexity and pain of poor Cordelia, who could not make out what he was talking about. It fell to the lot of the present writer to discover, one Sunday afternoon as she was sitting by his bedside, that the umbrella was a birthday present which Carr had intended to give to Cordelia, her birthday being, as the reader will perhaps remember, on March 28th. He was very anxious that this umbrella—silk, expensive, of fashionable shape and hue—should be bought and paid for at once. The present writer tried to soothe him by saying that he would soon be about again and able to choose the present himself. Carr looked at her in wide-eyed astonishment, and observed simply: "But it isn't till the end of the month. I shan't be here." The present writer was naturally very much affected by this characteristic concern on Carr's part for the welfare and happiness of those he loved, even when he himself did not expect to be there to see it; and the umbrella was bought next day in Hudley and shown to Carr, to his great relief and pleasure. During the next two days he often reverted anxiously to the topic of the umbrella, but as soon as Cordelia or the nurse began to explain that it was already bought he smiled, made an acquiescing movement of head and hand to show that he remembered, and murmured self-accusingly: "Silly! Of course!"

On the afternoon of March 16th the present writer, while on duty at school, was summoned home by a telephone message from Hammond; Carr was much worse, a day nurse had been secured, and Cordelia required companionship and support. Carr's granddaughter returned to Fallingroyd House at once, to find Cordelia weeping bitterly in the little dining-room—the doctor had mentioned the dreaded word "pneumonia" in her hearing. There was indeed a pronounced and obvious change in Carr, and from that time forward he communicated but little with those around him. His breathing continued to be terribly strained, but for the most part he was in a state of coma, and seemed not to feel any real distress or pain. He had, however, lucid intervals, in one of which the twins were brought in for him to see. Anything in the nature of a sentimental farewell or deathbed scene would have been repugnant to Carr's essentially modest and sincere character; and accordingly he said little to the boys, regarding them, however, with bright pleased eyes and a half-smile. From March 17th onward Hammond slept at Fallingroyd House; and about three o'clock on the morning of Monday, March 21st, he roused the present writer with the intimation that the end was at hand. There were, however, still a few hours of Carr's life left. For the most part he lay in a state of coma, with only his heavy rattling breathing to show that he still lived; but from time to time he seemed to rouse himself, his eyes took on expression, he appeared to be thinking, and occasionally a dim vague word or two fell from his lips and indicated what was passing in his mind. Just at the last, when the sun was climbing over the eastern shoulder of High Carr, he seemed greatly troubled because, as he vaguely murmured, he had never done anything great or important in his life. Cordelia—whose pure loving face, worn by grief, looked singularly beautiful in the wan morning light—bent over him and told him soothingly: "You've done your best." He stared at her, apparently much struck by this, and seemed to be busy thinking it out when he died.

And here Carr's granddaughter wishes to take a liberty—the only one of its kind in this work—and present to the reader Carr's thoughts, as he lay there dying, in the way she imagines they must have passed through his mind. Her excuse for this is that Carr's vague words, his changes of expression, the look in his eyes, which conveyed so accurately and vividly to her what he was thinking, would not have the same effect upon strangers unfamiliar with his ways. For many years past Carr's granddaughter had been wont to study him and to enter sympathetically into his thoughts, while Cordelia had that instinctive comprehension of his feelings which comes from a life spent side by side; and these two are agreed that the account which follows is substantially the truth.

Carr's thoughts, then, flew back to his youth; to his mother, to William Ainsley, to Carr Fold and Joshua and Catherine. He saw so clearly now, so very very clearly, that William Ainsley had meant him to marry Catherine—for had he not wanted to marry Hammond off to Suzanne Whiteley? He understood now so clearly, so very clearly, how his mother had felt when he had married Taylor Eastwood's daughter—for had he not felt the same when Hammond married Chrissie Hallas? How different young P. J. Carr's life would have been if he had carried out his uncle's plan! The sun was rising now, and through the window High Carr stood out black across the valley against the fiery sky. He could have been master of Carr Fold, could have owned Carr Carr and Ainsley—but then he would have had to give up his beautiful Cordelia. At this he mildly shook his head and murmured "Dell!" He saw her pure, sweet, well-loved face bending over him, he felt her soft kiss on his cheek; her hand with its well-worn wedding ring closed over his own; he smiled, and did not regret Carr Carr and Ainsley. His thoughts wandered back again into the past, to the picnic, to Taylor Eastwood and his sticks of celery, to Cherry clawing at his leg—there was a cat for you!—to the *Venetia* waltz and Cordelia weeping on her wedding day; back further still to the night he had first met his love. He recalled her haughty, angry little face above the sealskin coat, and Catherine's blue dress, and Lomas singing. Ah yes, Lomas! Poor Catherine! Living that idle, useless life down there, with a worthless husband and no children to work and hope for. Poor Catherine! Poor thing! Poor thing! He remembered how he and she had talked of their ambitions, that fine May evening long, long ago, while the moon came out and the lights sprang up in the Carr Foot cottages. They were so sure they were going to make a finer thing of life than the previous generation! Well, their ambitions had not come to much for either of them; for Catherine's life was wasted, and what had *he* done? Nothing! Nothing at all! simply scraped a moderate living for his wife and family all through the years, and that more by good luck than by management. He saw the beautiful Carr Foot Mills chimney swaying through the air, his heart grew sadder still, and he reproached himself severely. Charlie Gill, now—there was a career for you! And there was Bales Newton had made a name for himself, and so had Nicholas Whiteley, and even Lomas had gathered wealth; but Philip Joseph Carr, as far as he could see, had never done anything at all except just live. *He* had improved nothing, invented nothing, made no name. Dell said he'd done his best. Well, so he had, but was it worth while for that, the pain, the struggle, the defeat of life? Of course he had had his beautiful Cordelia, and Hammond, and Eugene—poor Eugene! *there* was a fellow might have done something in the world! But he was dead with a bullet through his heart; poor Eugene!—and he had had that darling baby girl whose name he could not quite remember; and there was his granddaughter, and those splendid boys, and after all he had, as Dell said, done his best. Did he really envy Lomas? Well, no, after all he thought not; he thought on the whole he would rather die as P. J. Carr than Lomas Eastwood. He had improved nothing, invented nothing, it was true; but then as far as he could judge he had spoiled nothing either. Truth and justice, decency and honour, love and kindness, laughter and joy—they were all still in mankind's firmament as far as he was concerned; they had at least suffered no diminution at his hands; he had passed them on to his grandchildren intact, and that was something. Had it been worth while for that, the pain, the struggle, the defeat? Well, yes; on the whole perhaps it had.

He smiled vaguely, his head sank back on the pillow, his heavy breathing abruptly ceased; Philip Joseph Carr was dead.

XII

CARR'S PLACE IN LIFE AND LITERATURE

In estimating Carr's place in life and literature the present writer has been very much helped, first, by Carr's own estimate of himself as recorded in the last chapter, and second, by Eugene's important note on his father's career, at the head of which appears the invaluable reference Ecclesiasticus xxxviii. 32–34.

It must be stated frankly that Carr's modest opinion of himself, which has appeared over and over again in this record of his life, is the correct one. He was a completely ordinary man. He accomplished no great thing. He did not invent anything, or improve anything, or make a name for himself in any branch of human activity. His place in literature and in history is, undoubtedly, as one of the crowd. Every important action in history or in literature must have a background of human beings for whom and in regard to whom the action is performed; and Carr belongs to this background of average, non-eminent human beings, who, be it remembered, form the large majority of the world's population. For if we regard each generation as setting out boldly in their youth to tell the king the sky is falling, we are bound to reach the conclusion that in each generation only a few are able to improve mankind's sky, only a few have the ability to redecorate it, to reconstruct it, to add to its beauty and to make it more suitable for the purpose for which it was designed. But the remainder of each generation have at least the task of holding it up while these reconstructions and redecorations are going on. It is their part to maintain and to transmit, as the writer of Ecclesiasticus knew very well. "Without these," he writes—meaning average men such as Carr—

"Without these cannot a city be inhabited: and they shall not dwell where they will, nor go up and down:

"They shall not be sought for in publick counsel, nor sit high in the congregation: they shall not sit high in the judges' seat, nor understand the sentence of judgment: they cannot declare justice and judgment; and they shall not be found where parables are spoken.

"But they will maintain the state of the world. . . ."

Without the average man to maintain what has already been gained of truth and justice, decency and honour, love and kindness, laughter and joy, and to hand them on intact to the next generation, while the eminent man is experimenting with improvements, these qualities would perish from the earth. Why then should not one of the crowd, one of those who maintain, those who transmit, have a standard biography written for him with as much justification as one of the celebrities, one of those who improve?

Such at any rate was the line of reasoning which impelled the present writer to the preparation of this biography; it is for the reader to decide whether it is justified by the completed work.

APPENDIX A

NOTE ON THE PRESENT DISTRIBUTION OF THE AINSLEY PROPERTY

On November 18th, 1927, Catherine and Lomas went to London for one of their customary week-end jaunts. While there Catherine caught influenza, but attributing her feeling of distress merely to a bad cold, she said nothing to Lomas, but journeyed back to Torquay with him on the following Wednesday. On the Thursday she had to be removed to a nursing home, and she died on the following Tuesday, November 29th. Lomas had already become infected with the influenza germ, and his death followed immediately upon hers, taking place on the Saturday of that week. It may interest the reader with a taste for irony to see extracts from the obituary of Lomas given in the *Hudley News* for the following Saturday, December 10th. It is headed: "Mr. Lomas Eastwood: Death of a Hudley Artist," and reads as follows.

"The death took place on Saturday, at Torquay, of Mr. Lomas Eastwood, formerly of Hudley and Carr Foot." (Here follows an account of the circumstances of the death of Lomas and Catherine.) "Mr. Eastwood was well known here as an artist of great ability. For many years he acted as designer at Denbridge Mills, being a close friend of Sir Charles Gill, of whom he was a schoolfellow (*sic*). He left Carr Foot to reside in Torquay some thirty years ago, feeling that he could find greater expression for his artistic aspirations and talents there. Mr. Eastwood's specialty was water-colour, and he has several times sent samples of his work to the Hudley Arts and Crafts Exhibition. He will be lamented by a large circle of friends in Hudley and Torquay."

The result of these two deaths was to enrich the Carr family as follows. Catherine's will, after various rather large charitable bequests, bequeathed approximately two-thirds of her remaining wealth to her husband, and one-third to Carr, or, if he had predeceased her, in equal shares to Hammond and the present writer (as Eugene's descendant) respectively. (Carr's will had left all his property—of which there was not a great deal—to Hammond in trust for Cordelia.) Lomas's will left everything of which he died possessed to be divided equally between the twins Hammond Taylor Carr and Philip Taylor Carr. This is the last available piece of evidence on the question of Lomas's alleged paternity of Chrissie Hallas; the reader can now make his own decision on this interesting point. The wealth of William Ainsley was therefore unexpectedly divided among the Carrs in the following (approximate) proportions: Hammond had one-sixth and the present writer one-sixth, while each twin had one-third.

It has been objected by some critics that this information should have found a place in the body of this biography rather than in an appendix; but with this the present writer cannot agree. Carr did not live to see the accidental enrichment of his descendants, and therefore it has no place in his life; it forms rather one of those strands alluded to on p. 373, which, having their origin in events which occurred before Carr's birth, will continue to colour the lives of his grandchildren and their descendants long after his death.

That other important piece of William Ainsley's property, Carr Fold, at the time of writing (March 1929) remains in the hands of Sir Charles Gill's two sons, who are acting as his executors, Sir Charles having died suddenly on October 5th, 1928, of an apoplectic seizure following a violent argument with the Chairman of the Denbridge Vale U.D.C. Whether Carr Fold will ever come into the hands of the Carrs is an open—and a very interesting—question.

It only remains to add that Catherine's death placed her diary at the present writer's immediate disposal, and enabled her to begin work on Carr's biography without delay. The last entry in the diary is dated March 22nd, 1927—the day after Carr's death. It reads: "Phil died yesterday, and all the world is dark to me." The words after "yesterday" are repeatedly crossed through, and then written in again above the line, as though Catherine had decided to cease keeping her diary and to place that volume in the bank with the others, and therefore felt that she might allow herself this final expression of feeling about her cousin. Poor Catherine!

APPENDIX B

CHRONOLOGICAL SUMMARY OF EVENTS

1854.	Feb.	29.	Birth of Annie Hallas.
1857.	May	20.	Birth of Lomas Eastwood.
1858.	"	13.	Interview between Taylor Eastwood and Hammond Carr.
	"	14.	Hammond Carr absconds.
	"	15.	Birth of Philip Joseph Carr.
	Nov.	18.	Birth of Catherine Ainsley.
1859.	Mar.	28.	Birth of Cordelia Mary Eastwood.
1862.	Jan.	22.	Death of Walter Carr.
1866.	Oct.	3.	Death of Edmund Carr.
1867.	Sept.	30.	Carr enters Hudley Grammar School.
	Dec.	3.	Death of Hammond Carr.
	"	28.	Adelaide Ainsley very ill, but recovers.
1874.	Sept.	1.	Carr apprenticed at Carr Foot Mills.
1879.	Jan.	4.	Carr Foot Weslcyan Chapel destroyed by fire.
	May	15.	Deed of partnership signed between P. J. Carr and William Ainsley.
			Carr Foot concert. Carr meets Cordelia.
	June	7.	Picnic to Bolton Woods.
	"	12–14.	St. Marks Bazaar.
	"	21.	Flower Show.
	"	23–30.	Hudley Fair.
	July	9.	Cricket Match; Hudley Grammar School *v.* Old Boys.
	"	17.	Black Dike Band in Hudley.
	"	23.	Hudley Grammar School Athletic Sports.

1879. Aug. 8–22. Cordelia in St. Anne's.
" 5–25. Carr in Belgium.
Sept. 20. Morning Performance of *H.M.S. Pinafore.*
" 30. Lecture by Archibald Forbes on Zulu War.
Oct. 9–11. Monsieur Crowther at Roller-Skating Rink.
Nov. 18. Charlie Gill engaged to Amelia Barker.
Dec. 3. Party at the Gills.
Quarrel between Carr and Cordelia.
" 4–18. Letters between Carr and Cordelia.
" 24. Cordelia posts Christmas Card to Carr.
" 25. Carr visits Majorca Road. Taylor practically ejects him.
" 27. Skating. Cab incident.

1880. Feb. 14. Taylor Eastwood discovers Cordelia's valentine from Carr.
" 16. Cordelia sent to Scarborough.
" 17. Mrs. Carr receives letter from Taylor Eastwood.
" 20–April 3. Correspondence between Carr and Cordelia.
Mar. 28. Easter Sunday. Cordelia's twenty-first birthday.
" 31. Hudley Election.
April 3. Carr arrives in Scarborough.
" 6. Marriage of Carr to Cordelia Mary Eastwood.
" 10. Carr and Cordelia meet Gill at the Opéra Comique.
" 12. Return of Carr and Cordelia to Hudley.
" 19. Death of Ellen Carr.
" 22. Funeral of Ellen Carr.
" 23. Carr and Cordelia begin residence at Atack Place.

1881. Feb. 12. Birth of Hammond Taylor Carr.
Mar. 15. Christening of Hammond Taylor Carr.
April 10. Eastwoods dine at Atack Place. Anger of Cordelia against her brother.

1881.	May	7.	Catherine lays foundation stone of Carr Foot Chapel.
	June	14.	Marriage of Charlie Gill to Amelia Barker.
			Lomas Eastwood proposes to Catherine.
	July	12.	Letter from Fräulein Kirchner.
	Nov.–May 1882.		Mr. and Mrs. Ainsley in France, etc. with the Royal Commission on Technical Education.
			Catherine in Leipzig. Carr and Cordelia at Carr Fold.
1882.	May	27.	Ainsleys return to Carr Fold.
			Carr and Cordelia resume residence at Atack Place.
	June	11.	Scene between Carr and Cordelia about bills.
	July	2.	Birth of Philip Eugene Carr.
	Nov.	18.	Catherine's birthday.
			Taylor Eastwood's letter in *Hudley News*.
			Cordelia has a nervous breakdown.
	"	28.	Adelaide, Catherine and Cordelia at Scarborough.
	Dec.	9.	Letter from Carr to Cordelia.
	"	13.	Fatal accident to William Ainsley.
	"	16.	Funeral of William Ainsley.
1883.	Feb.	14.	Carr begins residence at Hough Hall.
	May	20.	Lomas Eastwood proposes to Catherine.
	June–Sept.		Mrs. Ainsley and Catherine in Bournemouth.
	Oct.	15.	Catherine begins to study nursing.
1884.	Feb.	12.	Birth of Suzanne Whiteley.
	May	15.	Incident between Lomas and Annie Hallas.
	"	19.	Lomas moves into lodgings in Prince's Road.
	"	20.	Lomas Eastwood proposes to Catherine.
	June	4.	Catherine wishes to adopt a child.
	"	13.	Catherine abandons her adoption scheme.
	Oct.	12.	Lomas at Carr Fold for dinner.

1885.	Feb.	5.	Death of Mrs. Eastwood.
	Mar.	10.	Scene between Taylor and Lomas.
	"	11.	Interview between Cordelia and Catherine.
	"	14.	Taylor informs Annie Hallas of Lomas's matrimonial views.
	May	20.	Lomas Eastwood proposes to Catherine.
1886.	Jan.	13.	Birth of Mary Elizabeth Carr (the first).
	May	20.	Lomas Eastwood proposes to Catherine.
1887.	Jan.	22.	Carr and Cordelia see *Ruddigore*.
	May	20.	Lomas proposes to Catherine.
	Aug.	4.	Death of Mrs. Enoch Barker.
1888.	May	20.	Lomas proposes to Catherine.
	June–Sept.		Quarrel between Enoch Barker and Charlie Gill.
	Oct.	3.	Carr and Cordelia see *The Yeomen of the Guard*.
1889.	May	20.	Lomas Eastwood proposes to Catherine.
	Dec.	7.	Carr and Cordelia see *The Gondoliers*.
	"	25.	Carr gives Catherine a leather case fitted with diary volumes.
1890.	May	20.	Lomas Eastwood proposes to Catherine.
	July	8–23.	The Carrs and the Whiteleys in Switzerland together.
	"	16.	Photograph of Hammond, Eugene and Mary Elizabeth Carr.
	"	27.	Death of Mr. Nicholas Whiteley, senior.
1891.	Jan.	30.	Death of Charles Bradlaugh.
	Feb.	3.	Taylor Eastwood attends Bradlaugh's funeral.
	"	4.	Taylor Eastwood ill. Mary Elizabeth Carr begins to be ill.
	"	5.	Hudley Mayor's Ball. M. E. Carr develops pneumonia.
	"	6.	Catherine engaged to Lomas Eastwood.
	"	9.	Death of Mary Elizabeth Carr.
	"	11.	Funeral of Mary Elizabeth Carr.

1891.	Feb.	13.	Taylor Eastwood again dangerously ill, but recovers.
	May	20.	Marriage of Catherine Ainsley to Lomas Eastwood.
	July	1.	Lomas and Catherine begin residence at Carr Fold.
	Sept.	8.	Didymus killed in carriage accident.
	Oct.	9.	Lomas leaves the firm of Gill and Barker.
1892.	Jan.	23.	Mrs. Ainsley removes to Atack Place.
			Cessation of Catherine's diary.
	Dec.	28.	Death of Mrs. Ainsley.
1894.	June	25.	Statue to Bradlaugh unveiled in Northampton.
			Taylor, Lomas and Annie present at unveiling.
	Sept.	30.	Death of Taylor Eastwood.
1895.	Feb.	26.	Birth of Christabel (Chrissie) Hallas at Blackpool.
	"	28.	Rupture between Catherine and Lomas.
			Catherine at Hough Hall.
	Mar.	1.	Carr interviews James Hallas and Nicholas Whiteley.
			Cordelia goes to Blackpool.
			Catherine returns to her husband, and they leave Carr Fold.
	"	2.	Nicholas Whiteley receives Catherine's notice of withdrawal from Carr Carr and Ainsley, and communicates it to Carr.
	Sept.	2.	Catherine withdraws from Carr Carr and Ainsley.
1896.	Feb.	12.	Fire at Carr Foot Mills.
	Aug.	19.	Catherine and Lomas begin residence at Torquay.
	Oct.	6.	Insurance claims on Carr Foot Mills settled for four-fifths of the original demands.
	Nov.–June 1897.		Voluntary liquidation of Carr Carr and Ainsley.

1897.	June 18.	Carr Foot Mills main chimney felled.
	Sept. 8.	Foundation of firm of Carr and Carr, dyers.
		Hough Hall sold to George Newton.
	" 22.	The Carrs take up residence at Fallingroyd House.
	Oct. 7.	George Newton takes up residence at Hough Hall.
1900.	July 17.	Eugene Carr wins a scholarship to Oxford.
	Aug. 12.	Catherine seriously ill, but recovers.
	Oct. 24.	Eugene at Balliol College, Oxford.
	Nov. 19.	Death of Mr. Enoch Barker.
1903.		Eugene secures appointment in Public Record Office.
	Aug. 13.	Engagement of Eugene Carr to Suzanne Whiteley.
	Sept.	Messrs. Carr and Carr become finishers as well as dyers.
1904.	June 8.	Marriage of Eugene Carr to Suzanne Whiteley.
	Oct. 12.	Eugene and Suzanne begin residence in Hammersmith Terrace.
	Dec. 9.	Death of Annie Hallas.
1905.	" 24.	Birth of Mary Elizabeth Carr (the second).
1909.	May 9–29.	Nicholas Whiteley ill with pleurisy, but recovers.
1910.	Feb. 14.	Catherine has a nervous breakdown.
	Mar.–Sept. 1911.	Lomas and Catherine tour the world.
1911.	Jan. 12.	Suzanne has a serious miscarriage.
	May 15.	M. E. Carr presents a poem to Carr.
	Nov. 15.	Lomas and Catherine begin residence at the Hotel Quita, Tourquay.
1912.	Dec. 3.	Messrs. Carr and Carr formed into a limited company.
1913.	Nov.	Hough Hall monkey-puzzle tree cut down.
1914.	June 13.	Death of Mrs. Nicholas Whiteley.

1914.	Aug. 4.	Outbreak of war between England and Germany.
		Hammond Carr mobilised.
	Nov.	Eugene enlists in the 10th (S.) Batt. Prince of Wales's Own West Yorkshire Regiment.
		House in Hammersmith Terrace sold.
	Dec. 2.	Eugene gazetted second lieutenant.
1915.	April 14.	Hammond in France with the 1/4 Battalion Duke of Wellington's (West Riding) Regiment.
	July 15.	Eugene in France.
	Aug. 14.	Hammond wounded—shrapnel in leg.
	" 20.	Cordelia visits Hammond in Glasgow hospital.
	Nov. 16.	Mr. Charles Gill buys Carr Fold.
1916.	Jan. 1.	Mr. Charles Gill knighted.
	Feb. 15.	Eugene gazetted first lieutenant.
	Mar. 22.	Eugene and Suzanne meet Lomas and Catherine in a London hotel.
	Nov. 19.	Death of Frau Schröter.
1917.	July 12.	Hammond gazetted captain.
	" 30.	Eugene wounded—blown up by mine.
	Aug.–Nov.	Suzanne, Carr and Cordelia in London from time to time to see Eugene.
	Sept. 14.	Catherine and Lomas to see Eugene in hospital.
	" 18.	Catherine's diary resumed.
1918.	May 30.	Eugene killed in France.
	June 4.	News of Eugene's death received at Carr Fold.
	" 7.	Hammond at Carr Foot on leave.
	" 12.	Hammond goes to London.
	" 14.	Suzanne and Nicholas Whiteley go to Whitby.
		M. E. Carr (the second) at Carr Foot.

1918. June 15. Marriage of Hammond to Chrissie Hallas.
" 17. News of Hammond's marriage received at Carr Foot.
" 21. Hammond returns to France.
" 26. Hammond wounded in arm near Vlamertinghe.
Sept. 14. Hammond's arm amputated near elbow.
Dec. 6. Hammond invalided out of the army.
1919. April 11–25. Carr ill with bronchitis.
May 8–22. Carr and Cordelia in Torquay.
" 21. Interview between Lomas and Cordelia.
Aug. 31. Birth of Hammond Taylor Carr (the second) and Philip Taylor Carr.
Sept. 6. Death of Chrissie Carr.
1921. June 7–14. Carr and others visit Eugene's grave.
1922. Sept. 21. Second marriage of Suzanne.
Nov. 14–Dec. 2. Carr ill with bronchitis.
1923. Jan. 4–18. Carr ill with bronchitis.
Oct.–July 1926. M. E. Carr at Lady Margaret Hall.
Nov.–Dec. Carr ill with bronchitis.
1924. " 10. Death of Mr. George Newton.
" 14–Dec. 20. Carr ill with bronchitis.
1925. Feb. 2. Hough Hall pulled down.
" 10–27. Carr seriously ill with bronchitis, but recovers.
April 6–May 29. Carr and Cordelia in Bournemouth.
1926. Aug. 24. Last photograph of Carr.
Sept. 21. M. E. Carr at Hudley High School.
1927. Feb. 6. Beginning of Carr's last illness.
Mar. 21. Death of Carr.
Nov. 29. Death of Catherine.
Dec. 3. Death of Lomas Eastwood.
1928. Oct. 5. Death of Sir Charles Gill.